MINDW🧠RKS
LEFT AND RIGHT
BRAIN TRAINING
— ULTIMATE EDITION —

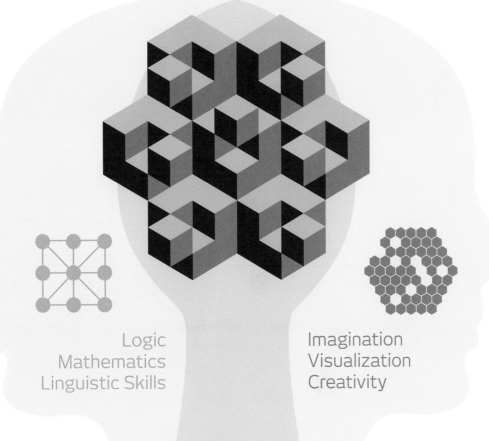

Logic
Mathematics
Linguistic Skills

Imagination
Visualization
Creativity

hinkler

Published by Hinkler Books Pty Ltd
45–55 Fairchild Street
Heatherton Victoria 3202 Australia
www.hinkler.com

hinkler

Design © Hinkler Books Pty Ltd
Puzzles and text © Book Creation Ltd

Printed and bound in Malaysia

ISBN: 978 1 4889 2399 9

CONTENTS

Introduction

Have you ever noticed that some tasks feel easier than others, and certain types of problems seem harder to solve? Our abilities are linked to the two hemispheres of our brain, which are responsible for distinct functions. If you'd like to improve your skills, it might be time to do some brain training! The more you practise a particular activity, the better you'll become at it. And the best way to improve certain abilities is to train the area of your brain responsible for them.

The brain's left hemisphere is where words and numbers are processed. It's also the center of problem—solving, mental arithmetic, deductive and intuitive reasoning, logic, and lateral thinking. If you've ever had to whip out your phone to calculate a tip, or you want to improve your crossword skills, you might find left—brain training helpful. The right hemisphere is the center of visual cognition and perception, and the source of skills such as spatial awareness, musical talent and imagination. If you've ever struggled to figure out which of your keys fits your front door, or you want to improve your memory, you might benefit from right—brain training.

Mindworks Left and Right Brain Training is packed with exciting activities to help you keep both the left and the right brain limber. The first part contains puzzles to give the left hemisphere of your brain a good workout. Deductive Puzzles are designed to help you hone your problem—solving, lateral—thinking and word—processing abilities. You'll need to find solutions based on patterns, known facts or principles, and logic and reasoning. Numeric Puzzles has number—based games and challenges to help improve the speed and accuracy of your mental calculations.

The second part of this book includes puzzles to challenge your brain's right hemisphere. Perceptual puzzles are designed to help sharpen your 3—D cognition, your memory and your ability to see the bigger picture. Mazes, spot—the—difference puzzles, and dice and domino games will help you train your brain to look past abstract shapes and patterns and focus on the overarching principle of the puzzle. Spatial puzzles are for those who want to improve their spatial awareness—here you'll find geometry—based games intended to improve your ability to perceive things in three dimensions.

Power through the challenges on your own, or start a game with friends and family. However you choose to solve the puzzles and no matter what your level of ability is, there's plenty of fun brain training here for you! ✪

MINDW⚙RKS
BRAIN TRAINING

Left-brain Puzzles

Deductive Puzzles is a brand-new, user-friendly tour around the world of puzzles for those who get a kick out of getting the right answer.

Everything in here is all black or white, right or wrong, so there'll be no arguments—apart from whose turn it is to try the next puzzle!

Deduction is a form of logic that can be used to find the solution to a problem based on a set of known facts or principles. A simple example of deductive reasoning is as follows:

1. Only birds have feathers.
2. An ostrich has feathers.
3. Therefore, an ostrich must be a bird.

If the first two statements are known to be facts, then the third statement can be deduced from them.

Deductive reasoning is a skill powered by the left-hand side of the brain. The puzzles in this section have been specifically designed to train your left brain by triggering problem-solving, deductive and intuitive reasoning, logic and lateral-thinking.

Nuances of logic can be surprisingly subtle. For example, suppose we asked you to describe whether the statement "Some birds have black feathers" is always, sometimes, or never true. Many people are tempted to choose "sometimes" because the statement appears conditional. However, the correct answer is "always" because there are always some birds somewhere in the world that have black feathers. What if we asked you to describe the truth of the statement "Some birds are ugly"? In this instance, none of the three answers can be chosen because the statement is a matter of opinion and there's no right or wrong answer. These distinctions, subtle though they are, form the basis for some branches of philosophy.

So if you're dying to test out your own powers of deduction, where to head next? You could go straight through this section tackling each one as it comes. However, if you want to ease yourself in more gently, look for our special grading system. Each puzzle is rated from 1 to 10 stars. Low numbers of stars indicate that the puzzle shouldn't deter you too long. An 8-, 9- or 10-star problem means you're likely to be taxed to your limit. Furthermore, there are time limits to keep an eye on, just to increase the tension that little bit more.

Every question is numbered and has its answer clearly marked in the back of the section. But be sure to try all avenues before resorting to the solutions—things are not always what they seem at first!

By the end of this section, you'll be a master of deducing right from wrong. And that's the truth. ✪

1 DIFFICULTY ⬤⬤⬤⬤⬤☆☆☆☆☆   ⏰ **5** Minutes

If you think tic-tac-toe is boring, try this interesting variation. The aim of the game is to avoid winning—in other words, if you get three of your symbol in a horizontal, vertical, or diagonal line, you lose the game.

In the sample game shown, it is O's turn. Can you see which of the four possibilities (A, B, C, or D) will lead to a guaranteed win?

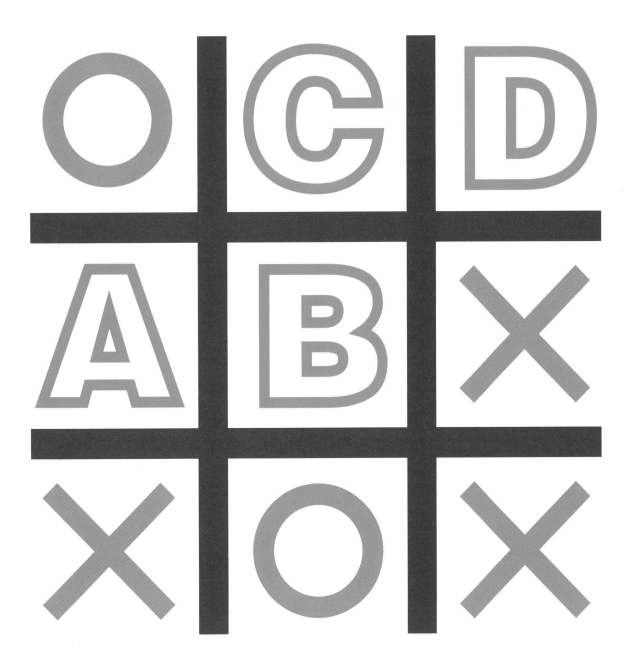

2 DIFFICULTY ★★★★★★☆☆☆☆   ⏱ **7** Minutes

Can you crack the safe? First decide which of the 14 statements given are false, then shade out the areas on the combination lock that are labeled with the letters of those false statements (so if you think statement A is false, shade out area A). The remaining lit segments will give you the digital combination required.

Hint: three of the statements are false.

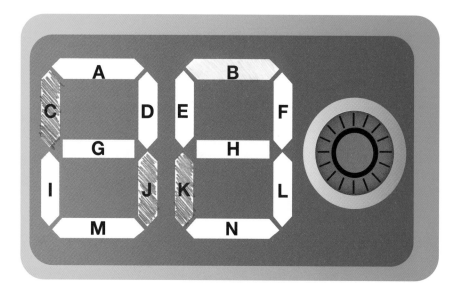

A. The upper number in a fraction is the numerator.
B. The ratio of a circle's circumference to its diameter is called pi.
C. A league is the term for a nautical mile.
D. Euclid wrote a famous work on geometry.
E. The Roman numeral for 500 is D.
F. An irrational number cannot be expressed as a fraction.
G. The longest side of a right-angled triangle is the hypotenuse.
H. Andrew Wiles famously proved Fermat's last theorem.
I. Integral and differential are types of calculus.
J. Hexadecimal is the number system for counting in groups of 12.
K. A reflex angle has between 90 and 180 degrees.
L. A heptagon has seven sides.
M. A perfect number is equal to the sum of all of its factors.
N. Originally, a myriad was equal to 10,000.

3 DIFFICULTY ✪✪✪✪☆☆☆☆☆☆ **3** Minutes

Each block is equal to the sum of the two numbers beneath it.
Can you find all the missing numbers?

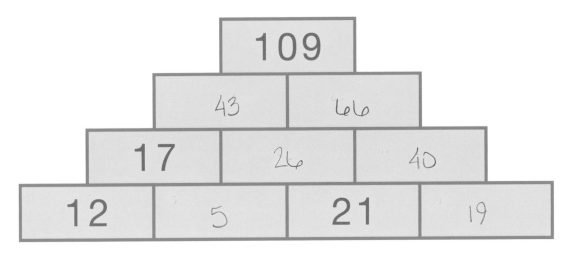

4 DIFFICULTY ✪✪✪✪☆☆☆☆☆☆ **6** Minutes

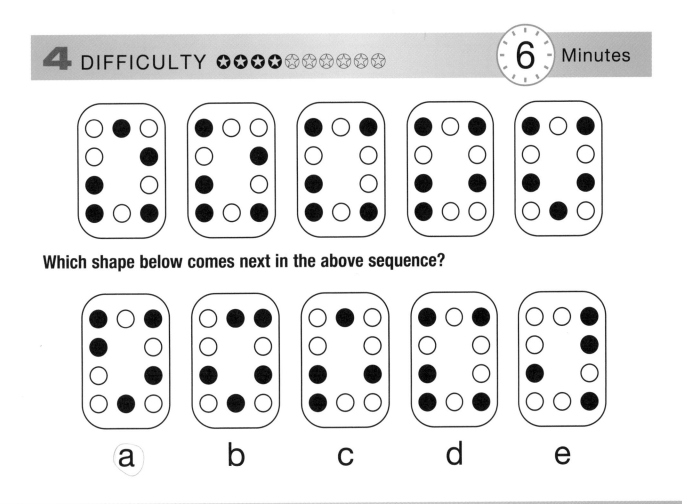

Which shape below comes next in the above sequence?

a   b   c   d   e

5 DIFFICULTY ✪✪✪☆☆☆☆☆☆☆   **6** Minutes

Can you fit these numbers into the grid? One number has already been inserted to help you get started.

3 DIGITS
~~135~~
~~208~~
424
~~650~~

4 DIGITS
~~1543~~
2246
4225
~~5890~~
~~6134~~
~~7979~~
~~8199~~
~~9484~~

5 DIGITS
~~18915~~
~~21266~~
24437
~~32791~~
~~43420~~
~~55159~~
~~61605~~
~~79937~~
82314
~~90556~~

6 DIGITS
~~130471~~
~~530395~~
~~766860~~
~~897030~~

7 DIGITS
1767463
~~2096913~~
2678374
~~3235488~~
4937541
~~4965907~~
5244243
~~5997845~~
6583226
~~6796588~~
~~7216860~~
~~8822997~~
9124965
~~9721305~~

6 DIFFICULTY ★★★★★☆☆☆☆☆  **6** Minutes

Each row and column contains the same numbers and signs, but they are arranged in a different order each time. Find the correct order to arrive at the final totals shown.

2	**+**	**6**	**x**	**3**	**−**	**4**	**= 20**
x		x		+		+	
3	−	2	x	4	+	6	**= 10**
−		÷		−		÷	
4	x	3	+	6	−	2	**= 16**
+		+		x		x	
6	+	4	x	2	−	3	**= 17**
=		**=**		**=**		**=**	
8		**13**		**2**		**24**	

7 DIFFICULTY ⚫⚫⚫⚫⚫☆☆☆☆☆   **5** Minutes

Make a calculation totaling the figure on the right by inserting the four mathematical operators (+, −, ÷, x) between the numbers shown.

They can be inserted in any order, and one of them has been used twice.

$$2 \times 3 + 8 \div 7 \times 5 - 4 = 6$$

8 DIFFICULTY ⚫⚫⚫⚫⚫☆☆☆☆☆   **8** Minutes

Five hopefuls brought their animals to the county fair. Can you figure out whose animal won which prize, and what kind of animal it was?

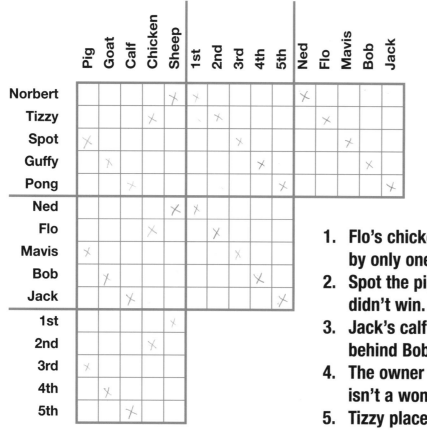

1. Flo's chicken was beaten by only one other animal.
2. Spot the pig wasn't last, but he didn't win.
3. Jack's calf came in 5th—one place behind Bob's Guffy.
4. The owner of Norbert the sheep isn't a woman.
5. Tizzy placed better than Pong.

Study these shapes for one minute, then see if you can answer the questions on the next page.

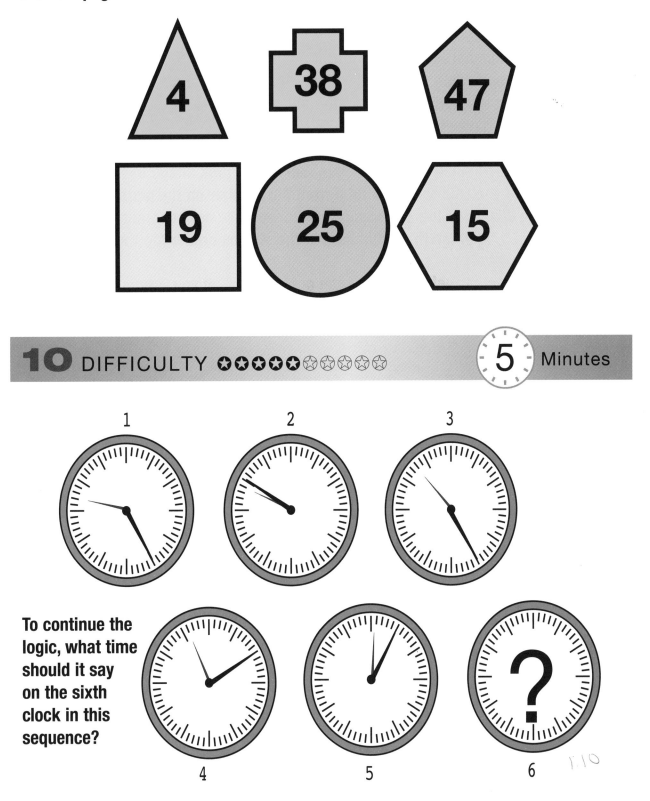

To continue the logic, what time should it say on the sixth clock in this sequence?

[9] DIFFICULTY ✪✪✪✪✪☆☆☆☆☆  ③ Minutes

Can you answer these questions about the puzzle on the previous page without looking back?

1. How many shapes have odd numbers?
2. Which three numbers will total a fourth number shown?
3. What is the total when you multiply the number on the blue shape by that on the shape directly above the blue shape?
4. Which shapes have even numbers?
5. What is the total of the numbers on the green shapes?
6. What is the total when you add the number on the pink shape to that on the circle, then subtract this total from the number on the pentagon?
7. Which two shapes of the same color are horizontally next to one another?
8. What is the total of the three numbers in the shapes on the top row?

11 DIFFICULTY ✪✪✪✪☆☆☆☆☆☆ ⑦ Minutes

There is a hidden phrase in the grid of letters. Place the right-hand grid over the letter grid in three different ways and then reassemble the resulting letters to see what you have "won."

12 DIFFICULTY ★★★★★★★☆☆☆

 30 Minutes

You'll be flying high if you solve this numeropic. Use the rules below to help you understand how to complete this puzzle.

How to do a numeropic:

Along each row or column, there are numbers that indicate how many blocks of black squares are in a line. For example, "3, 4, 5" indicates that from left to right or top to bottom, there is a group of three black squares, then a group of four black squares, then another group of five black squares.

Each block of black squares on the same line must have at least one white square between it and the next block of black squares. Blocks of black squares may or may not have a number of white squares before and after them.

It is sometimes possible to determine which squares will be black without reference to other lines or columns. It is helpful to put a small dot in a square you know will be empty.

13 DIFFICULTY ✪✪✪✪✪✪☆☆☆☆ ④ Minutes

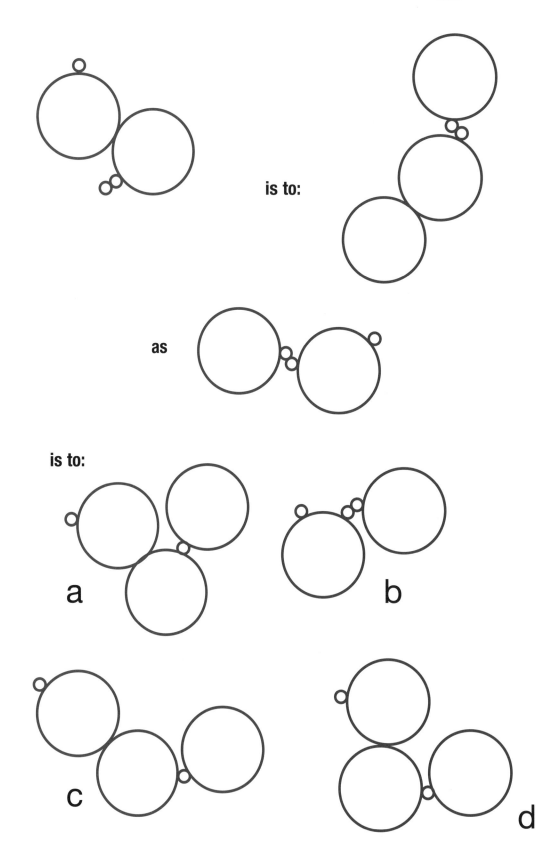

is to:

as

is to:

a

b

c

d

14 DIFFICULTY ✪✪✪☆☆☆☆☆☆☆  2 Minutes

In what way are the start and end of each of these six times identical?

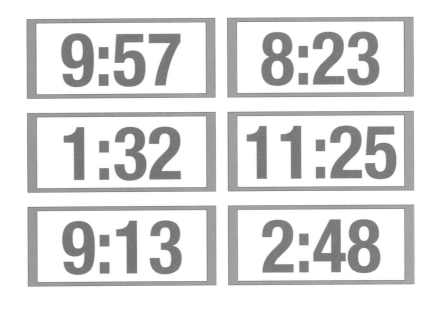

15 DIFFICULTY ✪✪✪✪✪☆☆☆☆☆ 5 Minutes

Place the remaining pieces in the grid so that:
* each row and column has two red and two yellow squares, and
* no row or column has two of the same digit.

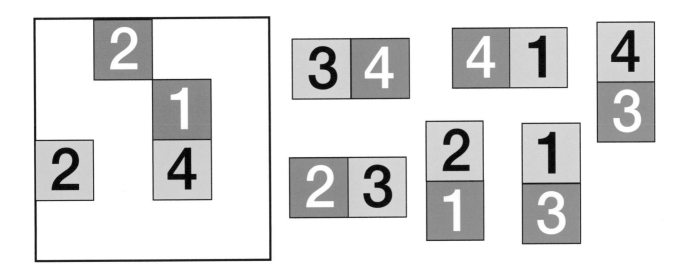

16 DIFFICULTY ★★★★☆☆☆☆☆☆ ③ Minutes

Which of the four boxed figures (a, b, c, or d) completes the set?

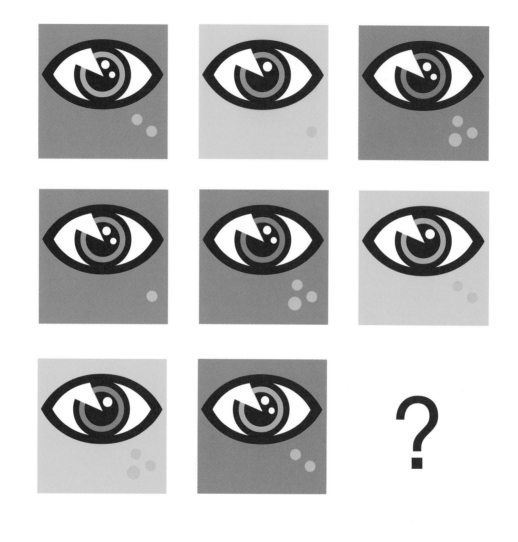

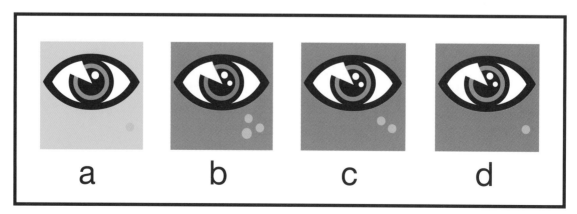

| a | b | c | d |

Try to get from the top left red square to the bottom right red square by making a series of calculations. You must always move from each square to an adjacent one and may not move diagonally.

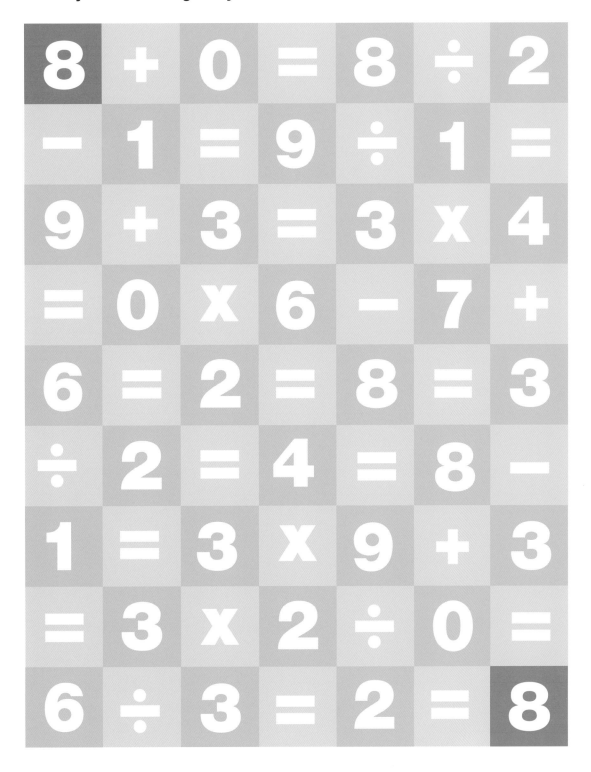

8	+	0	=	8	÷	2
−	1	=	9	÷	1	=
9	+	3	=	3	x	4
=	0	x	6	−	7	+
6	=	2	=	8	=	3
÷	2	=	4	=	8	−
1	=	3	x	9	+	3
=	3	x	2	÷	0	=
6	÷	3	=	2	=	8

The number 123987 appears just once in this grid and occurs in a straight line, running either backward or forward in a horizontal, vertical, or diagonal direction. Can you locate it?

9	3	2	1	7	3	1	2	3	8	9	7
7	8	2	2	8	9	1	2	3	9	8	2
1	3	1	7	3	2	2	2	2	9	3	1
9	2	2	8	3	1	3	9	1	8	2	2
7	8	3	1	2	3	7	7	7	3	1	3
8	7	9	3	2	1	8	8	9	2	8	9
3	1	7	7	9	3	9	1	1	7	8	7
2	2	8	9	3	3	7	2	2	3	2	8
1	2	3	9	2	2	3	8	3	2	7	7
7	1	8	1	3	9	1	1	9	1	8	3
8	3	1	2	3	7	9	8	7	3	9	2
9	7	1	2	3	8	7	9	3	2	1	1

19 DIFFICULTY ✪✪✪✪✪☆☆☆☆☆   ⏱ 5 Minute

Each block is equal to the sum of the two numbers beneath it. Can you find all the missing numbers?

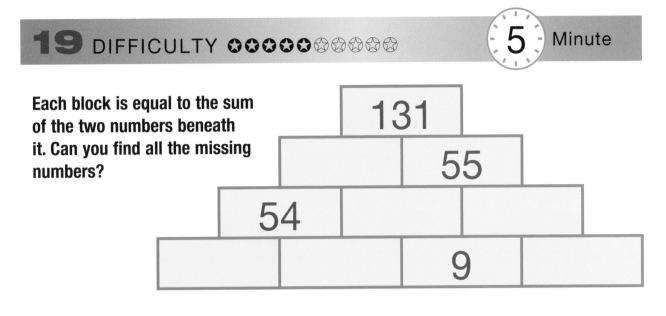

20 DIFFICULTY ✪✪✪✪✪✪☆☆☆☆   ⏱ 10 Minute

Take the cards to the left of the grid and place them so that each horizontal row and vertical column contains a joker plus four aces of different suits, and each shape (shown by the thick lines) also contains a joker plus four aces of different suits. Some cards are already in place.

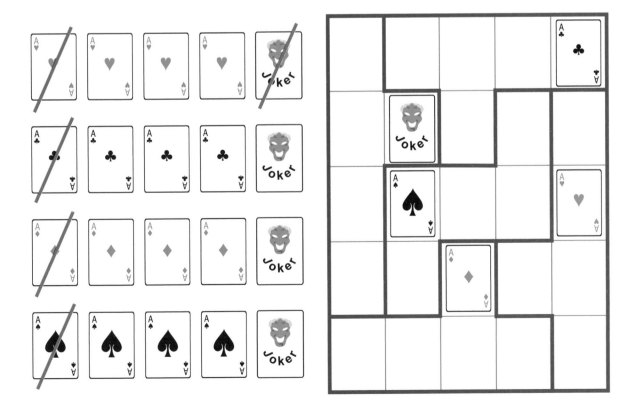

21 DIFFICULTY ●●●☆☆☆☆☆☆☆ ⏱ 3 Minutes

Make a calculation totaling the figure on the right by inserting the four mathematical operators (+, −, ÷, x) between the numbers shown.

They can be inserted in any order, and one of them has been used twice.

| 9 | | 3 | | 6 | | 2 | | 4 | | 5 | = | 10 |

22 DIFFICULTY ●●●●●☆☆☆☆☆ ⏱ 5 Minutes

Given that scales a and b balance perfectly, how many circles are needed to balance scale c?

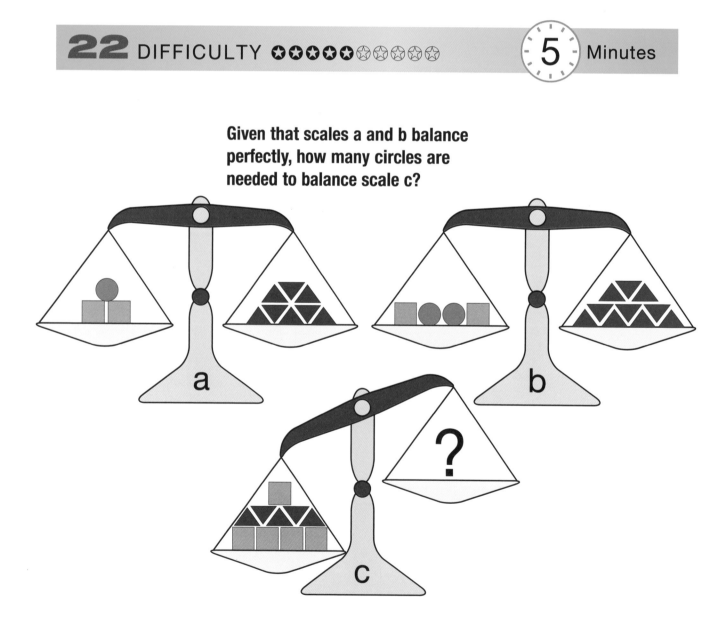

23 DIFFICULTY ✪✪✪✪✪☆☆☆☆☆

3 Minutes

Which of these configurations is the odd one out?

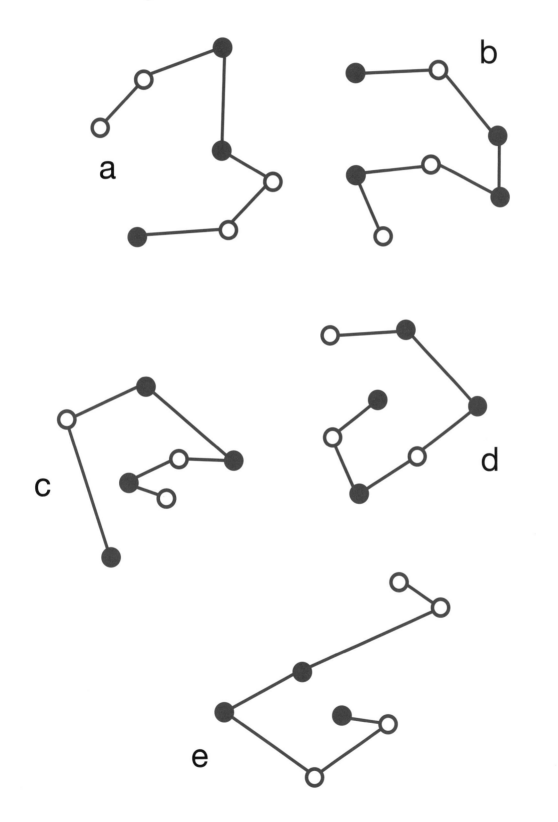

24 DIFFICULTY ●●●●●○☆☆☆☆ | 6 Minutes

Which of the four boxed figures (a, b, c, or d) completes the set?

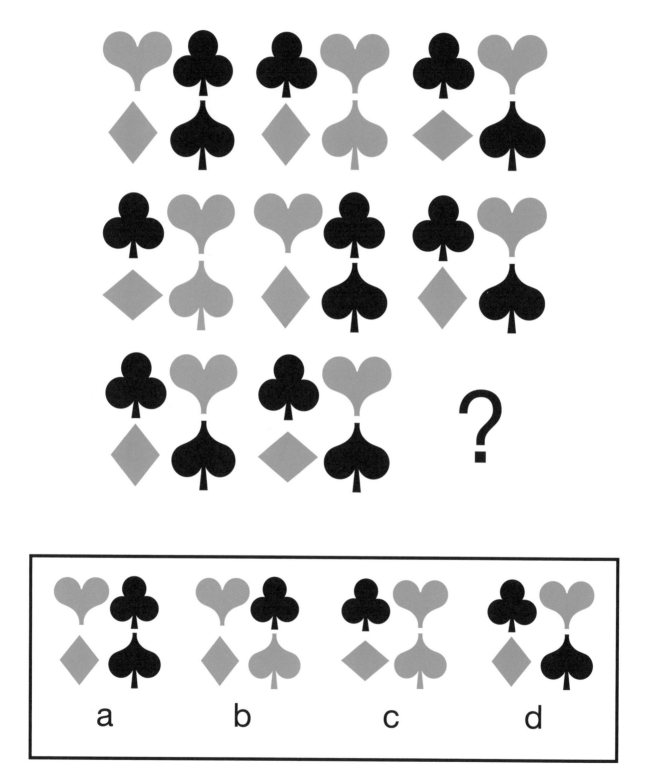

25 DIFFICULTY ✪✪✪✩✩✩✩✩✩✩ ⏱ **5** Minutes

Can you fit these numbers into the grid? One number has already been inserted to help you get started.

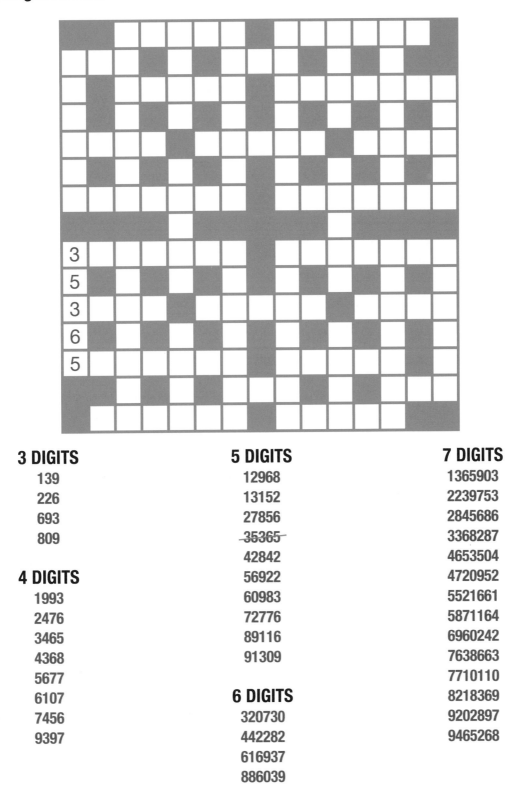

3 DIGITS
139
226
693
809

4 DIGITS
1993
2476
3465
4368
5677
6107
7456
9397

5 DIGITS
12968
13152
27856
~~35365~~
42842
56922
60983
72776
89116
91309

6 DIGITS
320730
442282
616937
886039

7 DIGITS
1365903
2239753
2845686
3368287
4653504
4720952
5521661
5871164
6960242
7638663
7710110
8218369
9202897
9465268

MINDWORKS BRAIN TRAINING

26 DIFFICULTY ●●●●●●○○○○ | 8 Minutes

Five models each wore one of five items by five designers on the catwalk. Can you figure out each model's last name and which item, by which designer, each wore?

1. Ms. Jones didn't wear Vergucci, carry a bag, or wear gloves or blue.
2. The pink hat wasn't Fundi or Tom Buick, and Kate didn't wear it.
3. Naomi Taylor didn't wear gloves or shoes.
4. The Vergucci bag wasn't red.
5. Manon works for Armande, which doesn't make hats or gloves.
6. Jody wore all black but not Canale, and she didn't wear a coat.
7. Miss Dupris wore gold but not by Fundi or Armande, and she didn't wear gloves.
8. Ms. Briant wore Canale.
9. Tom Buick's collection was all blue.

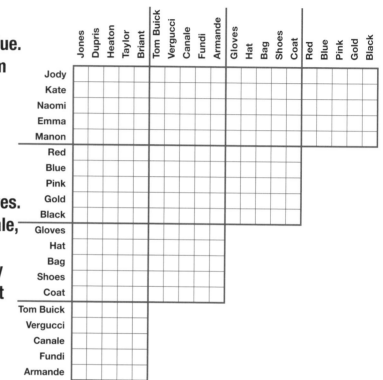

27 DIFFICULTY ●●●●●○○○○○ | 5 Minutes

Which pentagon from the selection below should replace the question mark?

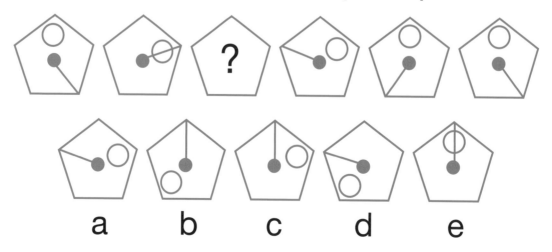

28 DIFFICULTY ★★★★★☆☆☆☆☆ (No target time)

Here's a very simple but effective game. Take 15 coins (it doesn't matter how they are arranged). Two players take turns picking up one, two, or three coins. Play continues until there are no coins left in the pile. The winner is the person who ends up with an odd number of coins.

Play the game a few times and see if you can figure out a winning strategy. The player who goes first always has the advantage, if he or she knows how to use it properly! For a variation, try starting with 13 coins.

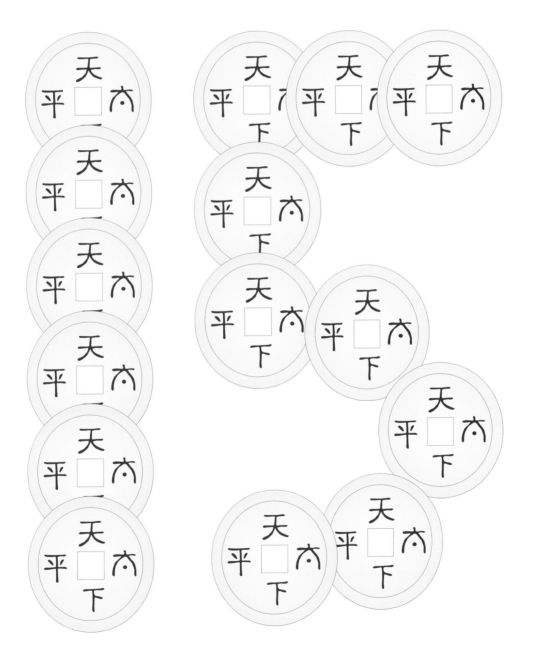

Given that scales a and b balance perfectly, how many gooseberries are needed to balance scale c?

30 DIFFICULTY ✪✪✪✪☆☆☆☆☆☆  3 Minutes

What number comes next?

49, 62, 70, 77, 91, 101, 103, ?

31 DIFFICULTY ✪✪✪✪☆☆☆☆☆☆ 4 Minutes

Which number is the odd one out?

7141   9187
3025   6140
8164   5149
2079   4193

32 DIFFICULTY ★★★★☆☆☆☆☆  4 Minutes

Each row and column contains the same numbers and signs, but they are arranged in a different order each time. Find the correct order to arrive at the final totals shown.

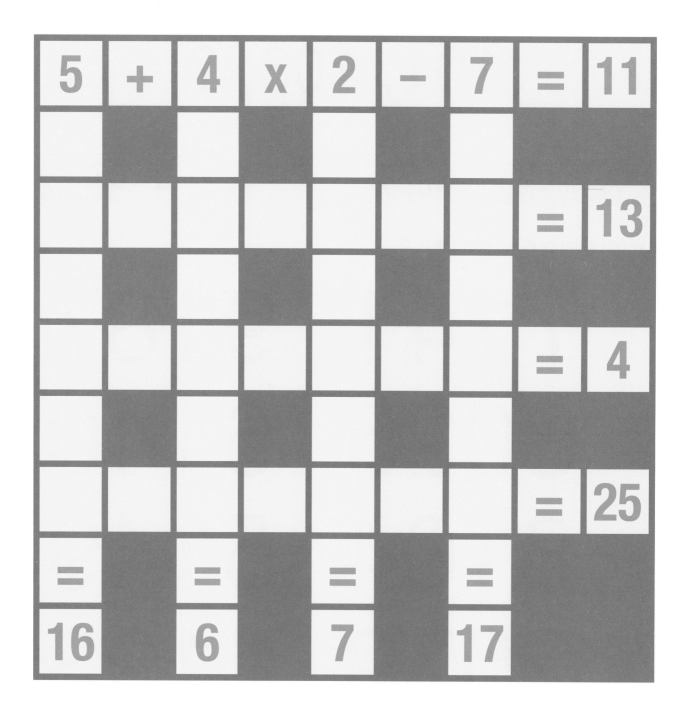

5	+	4	x	2	−	7	=	11
							=	13
							=	4
							=	25
=		=		=		=		
16		6		7		17		

33 DIFFICULTY ●●●●●✩✩✩✩✩

4 Minutes

The number 246135 appears just once in this grid and occurs in a straight line, running either backward or forward in a horizontal, vertical, or diagonal direction. Can you locate it?

2	4	6	2	4	6	1	6	4	2	5	4
4	4	3	5	6	5	3	5	6	3	3	5
6	5	6	6	4	2	3	2	1	5	1	1
1	3	3	1	2	5	4	3	2	3	5	3
3	1	4	2	4	6	3	1	5	6	3	6
2	6	2	6	4	2	6	4	2	5	6	4
3	4	4	1	2	4	5	1	1	6	4	2
1	2	6	4	4	1	3	6	2	4	2	4
6	4	5	2	6	3	4	4	5	2	3	6
4	6	1	4	1	2	2	2	6	4	2	1
2	3	2	6	2	3	1	6	4	2	4	2
5	6	1	2	4	6	1	3	2	5	2	5

34 DIFFICULTY ★★★★★☆☆☆☆☆ | ④ Minutes

Make a calculation totaling the figure below by inserting the four mathematical operators (+, −, ÷, x) between the numbers shown.

They can be inserted in any order, and one of them has been used twice.

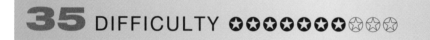

| 8 | 4 | 3 | 5 | 2 | 6 | = | 3 |

35 DIFFICULTY ★★★★★★★☆☆☆ | ⑥ Minutes

Here's a trickier one! Using the same principle as above try to complete the calculation. One of the mathematical operators has been used twice.

| 99 | 25 | 36 | 11 | 22 | 72 | = | 127 |

Given that scales a and b balance perfectly, how many red balls are needed to balance scale c?

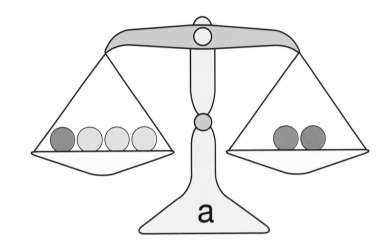

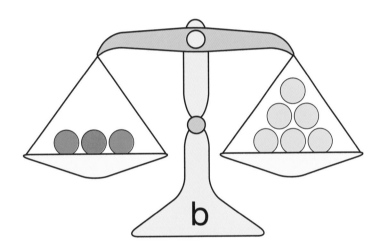

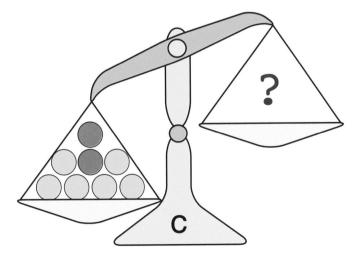

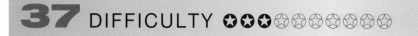 

MINDWORKS BRAIN TRAINING

37 DIFFICULTY ●●● ☆☆☆☆☆☆☆ ③ Minutes

The number 619362 appears just once in this grid and occurs in a straight line, running either backward or forward in a horizontal, vertical, or diagonal direction. Can you locate it?

1	3	9	1	4	2	6	4	9	1	2	4
2	2	6	3	6	9	3	2	6	4	6	3
6	4	6	9	2	1	2	1	9	3	6	2
3	6	2	4	3	6	9	3	1	2	9	6
9	2	9	1	9	3	4	4	9	6	3	3
1	2	1	6	6	1	3	2	6	3	6	6
2	9	6	3	1	9	6	3	9	2	2	1
6	1	2	3	6	4	9	6	1	3	1	9
3	9	3	1	9	3	6	2	2	6	6	6
9	4	2	9	2	1	3	1	9	2	1	2
1	2	1	3	1	3	6	4	3	1	4	1
4	6	9	1	3	2	6	3	1	9	6	9

Place the remaining pieces in the grid so that:
* each row and column has two red and two yellow squares, and
* no row or column has two of the same digit.

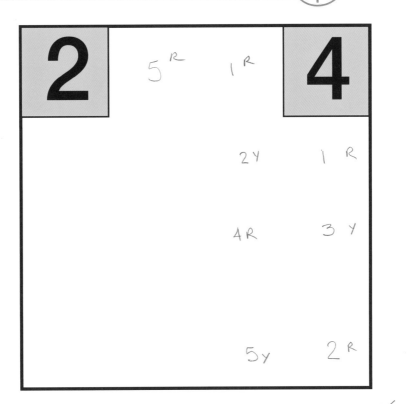

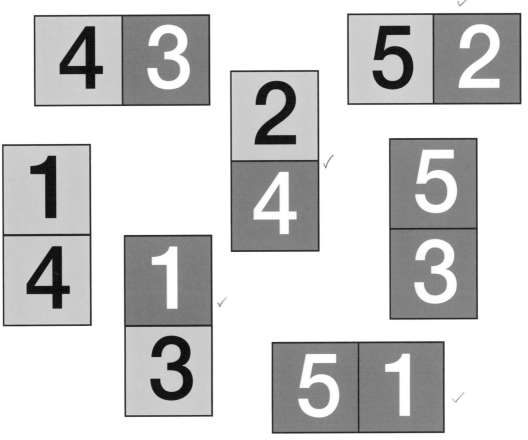

39 DIFFICULTY ✪✪✪✪✪✩✩✩✩✩ ④ Minutes

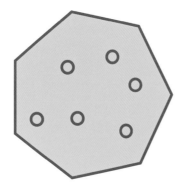

is to:

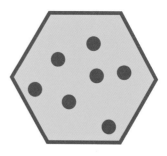

as

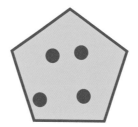

is to:

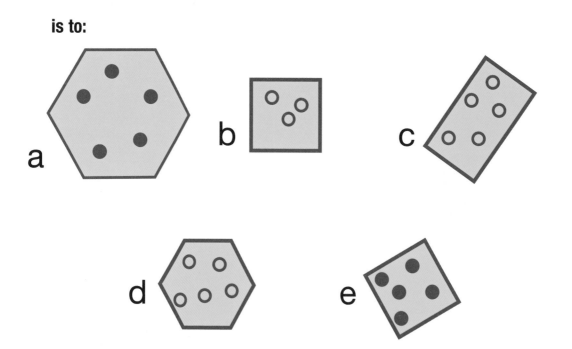

40 DIFFICULTY ★★★★★★☆☆☆☆

30 Minutes

See if you can rise to the challenge and complete this numeropic. See the panel in puzzle 12 for instructions on how to complete this type of puzzle.

Top (column) clues, read top to bottom:

```
                                    2
                  1     1       2   1
            1     2   6 1   8 2 1
  2 4 5 6 8    10 9   2 7 8 5 6   6 5 1 6 3 5
1 1 1 2 4 3 10 11 12 4 6 1 1 6 6 8 6 9 7 7 6 3 7 1 13   9 6 5 1
2 2 4 2 4 2 4 3 3 1 1 7 11 2 6 1 10 7 1 1 5 1 4 6 6 11 7 6 3 1
1 1 1 7 1 1 1 1 2 1 1 13 1 1 1 2 1 1 12 1 1 2 1 1 1 1 1 10 1 1 1 1
```

Left (row) clues, read top to bottom:

```
                        8
                      3 3
                      4 3
                3 1 5 2
                  4 7 2
                  5 5 3
                  6 5 5
                  6 7 6
          8 1 1 1 1 6
                    8 7
                  7 8 5
                  7 9 4
                  7 10 3
                  6 10 3
                  6 10 2
              5 2 3 3 2
    1 1 4 2 1 1 1 2 2
      1 1 2 2 3 3 1 1
            1 1 1 13 1
                5 13 1
                  19 2
                  17 5
                  14 6
                3 4 4 7
                5 2 2 9
                5 2 2 7
                3 4 3 5
        1 1 1 1 1 1 1 1 1
          1 1 1 1 1 1 1 1
                      30
```

41 DIFFICULTY ⚫⚫⚫⚫⚫☆☆☆☆☆   ⏱ 5 Minutes

Each block is equal to the sum of the two numbers beneath it. Can you find all the missing numbers?

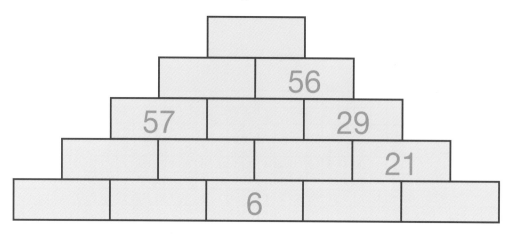

42 DIFFICULTY ⚫⚫⚫⚫☆☆☆☆☆☆   ⏱ 3 Minutes

Where should the hour hand point to on clock e?

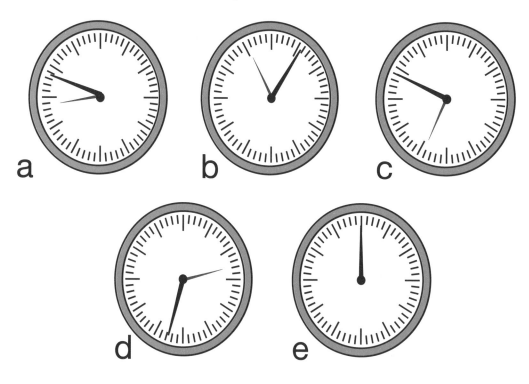

43 DIFFICULTY ★★★★★☆☆☆☆ **12** Minutes

The ace, 2, 3, and 4 in each of four suits should be placed in the grid below. Digits and letters showing the values A, 2, 3, and 4 and the suits have been shown at the beginning of each row across and column down to indicate which values and suits are contained in those rows and columns. Can you figure out the unique place for each card?

MINDWⓄRKS BRAIN TRAINING

44 DIFFICULTY ✪✪✪✪✪✪✩✩✩   ⏱ 30 Minutes

You'll probably be over the moon when you've completed this numeropic. See the panel in puzzle 12 for instructions on how to complete this type of puzzle.

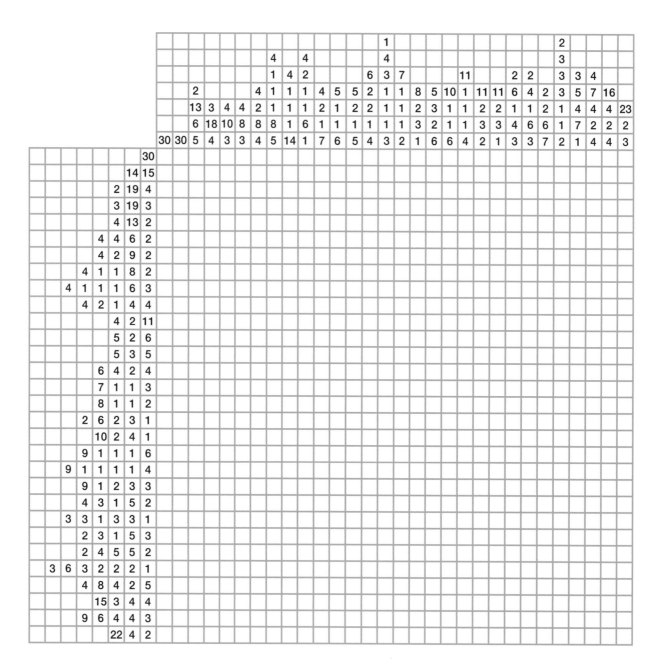

45 DIFFICULTY ✪✪✪✪☆☆☆☆☆☆ ③ Minutes

The number 302949 appears just once in this grid and occurs in a straight line, running either backward or forward in a horizontal, vertical, or diagonal direction. Can you locate it?

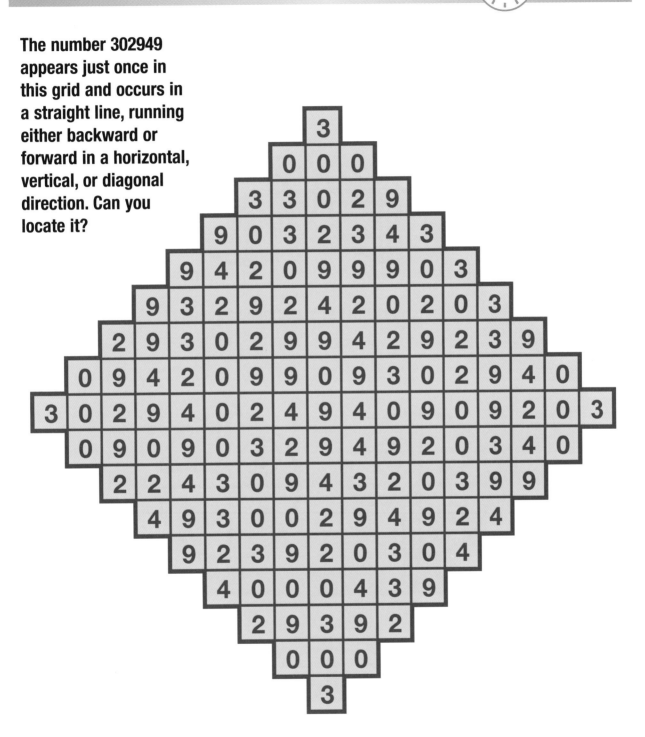

4 Minutes

What comes next in the above sequence?

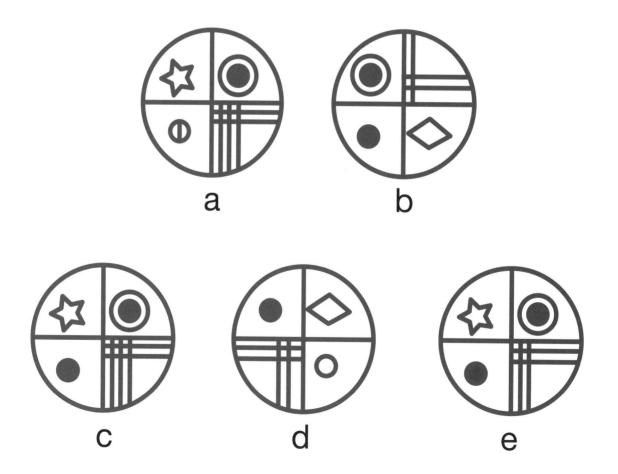

a   b

c   d   e

47 DIFFICULTY ✪✪✪✪✫✫✫✫✫✫  2 Minutes

Which is the odd one out?

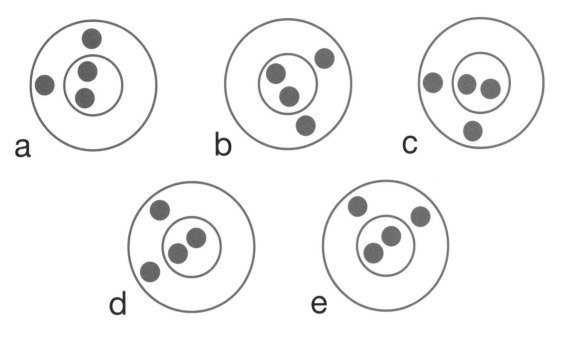

a   b   c

d   e

48 DIFFICULTY ✪✪✪✪✪✪✫✫✫✫ 4 Minutes

On petri dish a there are currently 5,000 bacteria that produce another 250 bacteria per hour. On petri dish b there are currently 12,000 bacteria, but 100 bacteria die per hour. When will both dishes have an identical bacteria population?

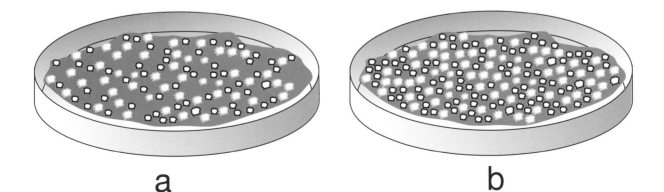

a   b

49 DIFFICULTY ✪✪✪✪✪☆☆☆☆☆ ⑤ Minutes

Can you fit these numbers into the grid? One number has already been inserted to help you get started.

3 DIGITS	**5 DIGITS**	**7 DIGITS**
376	17686	1266562
579	21019	1745427
798	33644	2137924
964	46399	2735436
	59575	3675684
4 DIGITS	66796	4487579
1560	74716	5997674
2258	84664	6337004
3065	94955	6727751
4696	99145	7178438
5862		7912329
7213	**6 DIGITS**	8148431
8024	546262	9467952
9332	695591	9945593
	782758	
	998230	

50 DIFFICULTY ✪✪✪✪✪✪✪☆☆☆ ⏱ 7 Minutes

Can you crack the safe? First decide which of the 14 statements given are false, then shade out the areas on the combination lock that are labeled with the letters of those false statements (so if you think statement A is false, shade out area A). The remaining lit segments will give you the digital combination required.

Hint: four of the statements are false.

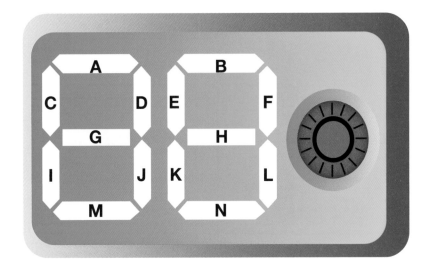

A. There are a dozen dozens in a gross.
B. 39 is a prime number.
C. 111 x 111 = 12,321.
D. 50 divided by 0.5 equals 25.
E. The total score you get from rolling two standard dice is 7, on average.
F. The positive square root of 121 is 11.
G. (1/2) x (2/3) x (3/4) x (4/5) = 1/5.
H. There are 1,440 minutes in a typical day.
I. If the digits of a whole number add up to 9, the number is divisible by 9.
J. "Threescore years and ten" equals 70 years.
K. If P x Q = Q, then P must be 1.
L. If two angles in a triangle are 36 and 54 degrees, the third angle is a right angle.
M. In Roman numerals, I + V + X + L + C + D + M = 1,666.
N. The cube of 5 is 225.

51 DIFFICULTY ✪✪✪✪✪☆☆☆☆☆   8 Minutes

Five owners brought their dragsters to race. Can you match each racer with his last name, name the cars, and find out each car's speed?

1. **Steve's Blisterine wasn't the fastest, and neither was the dragster owned by Zak Dupris.**
2. **Van Happs's Hot Stuff was 25 mph slower than one car, but only 10 mph slower than Jackson.**
3. **Marty was second quickest—20 mph quicker than Chicken Speed.**
4. **Fast and Loose wasn't the quickest, but it was quicker than Bubba.**
5. **Schwartz was quicker than Delaney.**

	Jackson	Delaney	Schwartz	Dupris	Van Happs	235	240	250	255	265	Rock Racer	Blisterine	Hot Stuff	Chicken Speed	Fast and Loose
Steve															
Zak															
Bubba															
Marty															
Kate															
Rock Racer																
Blisterine																
Hot Stuff																
Chicken Speed																
Fast and Loose																
235																
240																
250																
255																
265																

52 DIFFICULTY ✪✪✪☆☆☆☆☆☆☆   4 Minutes

Make a calculation totaling the figure on the right by inserting the four mathematical operators (+, −, ÷, x) between the numbers shown.

The mathematical operators can be in any order, and one of them has been used twice.

| 4 | | 6 | | 5 | | 2 | | 7 | | 3 | = 8 |

53 DIFFICULTY ✪✪✪✪✪✪✪✪☆☆ — 8 Minutes

Make your way from top left to bottom right in this number maze. You may only move to calculations that total either one more or one less than the previous sum.

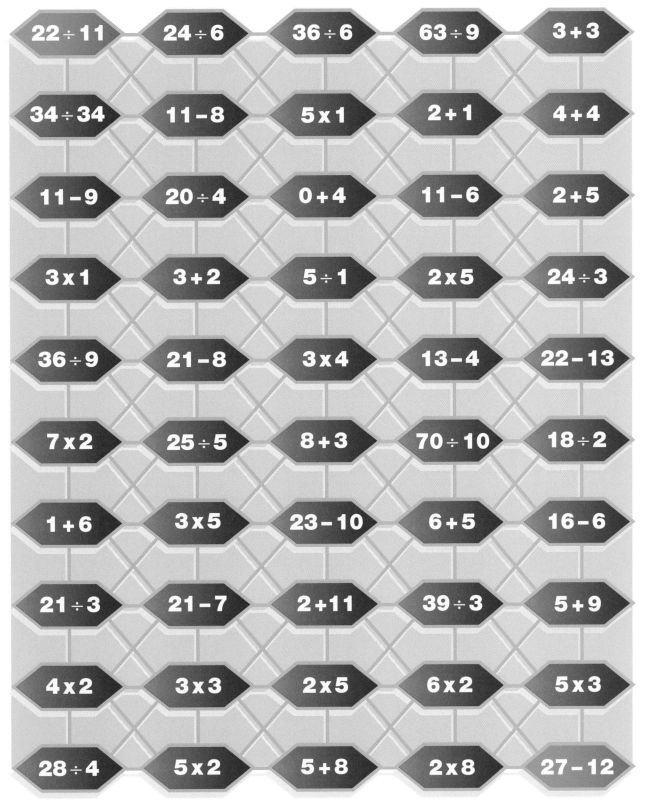

54 DIFFICULTY ✪✪✪✪✪✪☆☆☆☆ ⏲ 30 Minutes

Can you keep on the right track with this numeropic? Refer to the instructions on how to do this puzzle in puzzle 12 if you need any help.

55 DIFFICULTY ✪✪✪✪✪☆☆☆☆☆  5 Minutes

The number 295617 appears just once in this grid and occurs in a straight line, running either backward or forward in a horizontal, vertical, or diagonal direction. Can you locate it?

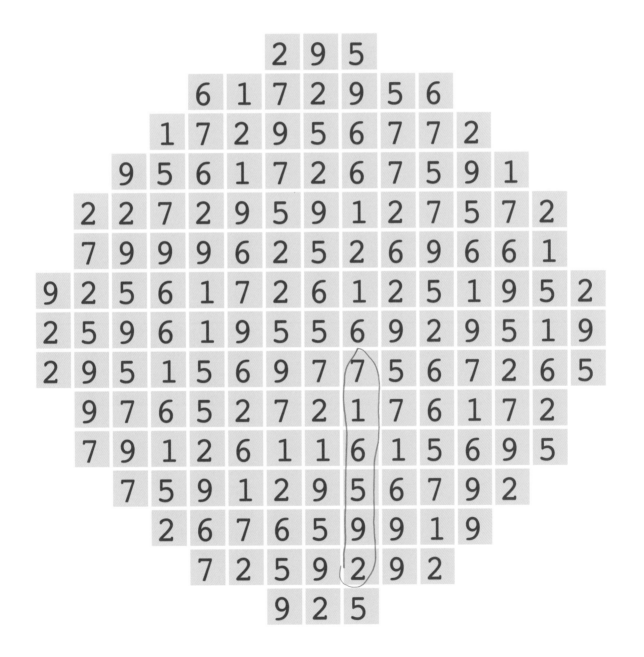

56 DIFFICULTY ✪✪✪✪✪✪✪☆☆☆

7 Minutes

Each block is equal to the sum of the two numbers beneath it. Can you find all the missing numbers?

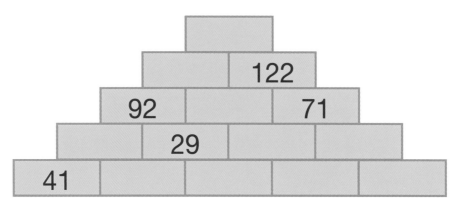

57 DIFFICULTY ✪✪✪✪✪☆☆☆☆☆

8 Minutes

Five workers at a candy factory all have different jobs on different lines. Can you match each first name to a last name, a product, and a job?

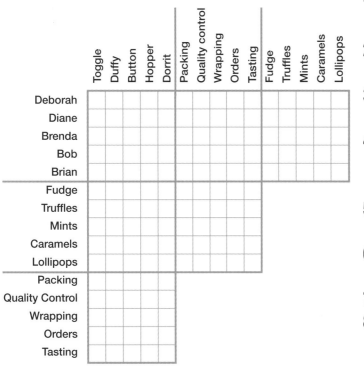

1. Mr. or Mrs. Dorrit works with fudge and not with Brenda.
2. Diane Toggle doesn't wrap and she doesn't work with mints or truffles.
3. Bob in orders doesn't deal with caramels.
4. No one with a first name that begins with "B" works in quality control.
5. There are no women in lollipops and no men in mints.
6. The truffle taster is a woman, but she isn't Deborah Duffy.
7. Bob doesn't work in lollipops.
8. Mr. or Mrs. Button works in packing. Caramels are not wrapped.

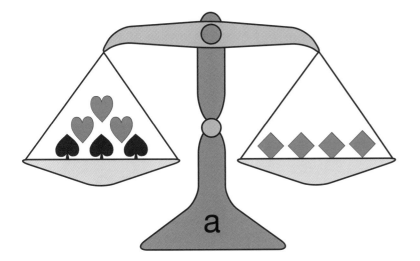

Given that scales a and b balance perfectly, how many hearts are needed to balance scale c?

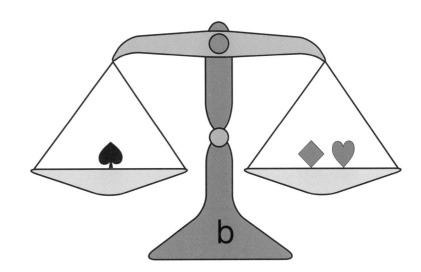

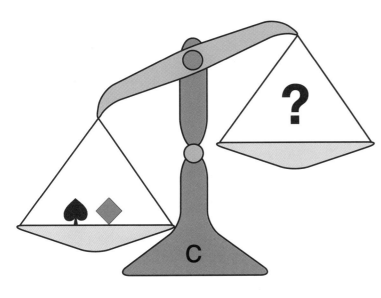

Each row and column contains the same numbers and signs, but they are arranged in a different order each time. Find the correct order to arrive at the final totals shown.

9	+	6	x	3	–	7	=	38
							=	28
							=	12
							=	33
=		=		=		=		
43		50		84		48		

We've given the cards shown here different values, so that an ace = 1, jack = 11, queen = 12, and king = 13, while all other cards have the same value as their numbers. Study this arrangement of cards carefully for one minute, then see if you can answer the questions on the next page.

[60] DIFFICULTY ✪✪✪✪✪✪✪☆☆☆ ⏰ 5 Minutes

Can you answer these questions about the puzzle on the previous page without looking back?

1. Which suit is the king?

2. Which number does not appear?

3. What is the lowest total value of four cards in a row?

4. What is the lowest total value of three cards in a column?

5. Which card is directly to the left of the 9 of diamonds?

6. What is the total value of the four corner cards?

7. Which suit is the ten?

8. Which card is directly above the 9 of diamonds?

61 DIFFICULTY ✪✪✪✪✪✪☆☆☆☆ ⏰ 4 Minutes

Make a calculation totaling the figure on the right by inserting the four mathematical operators (+, −, ÷, x) between the numbers shown.

They can be inserted in any order, and one of them has been used twice.

| 10 | 7 | 11 | 4 | 8 | 12 | = | 19 |

62 DIFFICULTY ●●●●●●●○○○

5 Minutes

Can you fit these numbers into the grid? One number has already been inserted to help you get started.

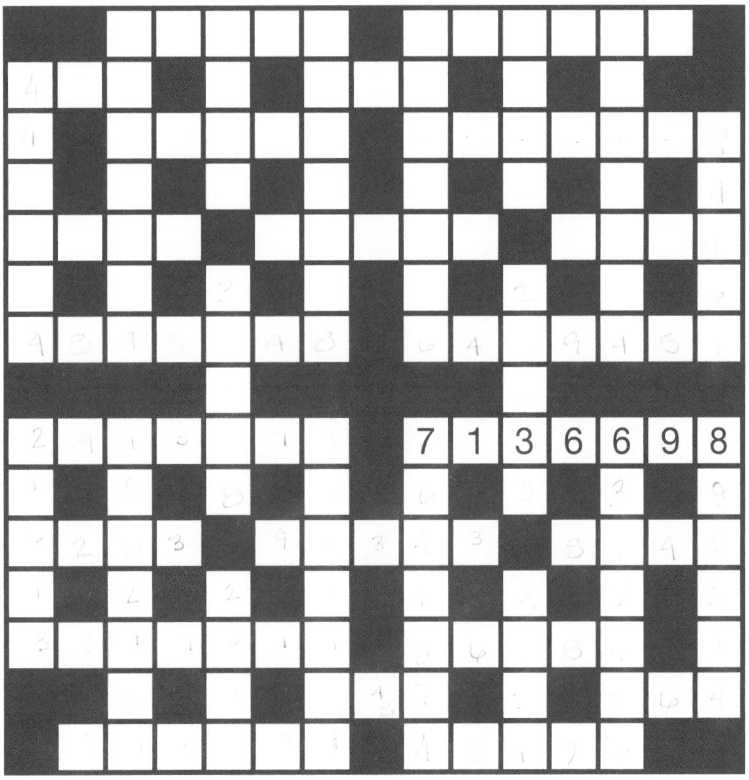

3 DIGITS
247
264
413
487

4 DIGITS
2528
3248
6283
6973
7184
8145
8831
9281

5 DIGITS
21643
28634
35138
38626
43196
54332
84461
86884
91798
95343

6 DIGITS
396889
442955
813158
895314

7 DIGITS
1582989
2413379
2757941
3396839
3397591
4845548
5558199
5597831
6317426
6489451
7136698
7641874
8744372
9159129

63 DIFFICULTY ✪✪✪✪✪☆☆☆☆☆ ③ Minutes

Take a close look at the patterned shields below. Which one is the odd one out?

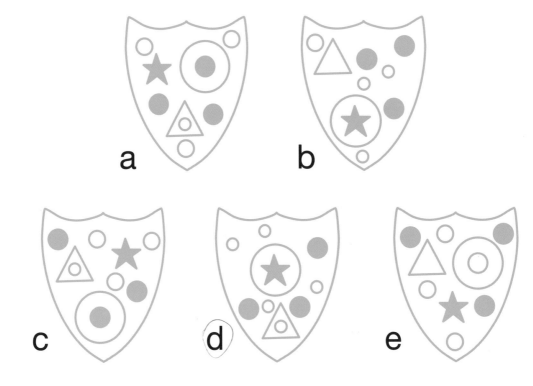

a   b

c   d   e

64 DIFFICULTY ✪✪✪✪✪☆☆☆☆☆ ② Minutes

What number comes next?

749326

239746

479236

???????

65 DIFFICULTY ✪✪✪✪✪✪✪☆☆☆ · ④ Minutes

The number 472596 appears just once in this grid and occurs in a straight line, running either backward or forward in a horizontal, vertical, or diagonal direction; however, as you can see, the numbers are reversed! Can you locate it?

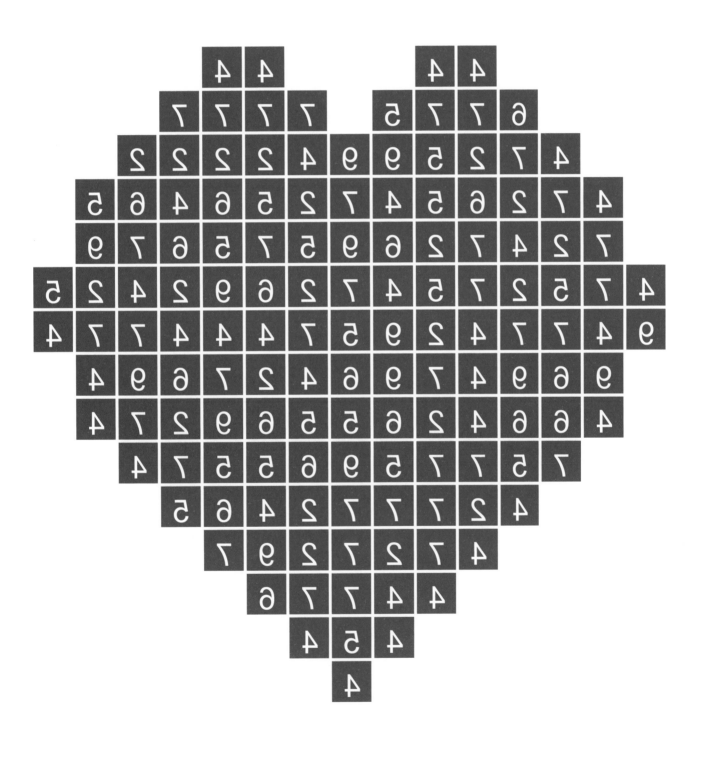

66 DIFFICULTY ★★★★★☆☆☆☆☆   (No target time)

For this game, you will need three coins or counters for each player. The first player chooses a circle on the board to place the first piece. The second player then does the same. Play continues in the usual manner until all the players have played their pieces.

The aim is to get your three pieces in a horizontal, vertical, or diagonal line. If there is no winner after the first six opening moves, the first player chooses any coin and slides it along a line to any available adjacent circle. The second player takes a turn and so on. The first player to make a line of three wins the game.

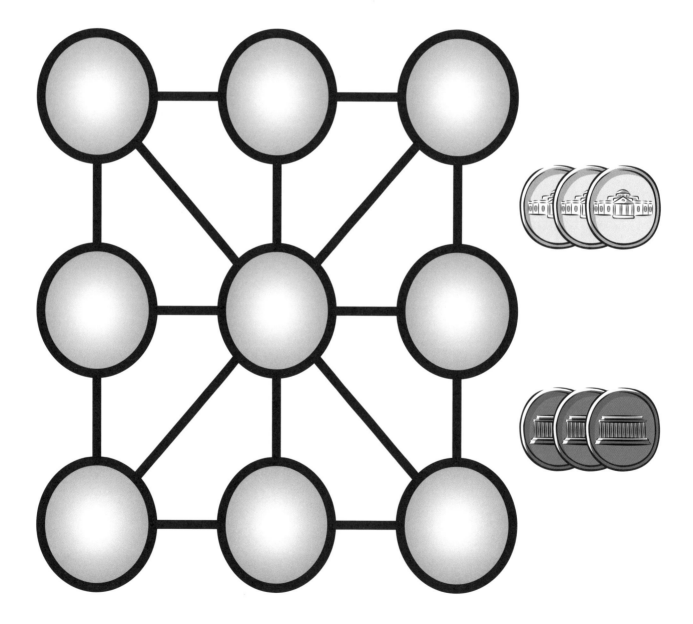

67 DIFFICULTY ✪✪✪✪✪✪✩✩✩✩ ⏱ 30 Minutes

Can you steam through this numeropic in record time? If you need any help in completing this puzzle, refer to the instructions in puzzle 12.

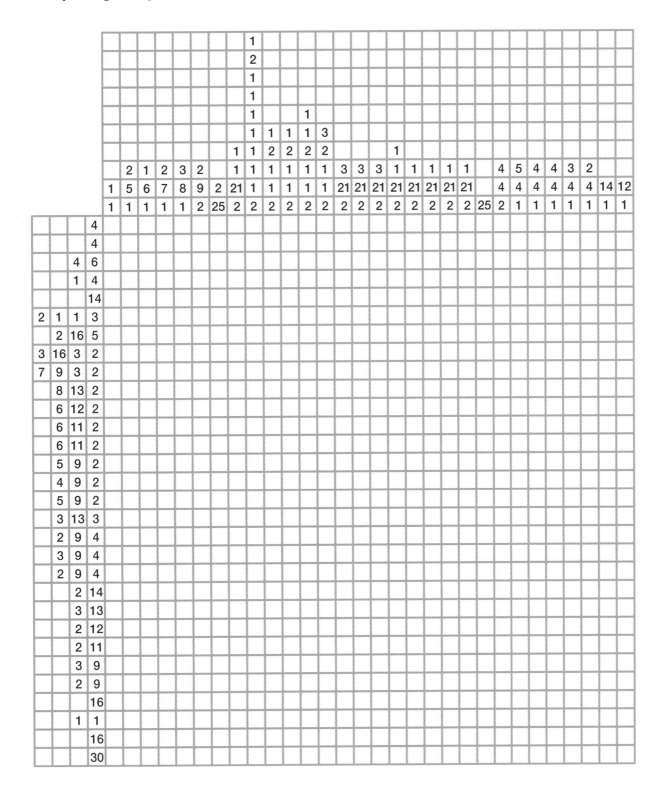

68 DIFFICULTY ✪✪✪✪✪✪☆☆☆☆

4 Minutes

Make a calculation totaling the figure on the right by inserting the four mathematical operators (+, −, ÷, x) between the numbers shown.

They can be inserted in any order, and one of them has been used twice.

| 20 | | 14 | | 9 | | 6 | | 18 | | 3 | = | 44 |

69 DIFFICULTY ✪✪✪✪✪✪☆☆☆☆

3 Minutes

Use your powers of logic to determine what number comes next in the sequence below.

36, 91, 21, 51, 82, 12, 42, ?

70 DIFFICULTY ⭐⭐⭐⭐⭐⭐⭐☆☆☆ ⏱ 5 Minutes

Each block in this number pyramid is equal to the sum of the two numbers beneath it. Can you deduce all the missing numbers?

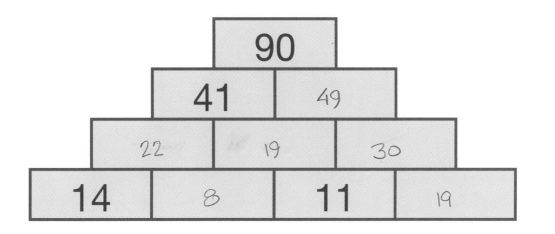

71 DIFFICULTY ⭐⭐⭐⭐⭐⭐☆☆☆☆ ⏱ 5 Minutes

If you saw these somewhat eccentric clocks on an office wall, what would be the logical time for GEORGETOWN?

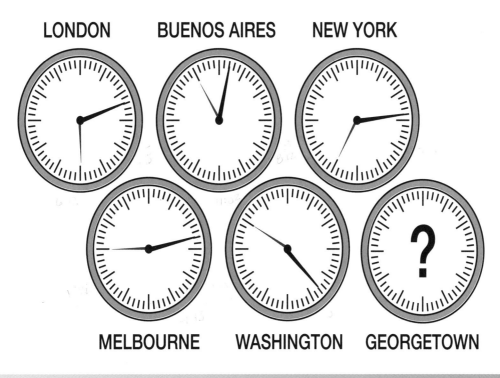

LONDON BUENOS AIRES NEW YORK

MELBOURNE WASHINGTON GEORGETOWN

63

72 DIFFICULTY ✪✪✪✪☆☆☆☆☆ ⏱ 5 Minutes

Which of the four boxed figures (a, b, c, or d) completes the set?

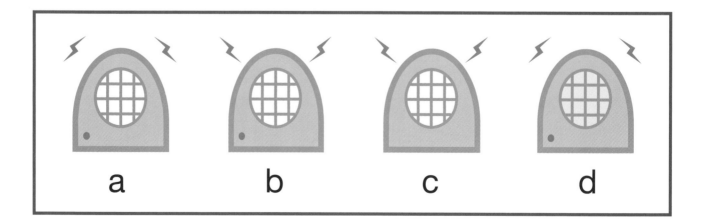

DIFFICULTY  7 Minutes

Place the loose tiles into the grid and ensure that:

* no row or column contains three tiles of the same color, and
* each row, column, and main diagonal adds up to 18.

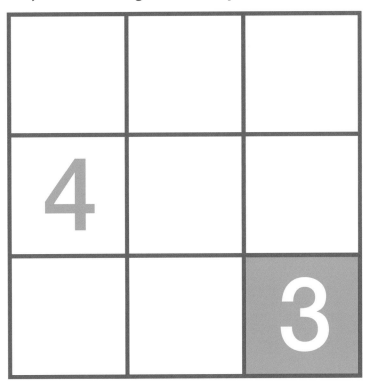

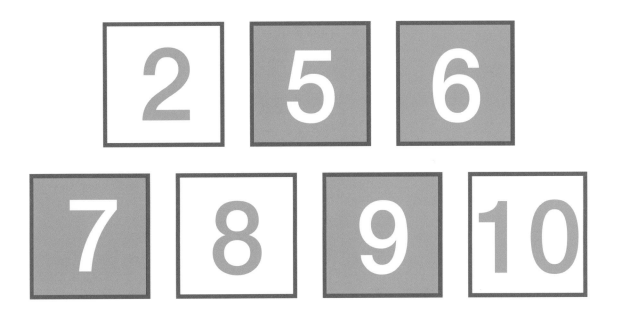

74 DIFFICULTY ✪✪✪✪✪✩✩✩✩✩   ⏱ 5 Minutes

Can you fit these numbers into the grid? One number has already been inserted to help you get started.

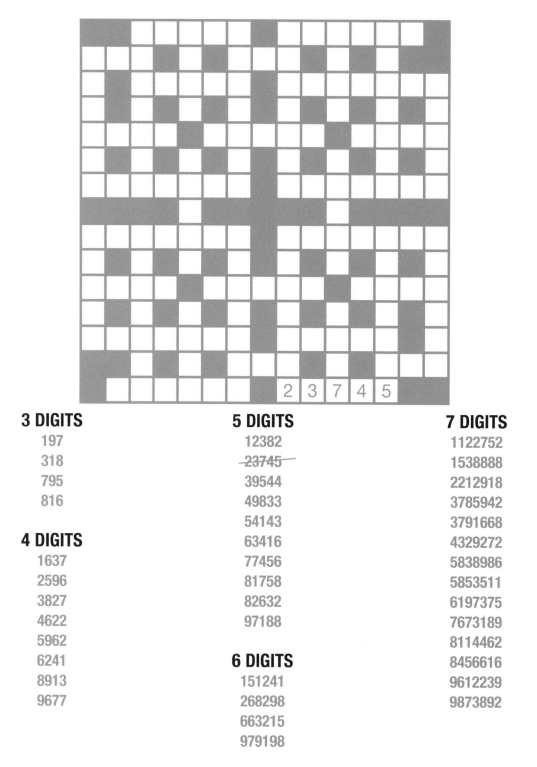

3 DIGITS	5 DIGITS	7 DIGITS
197	12382	1122752
318	~~23745~~	1538888
795	39544	2212918
816	49833	3785942
	54143	3791668
4 DIGITS	63416	4329272
1637	77456	5838986
2596	81758	5853511
3827	82632	6197375
4622	97188	7673189
5962		8114462
6241	**6 DIGITS**	8456616
8913	151241	9612239
9677	268298	9873892
	663215	
	979198	

75 DIFFICULTY ✪✪✪✪✪✪✪☆☆☆

1 Minute

Study these dice for one minute, then see if you can answer the questions on the next page.

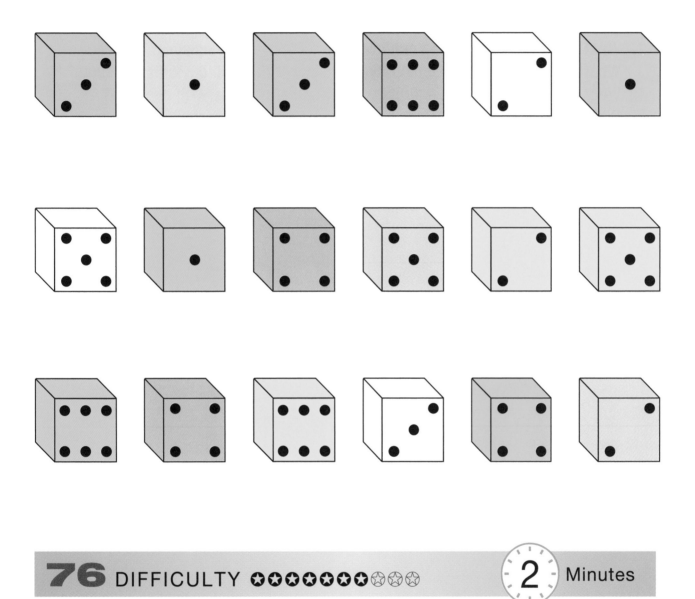

76 DIFFICULTY ✪✪✪✪✪✪✪☆☆☆

2 Minutes

A security guard is working a long night shift. At ten past one in the morning, he makes his first patrol. He patrols another four times at 70-minute intervals. He can then rest for a few hours before the patrol just after ten o'clock. He completes two more patrols with 70-minute gaps before clocking off at lunchtime. What superstition does he have?

[75] DIFFICULTY ✪✪✪✪✪✪✪☆☆☆ ⏱ **3** Minutes

Can you answer these questions about the dice on the previous page without looking back?

1. What is the color of the die directly below the white die that has five spots?
2. What is the sum total of the number of spots on the two most central dice?
3. What is the color of the die directly to the left of the blue die with two spots?
4. What is the color of the die directly above the orange die with one spot?
5. What is the sum total of the number of spots on all of the pink dice?
6. What are the colors of the three dice that have only one spot?
7. Only two dice of the same color are horizontally adjacent to one another: what is the sum total of the number of spots on these two dice?
8. Only two dice are identical: what is the color of these two dice?

77 DIFFICULTY ✪✪✪✪✪✪☆☆☆☆ ⏱ **3** Minutes

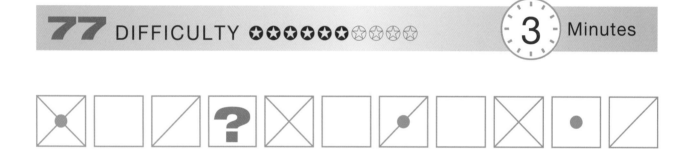

Which box below should replace the question mark in the above sequence?

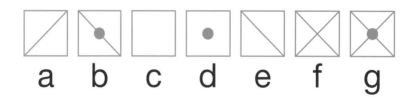

a   b   c   d   e   f   g

This puzzle uses the 16 face cards and aces from all four suits of a standard deck of cards. Complete the grid so that no row or column contains two cards of the same denomination or suit.

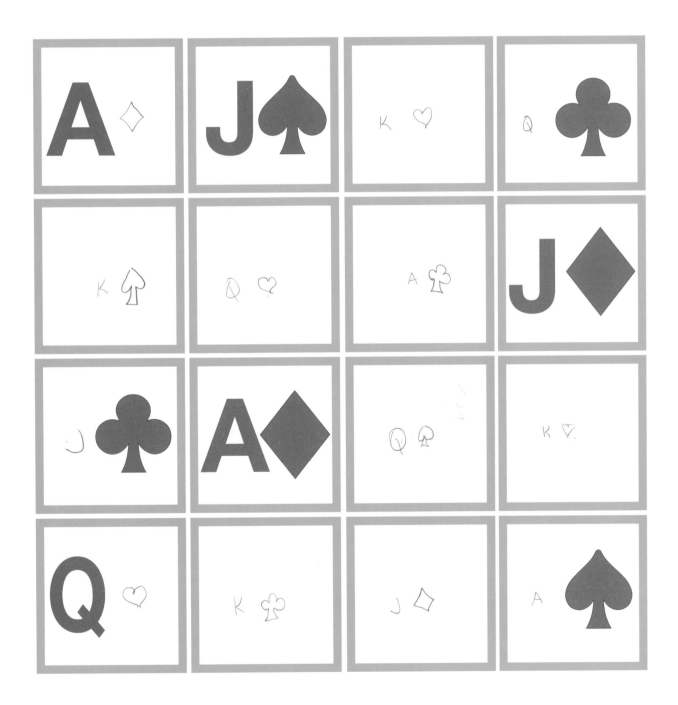

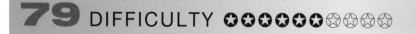
79 DIFFICULTY ○○○○○○○☆☆☆☆  **6** Minutes

Can you crack the safe? First decide which of the 14 statements given are false. Then shade out the areas on the combination lock that are labeled with the letters of those false statements (so if you think statement A is false, shade out area A). The remaining lit segments will give you the digital combination required.

Hint: five of the statements are false.

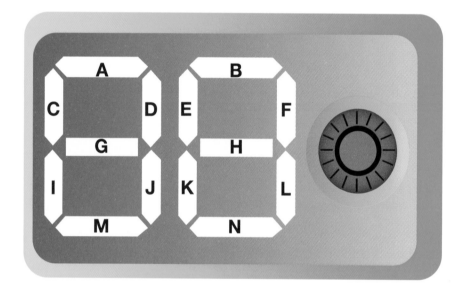

A. Ronald Reagan was the 40th president of the United States.
B. IQ stands for Intelligence Quota.
C. In architecture, a campanile is a bell tower.
D. In medieval times, a knight's glove was called a gauntlet.
E. The first Boeing 747 jumbo jet flew in February 1959.
F. A force 12 storm on the Beaufort scale is a hurricane.
G. Clint Eastwood won the Best Director Oscar for Unforgiven in 1992.
H. A lepidopterist collects coins.
I. Montezuma II was the last emperor of the Aztecs.
J. Limestone and chalk are forms of calcium carbonate.
K. Omega is the fourth letter of the Greek alphabet.
L. The real name of Batman is Bruce Wayne.
M. El Cid and Macbeth were born in the same century.
N. Cygnus cygnus is the Latin classification for the raven.

80 DIFFICULTY ✪✪✪✪✪✪✩✩✩✩ · 4 · Minutes

Complete the calculation totaling the figure on the right by inserting the four mathematical operators (+, −, ÷, x) between the numbers shown.

The mathematical operators can be in any order, and one of them has been used twice.

44　11　57　39　13　86 = 200

81 DIFFICULTY ✪✪✪✪✪✪✪✩✩✩ · 6 · Minutes

Take the cards around the outside of the grid and place them so that each horizontal row contains cards of six different values and each vertical column contains cards of four different values and four different suits. No card should be placed either horizontally or vertically next to one of the same color. The values of the cards are as per their numbers. Cards already in place should not be moved.

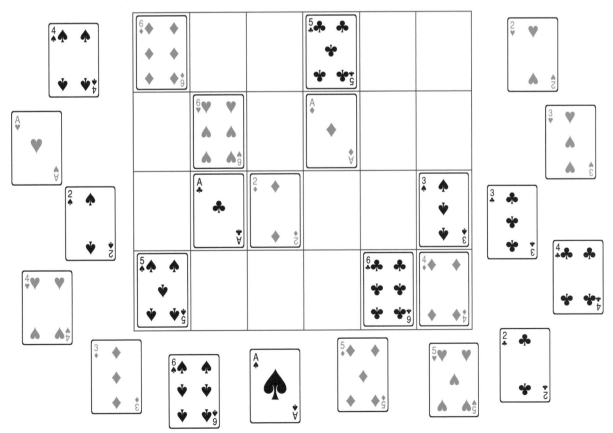

82 DIFFICULTY ✪✪✪✪✪✪✩✩✩✩

2 Minutes

Which number is the odd one out?

6839

7421

8243

2471

4283

3869

9263

83 DIFFICULTY ✪✪✪✪✪✪✪✪✪✩

5 Minutes

Each block in this especially difficult number pyramid is equal to the sum of the two numbers beneath it. Find the missing numbers.

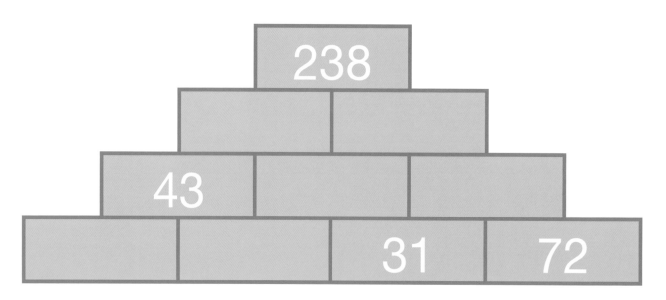

84 DIFFICULTY ✪✪✪✪✪✪☆☆☆☆ 3 Minutes

3682497

is to

9738642

and

285417

is to

751842

and

7186293

is to…

?

85 DIFFICULTY ✪✪✪✪✪✪✪✪☆☆ — ⏱ 5 Minutes

Each of the blocks in this challenging number pyramid is equal to the sum of the two numbers beneath it. Can you find all of the missing numbers?

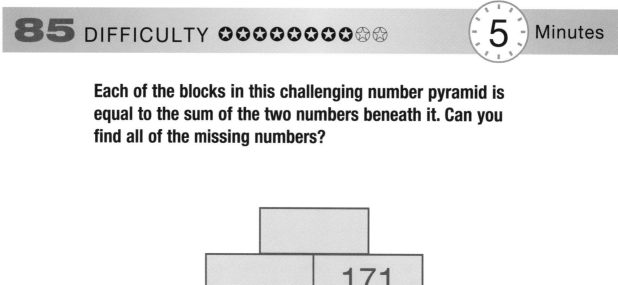

86 DIFFICULTY ✪✪✪✪✪☆☆☆☆☆ — ⏱ 4 Minutes

Make a calculation totaling the figure on the right by inserting the four mathematical operators (+, −, ÷, x) between the numbers shown.

They can be inserted in any order, and one of them has been used twice.

| 70 | | 86 | | 13 | | 66 | | 4 | | 27 | = | 171 |

87 DIFFICULTY ✪✪✪✪✪✪✪☆☆☆   10 Minutes

Five soccer players, playing in different positions, scored a varying number of goals for their teams. Can you match each first name with a last name, a team, a position, and a number of goals scored?

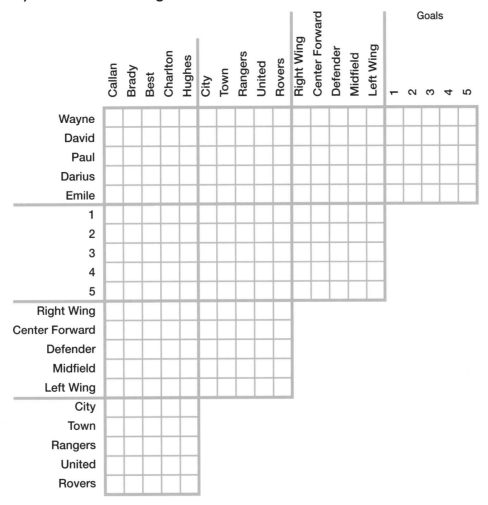

1. **Wayne Brady isn't a midfielder or a center forward. He scored more goals than Darius.**
2. **Rovers' Charlton scored more than Brady.**
3. **The Rangers' center forward scored two less than the Rovers' player.**
4. **Paul, playing for United, scored one more than David.**
5. **Hughes got four. He isn't a winger.**
6. **Emile, the left winger, scored two more than the center forward and one less than the Town player.**
7. **Callan got one less than the City defender.**

88 DIFFICULTY ●●●●●☆☆☆☆☆  (4) Minutes

Make a calculation totaling the figure on the right by inserting the four mathematical operators (+, −, ÷, x) between the numbers shown.

They can be inserted in any order, and one of them has been used twice.

| 14 | 5 | 33 | 19 | 4 | 15 | = | 36 |

89 DIFFICULTY ●●●●☆☆☆☆☆☆ (2) Minutes

Which number below is the odd one out?

3984 7456

1203 7896

5032 3527

90 DIFFICULTY ✪✪✪✪✪✪✪☆☆☆  **5** Minutes

Given that scales a and b balance perfectly, how many spoons are needed to balance scale c?

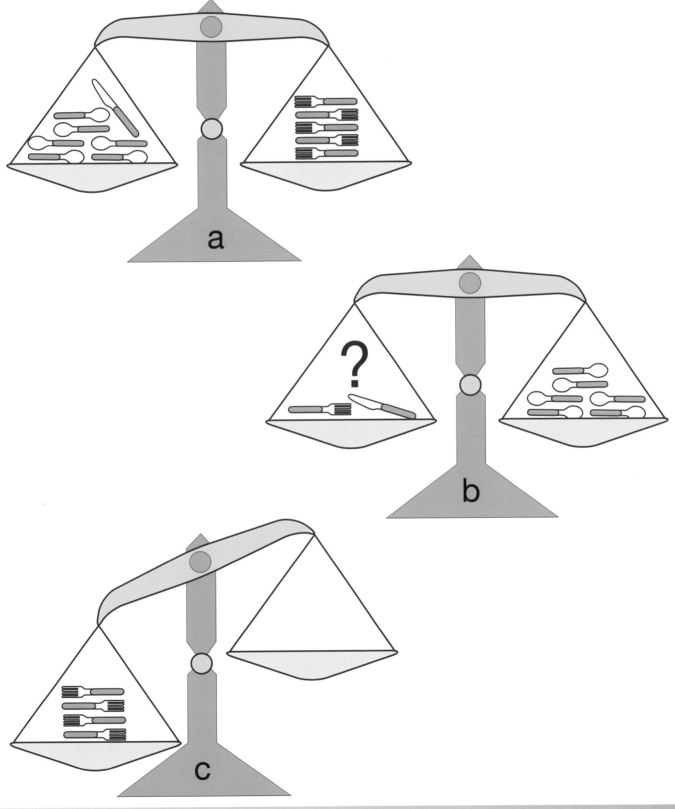

91 DIFFICULTY ✪✪✪✪✪✪☆☆☆☆　　⏰ 5 Minutes

This puzzle uses the 16 face cards and aces from all four suits from a standard deck of cards. Complete the grid by adding suits and face names so that no row, column, or main diagonal contains two cards of the same denomination or suit.

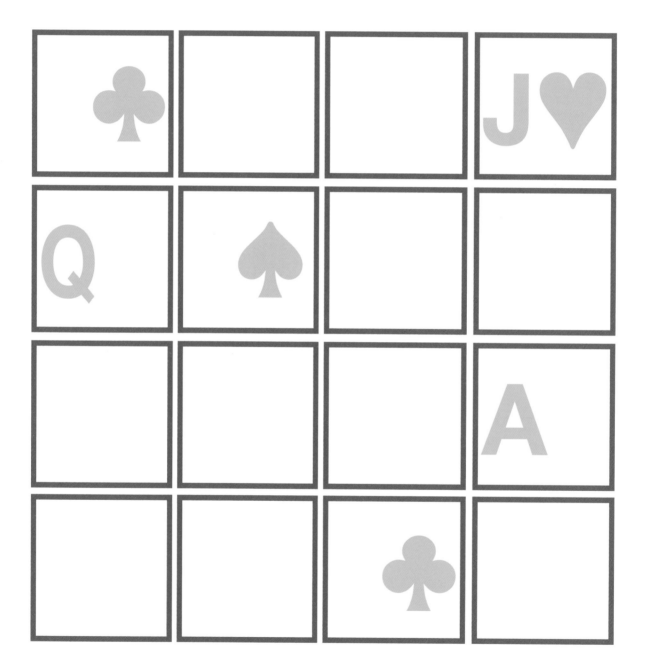

1

Square A is the correct move. It forces a win for Os. The other options will force a draw or possibly even a loss.

2

The combination is 29. Correct versions of false statements:

C. A league equals three nautical miles.

J. Hexadecimal is the number system for counting in groups of 16.

K. An obtuse angle has between 90 and 180 degrees.

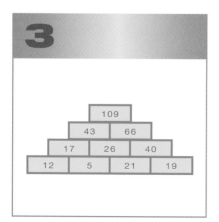

3

4

a; the dots change places in pairs working clockwise and starting with the top left/top middle dots.

5

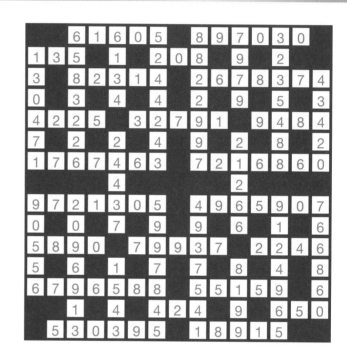

6

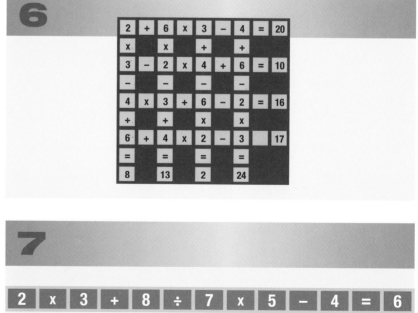

7

| 2 | x | 3 | + | 8 | ÷ | 7 | x | 5 | − | 4 | = | 6 |

8

Flo's animal is a chicken. The chicken was 2nd, so Flo was also 2nd (clue 1). Spot is a pig. Spot the pig didn't come 5th or 1st (2). Jack has a calf, and it placed 5th, so Jack placed 5th (3). Bob's animal is named Guffy, and it placed 4th, so Bob placed 4th (3). Norbert is a sheep, and his owner isn't Mavis or Flo (4), Guffy isn't a pig (2) or a sheep (4), and Bob doesn't have a calf (3) or a chicken (1). So Guffy must be a goat. Mavis doesn't own the chicken (1), the calf (3), or the sheep (4), and Bob owns the goat, so Mavis must own the pig, leaving Ned with Norbert the sheep. Mavis and Spot didn't come 5th or 1st (2), or 2nd (1), or 4th (3), so they came 3rd, leaving Ned and Norbert the sheep 1st. Guffy was 4th (3), and Tizzy placed higher than Pong (5), so Tizzy was 2nd and a chicken (1) and Pong was 5th and a calf (3).

Norbert—sheep—1st—Ned
Tizzy—chicken—2nd—Flo
Spot—pig—3rd—Mavis
Guffy—goat—4th—Bob
Pong—calf—5th—Jack

9

1. 4
2. 4+15+19=38
3. 4x19=76
4. Triangle (4) and cross (38)
5. 72
6. 7
7. The orange triangle and the orange cross
8. 89

10

Ten past one. Between any two clocks, 25, then 35, 45, 55, etc. minutes are added.

11

Nobel Peace Prize

12

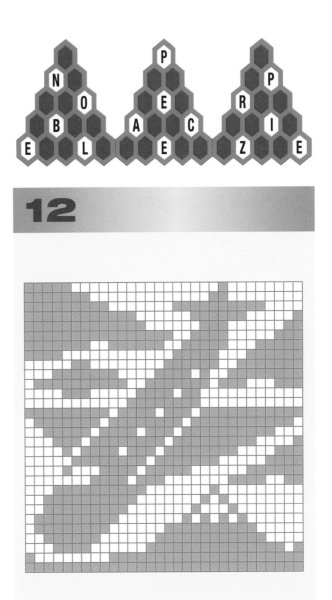

13

c; the figure retains the same shape, however, small circles change to large circles and vice versa.

14

They start and end with the same letter:

9:57   Nine fifty-seveN
8:23   Eight twenty-threE
1:32   One thirty-twO
11:25   Eleven twenty-fivE
9:13   Nine thirteeN
2:48   Two forty-eighT

15

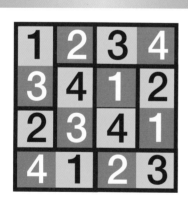

16

d; each vertical and horizontal line contains two dark-skinned and one light-skinned face. Each line contains a

face with one freckle, a face with two freckles, and a face with three freckles. Each line contains two eyes with two round highlights and one with a single round highlight. Finally, each line contains a blue eye, a brown eye, and a green eye. The missing image should be dark skinned with one freckle and a blue eye with two round highlights.

17

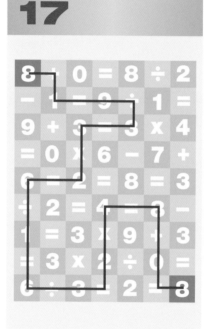

18

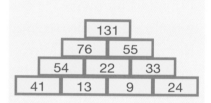

19

20

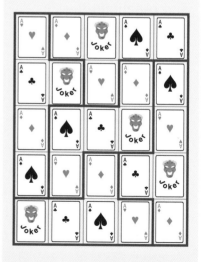

21

9 − 3 + 6 ÷ 2 − 4 x 5 = 10

22

10; one square and one circle weigh as much as five triangles. Thus one square weighs as much as three triangles, so a circle weighs as much as two triangles. Therefore, ten circles are needed to balance scale c.

23

d; a is the same string of dots as e, and b is the same string as c.

24

b; each vertical and horizontal line contains one red spade and two black ones. Each line also contains one image where the heart and club have been reversed and one image where the diamond has been turned on its side. The missing image should have a red spade, the club and heart should be reversed, and the diamond should be the right way up.

25

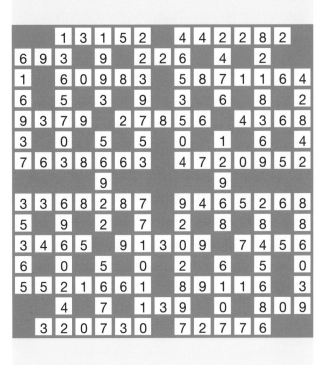

26

The gold item Dupris wore was not Tom Buick (8), Canale (8), Fundi, or Armande (7), so it must have been Vergucci and a bag (4). The black item was not then Vergucci, or Tom Buick (9), Canale (6), or Armande, so it must have been Fundi. The pink hat wasn't Tom Buick or Fundi (2), Vergucci (4), nor Armande (5), so it must have been Canale. The red item must then have been Armande and Manon's. The pink hat wasn't Jody's (6), Kate's (2), Naomi Taylor's (8), or Manon's (5), so it must have been Emma's and she must be Emma Briant (8). Naomi Taylor wasn't then wearing a hat, gloves, or shoes (3), or the bag (belonging to Dupris)—she must have been wearing the coat. Naomi Taylor's coat must have been blue, as it wasn't pink (2), gold (7), black (6), or red (Manon). So Naomi was also wearing Tom Buick (9) and the gold bag was Kate's, making her Kate Dupris (7). The gloves weren't then blue, pink (2), red (5), gold (bag), or blue (coat), so they must have been black and Fundi and belong to Jody (6), and the shoes must be red and Armande and belong to Manon.

Ms. Jones didn't wear gloves (1), so the red shoes are hers, making her Manon and leaving the Fundi gloves to Ms. Heaton, who must then be Jodie.

Jody Heaton—Fundi—gloves—black
Kate Dupris—Vergucci—bag—gold
Naomi Taylor—Tom Buick—coat—blue
Emma Briant—Fundi—bag—pink
Manon Jones—Armande—shoes—red

27

b; the circle moves one corner clockwise, then two corners, then three corners, etc., at each stage and the line moves one corner only counterclockwise at each stage.

28

To win the game, play first and take two coins. Whatever your opponent does, leave 1, 8, or 9 coins (if you have taken an odd number of coins), or 4, 5, or 12 coins (if you have an even number of coins).

29

8; three cherries and one gooseberry balance one banana, thus four gooseberries plus three cherries weigh as much as eleven cherries, and four gooseberries weigh as much as eight cherries. So two cherries weigh as

much as one gooseberry. This gives the equivalent of two-and-a-half gooseberries in scale a balancing one banana, so five gooseberries weigh as much as two bananas. There are two bananas (equal to five gooseberries) and six cherries (equal to three gooseberries) in scale c. Thus eight gooseberries are needed to balance scale c.

30

107; add the digits of the previous number each time, i.e., 49 (+ 4 + 9) = 62, 62 (+ 6 + 2) = 70, 70 (+ 7 + 0) = 77, etc. Therefore 103 (+ 1 + 0 + 3) = 107.

31

5149; in all the others, add the first and third digits to produce the second and fourth digits, for example, 7141, where 7 + 4 = 11.

32

5	+	4	x	2	–	7	=	11

5	+	4	x	2	–	7	=	11
+		x		x		+		
7	x	2	–	5	+	4	=	13
–		+		–		x		
4	+	5	–	7	x	2	=	4
x		–		+		–		
2	+	7	–	4	x	5	=	25
=		=		=		=		
16		6		7		17		

33

```
2 4 6 2 4 6 1 6 4 2 5 4
4 4 3 5 6 5 3 5 6 3 3 5
6 5 6 6 4 2 3 2 1 5 1 1
1 3 3 1 2 5 4 3 2 3 5 3
3 1 4 2 4 6 3 1 5 6 3 6
2 6 2 6 4 2 6 4 2 5 6 4
3 4 4 1 2 4 5 1 1 6 4 2
1 2 6 4 4 1 3 6 2 4 2 4
6 4 5 2 6 3 4 4 5 2 3 6
4 6 1 4 1 2 2 2 6 4 2 1
2 3 2 6 2 3 1 6 4 2 4 2
5 6 1 2 4 6 1 3 2 5 2 5
```

34

8 ÷ 4 x 3 + 5 – 2 – 6 = 3

35

99 – 25 + 36 x 11 ÷ 22 + 72 = 127

36

8; one blue ball weighs as much as three yellow balls, so two red balls also weigh as much as three yellow balls, and two red balls weigh as much as one blue ball. Thus eight red balls are needed to balance scale c.

37

```
1 3 9 1 4 2 6 4 9 1 2 4
2 2 6 3 6 9 3 2 6 4 6 3
6 4 6 9 2 1 2 1 9 3 6 2
3 6 2 4 3 6 9 3 1 2 9 6
9 2 9 1 9 3 4 4 9 6 3 3
1 2 1 6 6 1 3 2 6 3 6 6
2 9 6 3 1 9 6 3 9 2 2 1
6 1 2 3 6 4 9 6 1 3 1 9
3 9 3 1 9 3 6 2 2 6 6 6
9 4 2 9 2 1 3 1 9 2 1 2
1 2 1 3 1 3 6 4 3 1 4 1
4 6 9 1 3 2 6 3 1 9 6 9
```

38

```
2 5 1 4
4 3 2 1
5 1 4 3
3 4 5 2
```

39

c; the large 5-sided figure (pentagon) reduces its number of sides by one and becomes a rectangle. The number of dots that are contained in the figure increase by one and change from black to white.

40

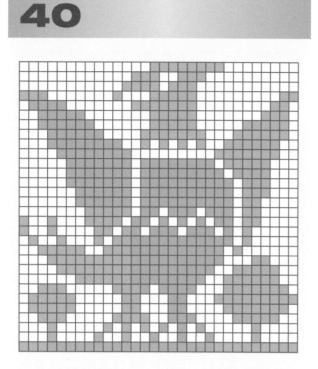

43

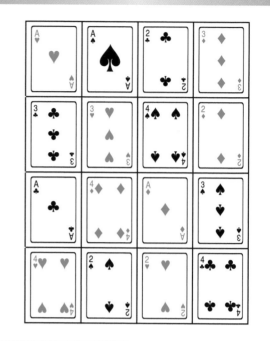

41

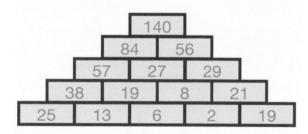

44

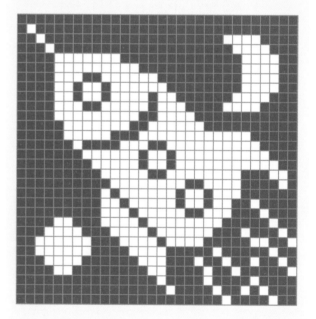

42

The hour hand should point to 7 o'clock. In the series, the minute hand is 30, 60, 90, 120, and 150 degrees clockwise from the hour hand.

45

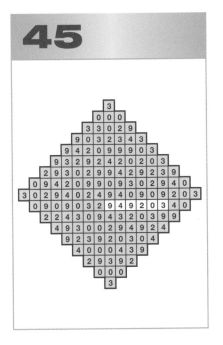

46

e; looking across the line of circles, the top left quarter alternates star/diamond, the top right quarter alternates circle with dot/circle, the bottom left quarter alternates white dot/ black dot/dot with line, and the bottom right quarter alternates one line/two lines/three lines horizontally, and three lines/two lines/one line vertically.

47

d; all the others are the same figure rotated.

48

5000 + 250x = 12000 − 100x. Hence, 350x = 7000, so x = 20. The numbers will be identical in 20 hours.

49

50

The combination is 64. Correct versions of false statements:

B. 39 is not a prime number because it is divisible by 13.

D. 50 divided by 0.5 equals 100.

K. If P x Q = Q, then P must be 1 as long as Q doesn't equal zero.

N. The cube of 5 is 125.

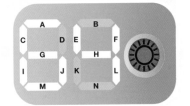

51

Blisterine is Steve's and didn't go 265 mph (1). Zak's last name is Dupris and he didn't go 265 either (1). Van Happs's car is Hot Stuff and it went 240 mph, and Jackson's went 250 mph (2). Marty went 255 mph and Chicken Speed went 235 mph. (3). Neither Blisterine (1), Hot Stuff (2), Chicken Speed (3), nor Fast and Loose (4) went 265 mph, so it must have been Rock Racer. Blisterine didn't go 265, 255, 240, or 235 mph, so it must have gone 250. Schwartz was faster than Delaney (5), so given that neither Dupris (1), Van Happs (2), or Jackson (2) went 265 mph, Schwartz must have. Zak Dupris didn't go 255 mph (3), so he must have gone 235, making his car Chicken Speed and leaving Delaney at 255, making his car Fast and Loose— and Delaney must be

Marty. Both Zak Dupris and Chicken Speed went 235 mph so that must be his car. Blisterine's owner is Steve (1), and Jackson's car and Blisterine both went 250 mph, so Steve is Steve Jackson. Fast and Loose was quicker than Bubba (4), so Bubba must have gone 240 mph, making him Bubba Van Happs, owner of Hot Stuff.

Steve Jackson—250 mph—Blisterine
Zak Dupris—235 mph—Chicken Speed
Bubba Van Happs—240 mph—Hot Stuff
Marty Delaney—255 mph—Fast and Loose
Kate Schwartz—265 mph—Rock Racer.

54

52

| 4 | + | 6 | ÷ | 5 | x | 2 | + | 7 | − | 3 | = | 8 |

53

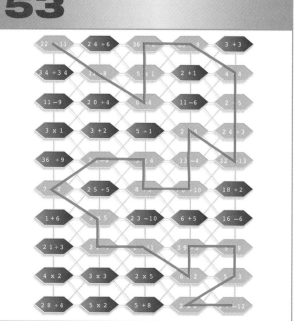

55

56

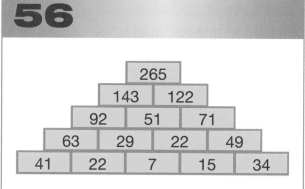

57

Dorrit works in fudge, Brenda doesn't and she isn't Dorrit (1). Diane is Diane Toggle and she doesn't work in wrapping, mints, truffles (2), or fudge (1). Bob works in orders, not with caramels (3). Neither Bob, Brian, nor Brenda work in quality control (4). Deborah, Diane Toggle, and Brenda don't work in lollipops, and Bob and Brian don't work in mints (5). Deborah is Deborah Duffy (6). The taster works in truffles and is not Deborah, Brian, or Bob (6). Bob doesn't work in lollipops (7), caramels (3), mints (5), or truffles (6), so he must work in fudge and fudge must be in orders (3). Neither Deborah Duffy, Diane Toggle, Brenda, nor Bob work in lollipops, so that must be Brian. Button works in packing (8). Caramels are not in wrapping (8). Dorrit isn't Brenda (1), Diane (2), nor Deborah (6), and Brian doesn't work in fudge (1) so Dorrit must be Bob and Dorrit must work in fudge and orders. The truffle worker is neither Diane Toggle (2), Dorrit (1), Deborah Duffy (6), nor Button (8), so it must be Hopper. Hopper then doesn't work with lollipops, and neither do Toggle (5), Duffy (5), nor Bob Dorrit (7), so the lollipop worker must be Button. So Button doesn't work in mints and neither does Bob Dorrit (5), Hopper the truffle taster nor Diane Toggle (2), so Deborah Duffy is the mint worker, leaving Diane Toggle to work in caramels. Diane Toggle doesn't work in wrapping (2), packing (8), or orders (3), and truffles are in tasting so Diane Toggle works in the quality control department, leaving wrapping to Deborah Duffy.

Deborah Duffy—wrapping—mints
Diane Toggle—quality control—caramels
Brenda Hopper—tasting—truffles
Bob Dorrit—orders—fudge
Brian Button—packing—lollipops

58

13; one spade weighs as much as one heart plus one diamond; thus three spades weigh as much as three hearts and three diamonds. So one diamond weighs as much as six hearts and one spade weighs as much as seven hearts. Thus thirteen hearts are needed to balance scale c.

59

60

1. Clubs
2. 2
3. 20: 4, 6, 9, and ace
4. 17: 5, jack, and ace
5. The 6 of hearts
6. 22: queen, 5, 4, and ace
7. Spades
8. The 8 of clubs

61

10 − 7 + 11 x 4 ÷ 8 + 12 = 19

62

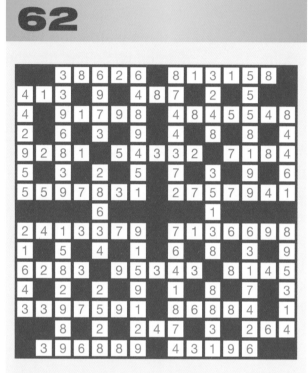

65

66

The center is very important. Try to restrict the movement of your opponent's coins (e.g., into a corner) so that there's more opportunity to make a winning line.

67

63

d; it contains five empty circles, whereas the other shields only contain four empty circles each.

68

20 + 14 − 9 x 6 − 18 ÷ 3 = 44

64

329476; each number is the third, fourth, and fifth digits of the previous number reversed, followed by the first, second, and sixth digits of the previous number in the same order.

69

73; they are the digits of the three times table (3, 6, 9, 12, 15, 18, 21, 24, 27, 30) rearranged in groups of two.

70

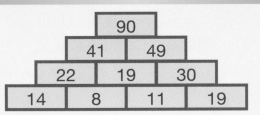

```
          90
      41      49
   22      19      30
 14      8      11      19
```

71

Seven minutes past ten. The hour hand points to the number of letters in the city's name. The minute hand points to the value of the first letter (i.e., 1 minute past equals A, 2 minutes past equals B, and so on).

GEORGETOWN

72

b; each vertical line and horizontal line contain two right-side-up pairs of lightning bolts and one inverted pair. Each line contains a black, a white, and a green central oval. Each line contains two green cages and one white wire cage over the oval. Finally, each line contains one image with two buttons, one with a single button, and one with no buttons. The missing image should have a pair of right-side-up lightning bolts and a white central oval with a green cage, and one button.

73

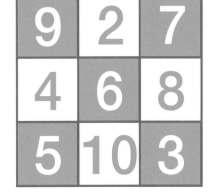

```
9  2  7
4  6  8
5 10  3
```

74

3	9	5	4	4		9	7	9	1	9	8
1	9	7		9		3	1	8		6		6

(Puzzle 74 is a number grid)

75

1. Orange
2. 9
3. Pink
4. Blue
5. 8
6. Blue, pink, and orange
7. 7
8. Purple

76

He does his patrols when his digital clock is displaying a palindromic time: 01:10, 02:20, 03:30, 04:40, 05:50, 10:01, 11:11, 12:21.

77

d; every fifth square contains a left diagonal line, every fourth square contains a red dot, and every third square contains a right diagonal line.

78

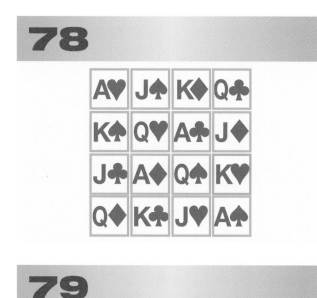

79

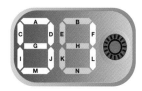

The combination is 81. Correct versions of false statements:
B. IQ stands for Intelligence Quotient.
E. The first Boeing 747 jumbo jet flew in February 1969.
H. A lepidopterist collects butterflies.

K. Omega is the final letter of the Greek alphabet.
N. Cygnus cygnus is the Latin classification for the swan.

80

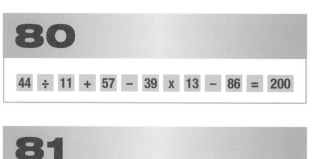

44 ÷ 11 + 57 − 39 x 13 − 86 = 200

81

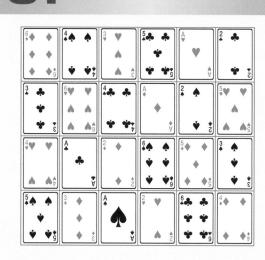

82

9263; all the others follow the pattern:
7421/2471
3869/6839
4283/8243
in which the first and third digits have swapped places.

83

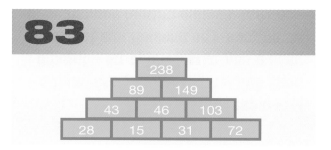

84

9731862; the numbers are rearranged so that all the odd numbers (in numerically descending order) are followed by all the even numbers (in numerically descending order).

85

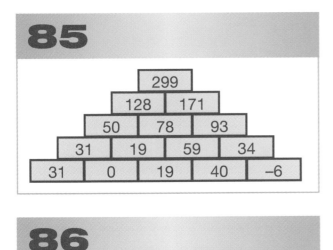

86

70 + 86 ÷ 13 x 66 ÷ 4 − 27 = 171

87

Wayne's second name is Brady. He isn't a center forward or a midfielder and he didn't score 1 goal (1). Darius didn't score 5 goals (1). Charlton plays for Rovers; he didn't score 1 goal, and Brady didn't score 5 (2). The center forward plays for Rangers and didn't score 5 or 4 goals (3). The Rovers' player, Charlton, didn't score 1 or 2 (3). Paul plays for United and didn't score 1 goal (4). Hughes scored 4 and isn't a winger (5). The left winger is Emile. He didn't score 1, 2, 5 (6), or 4 goals (5), so he must have scored 3. Callan didn't score 5 (7). Wayne Brady didn't score 1 (1), 5 (2), or 4 (5) goals. Emile scored 3, so Wayne must have scored 2. The Rangers' center forward didn't score 5, 4 (3), 3 (left winger), or 2 (Wayne Brady, not a center forward), so he scored 1. Paul scored one more than David, neither scored 2 (Wayne) or 3 (Emile) goals, so Paul must have scored 5 for United and David 4, leaving Darius with 1, which makes him the Rangers' center forward. The Rovers player scored two more than Darius (3), giving him 3 and making him Emile, in which case the Town player scored 4 (6). This leaves the City defender (7) with 2, making him Wayne Brady. Hughes scored 4 (5), so he's the Town player named David. Callan got 1 (7), making him Darius, the Rangers' center forward. Best then plays for United, making him Paul with 5 goals, and since neither Callan (center forward), Brady (defender), Hughes (5), nor Charlton (left wing) are right wingers, Paul Best must be one and David Hughes must be the midfielder for Town.

Wayne Brady—City—defender—2 goals
David Hughes—Town—midfield—4 goals
Paul Best—United—right wing—5 goals
Darius Callan—Rangers—center forward—1 goal
Emile Charlton—Rovers—left wing—3 goals

88

| 14 | x | 5 | + | 33 | – | 19 | ÷ | 4 | + | 15 | = | 36 |

89

3527; in all of the others, the sum of the first two digits is equal to the sum of the second two digits, e.g., 3984, where 3 + 9 = 8 + 4.

90

8; one knife and one fork weigh as much as six spoons, so two knives and one fork weigh as much as five forks. Thus one knife weighs as much as two forks. Three forks thus balance six spoons and one fork balances two spoons. Thus eight spoons are needed to balance scale c.

91

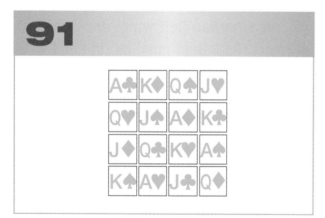

Numeric Puzzles is a compilation of puzzles for anyone who wants to maximize their mental arithmetic skills and sharpen their numerical "intuition."

No matter what your level of ability, a carefully graded series of challenges ensures that this section will have plenty for you.

The relationship between words and numbers is curious—words and numbers are both handled by the left hemisphere of the human brain and processed in the same way, regardless of their seeming differences. There are ten digits and twenty-six letters, yet numbers are infinite while the variety of words is finite. In spite of the fact that number puzzles use only ten digits along with the four basic mathematical operations (and perhaps the occasional square root or two), there is an amazing variety to be found in the world of number puzzles. Before you know it, you'll be completing sequences in a flash, dashing through the most difficult divisions, and scaling the heights of our number pyramids.

Traditional formats for word-based puzzles, such as crosswords and word searches, also get their own numeric treatments.

Each puzzle in *Numeric Puzzles* has been carefully graded according to a ten-star system—the more stars there are, the harder that puzzle will be. Remember that these ratings are based on an average performance, so don't be surprised if you breeze through a ten-star stumper (or are baffled by a three-star puzzler!) But it doesn't end there—since speed of calculation is just as important as accuracy, every challenge has been given its own time limit for you to work toward.

There are no sneaky tricks here. You don't need to know logarithms, calculus, or group theory (or even know what they mean). All of the puzzles are based on straightforward operations, although some are better disguised than others. If you find that you can't crunch through a particular calculation, the answers section at the back of this section will provide you with the solution. Every question in this section has been numbered—simply refer to the same number in the answer section and all will be revealed. But have one last attempt at solving the problem before resorting to the solutions, since the satisfaction of cracking a seemingly impossible problem is its own reward.

By the end of *Numeric Puzzles*, having honed your skills on these mathematical puzzles, you'll find yourself seeing numerical relationships and solving mathematical problems more quickly and easily than you ever imagined ✪

1 DIFFICULTY ★★★★★☆☆☆☆☆  ⑤ Minutes

Can you place the tiles in the grid so that:

★ each row and column contains two squares of each color, and

★ each row and column contains exactly one of each number?

2 DIFFICULTY ✪✪✪✪✩✩✩✩✩✩
Target time: 8 minutes

8 Minutes

Can you fit these numbers into the grid? One number has already been inserted to help you get started.

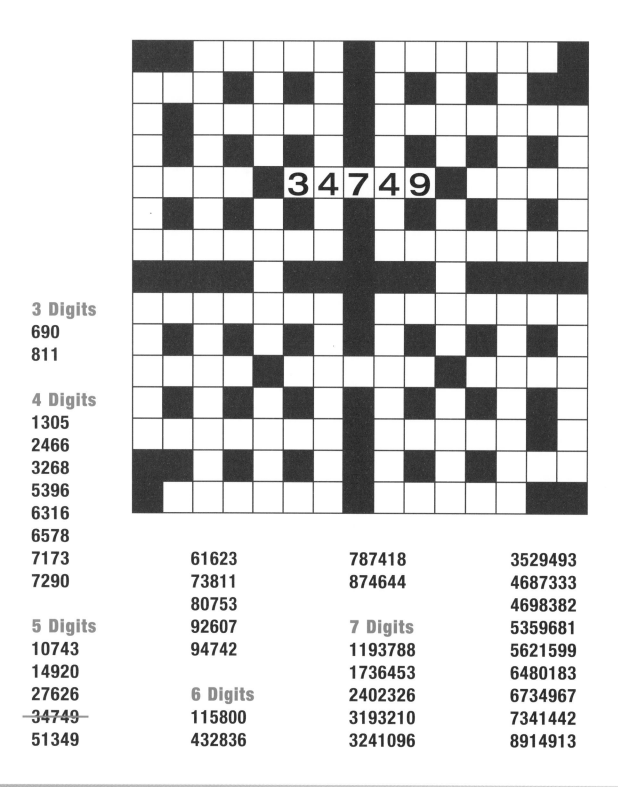

3 Digits
690
811

4 Digits
1305
2466
3268
5396
6316
6578
7173
7290

5 Digits
10743
14920
27626
~~34749~~
51349

61623
73811
80753
92607
94742

6 Digits
115800
432836

787418
874644

7 Digits
1193788
1736453
2402326
3193210
3241096

3529493
4687333
4698382
5359681
5621599
6480183
6734967
7341442
8914913

3 DIFFICULTY ★★★☆☆☆☆☆☆☆   3 Minutes

Make a calculation totaling the figure on the right, and using some or all of the numbers on the left with any of the four standard mathematical operators (+, −, x, and ÷).

3, 4, 5, 8, 9, 25 = 527

4 DIFFICULTY ★★★★★★★☆☆☆   5 Minutes
Target time: 5 minutes

Study these balloons carefully for one minute, then answer the questions on the next page without checking back.

[4] DIFFICULTY ✪✪✪✪✪✪☆☆☆☆ | 5 Minutes

Can you answer these questions about the puzzle on the previous page without checking back?

1. The numbers on two bunches of balloons add up to the same figure. What is it?

2. What's the total of the numbers on the pink balloons?

3. Which number appears twice?

4. On which colored balloons does it appear?

5. How many pink balloons have odd numbers?

6. Which odd number appears on a blue balloon?

7. Which even number appears on a yellow balloon?

8. How many balloons are green?

5 DIFFICULTY ✪✪✪✪✪✪☆☆☆☆ | 3 Minutes

Which clock face is the odd one out?

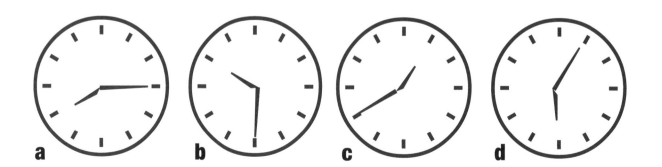

a   b   c   d

Starting with the yellow square on the top left corner, find the path through the squares, calculating each step to lead you to the solution on the bottom right corner. You may not pass through the same square more than once.

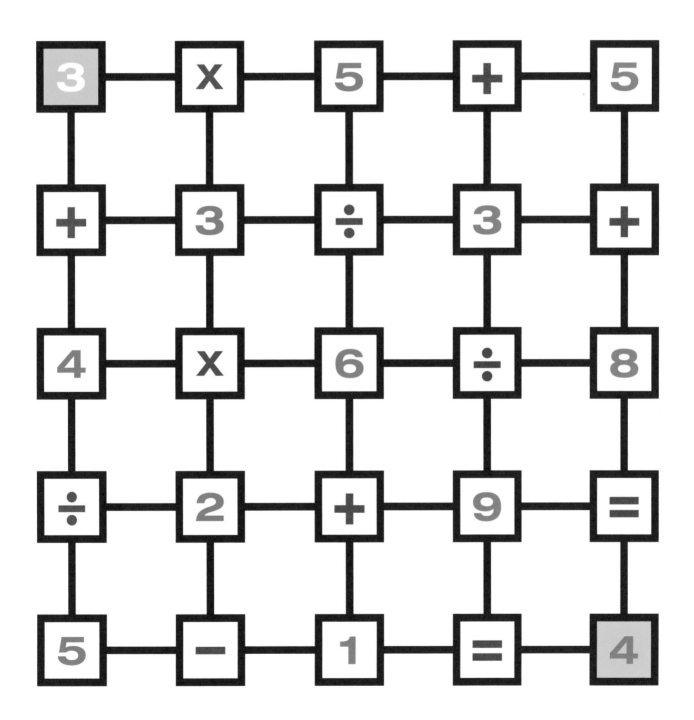

Consider the apples, bananas, and oranges shown below. Given that scales a and b balance perfectly, how many apples are needed to balance scale c?

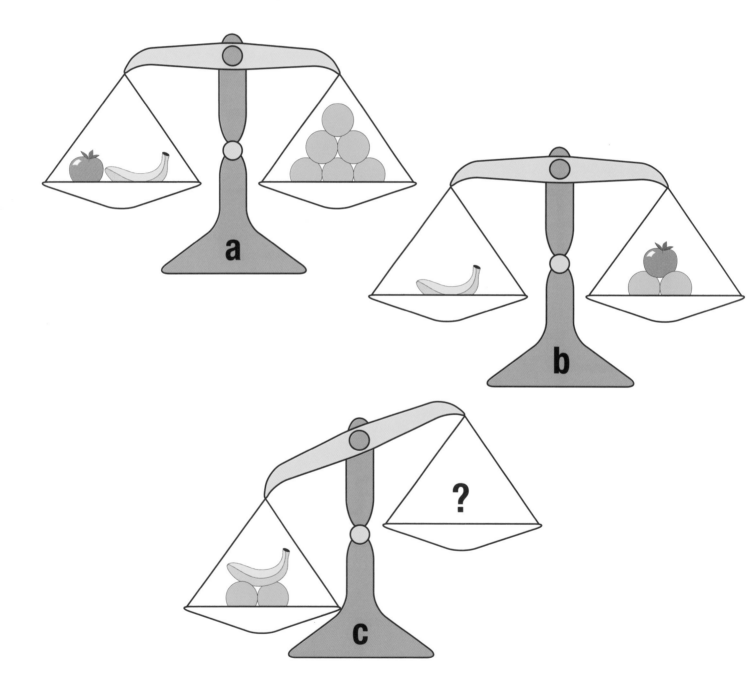

8 DIFFICULTY ★★★★★☆☆☆☆☆  **8** Minutes

Find the solutions to the following calculations in the grid, reading up, down, backward, forward, and diagonally!

1. 9 x 9 x 9 x 9
2. (40 x 40) + 400
3. (100 − 44) x 22
4. 8,989 + 1,111
5. 77 + 88 + 88 + 99
6. 1,234 x 5
7. 44 x 66

8. 666 + 334
9. 8,765 − 1,111
10. (9 + 9) x 99
11. (10,000 ÷ 20) + 20
12. 90,990 ÷ 3
13. (565 x 2) x 2

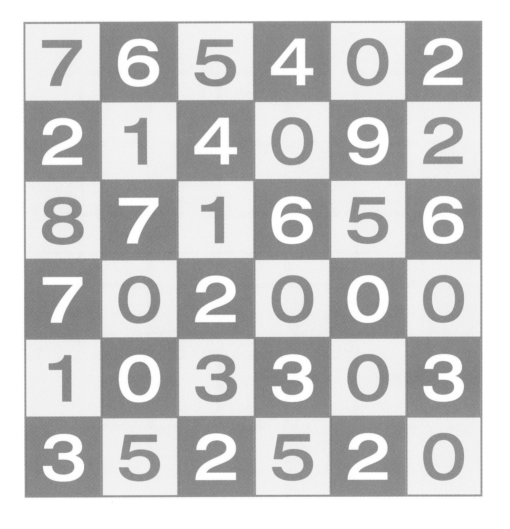

MIND WRKS BRAIN TRAINING

DIFFICULTY ✪✪✪✪✪☆☆☆☆☆☆   6 Minutes

Every row and column contains the same numbers and signs, but they are arranged in a different order each time. Find the correct order to arrive at the final totals shown.

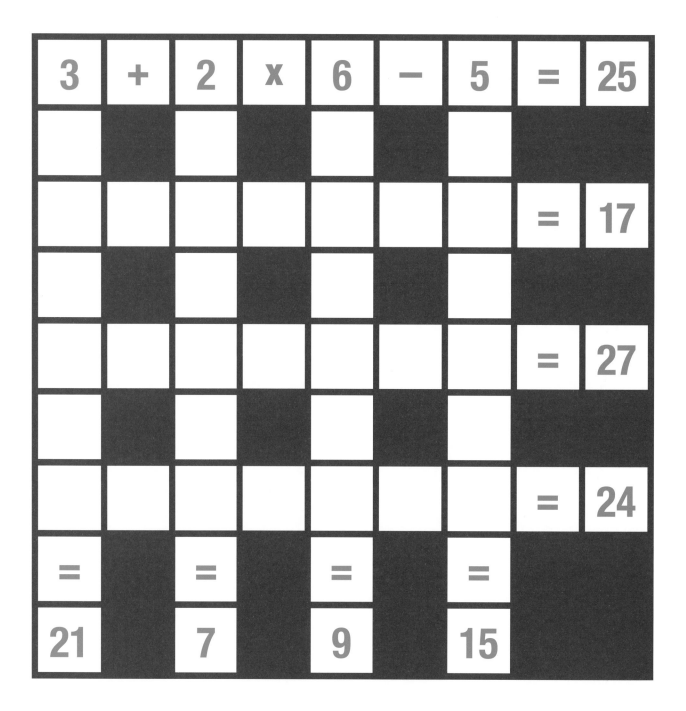

10 DIFFICULTY ✪✪✪✪✪☆☆☆☆☆
Target time: 5 minutes

5 Minutes

This is a two-player game. Players take turns removing as many coins as they like from one of the three rows. If you pick up the last coin, you lose the game. Once you've played the game a few times, see if you can work out how to guarantee a win by starting first.

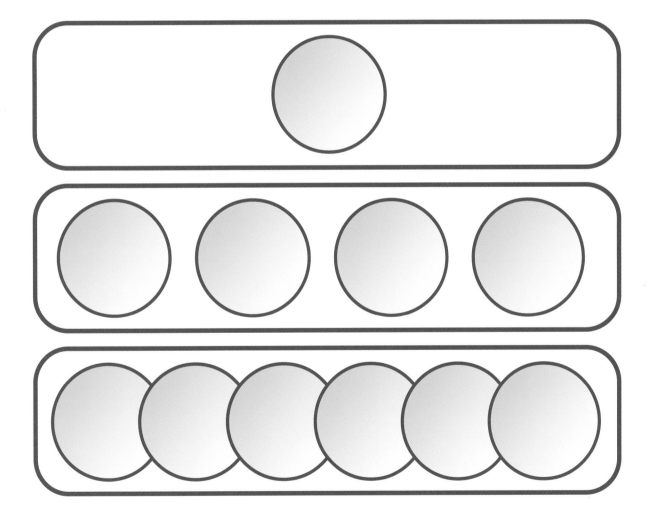

11 DIFFICULTY ✪✪✪✪✰✰✰✰✰✰ ④ Minutes

The number 543,789 appears just once in this grid and occurs in a straight line, running either backward or forward in a horizontal, vertical, or diagonal direction. Can you locate it?

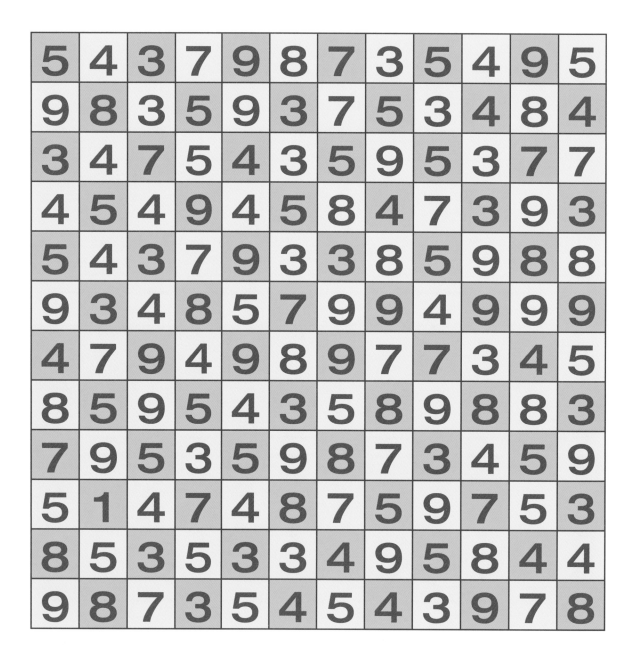

12 DIFFICULTY ✪✪✪✪✪✪☆☆☆☆ (10) Minutes

Can you fit these numbers into the grid? One number has already been inserted to help you get started.

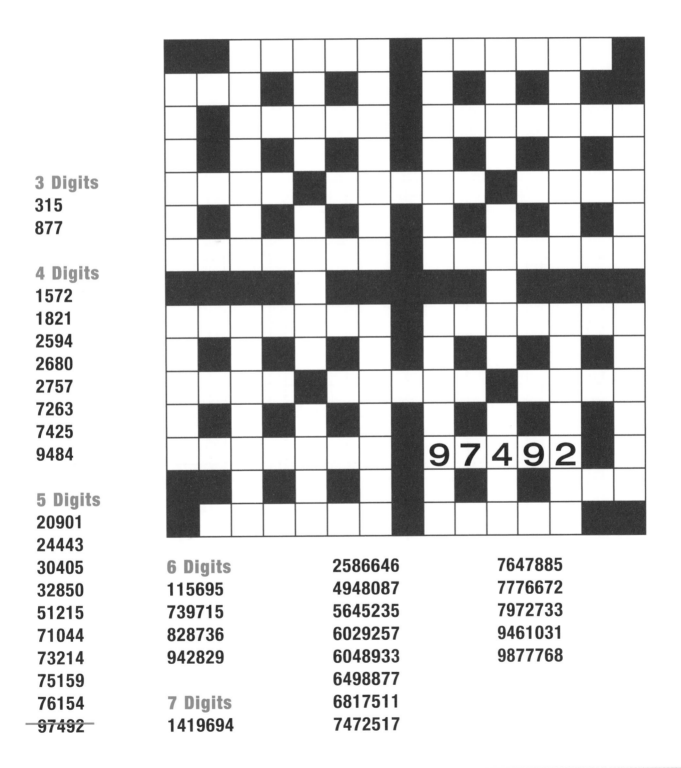

3 Digits
315
877

4 Digits
1572
1821
2594
2680
2757
7263
7425
9484

5 Digits
20901
24443
30405
32850
51215
71044
73214
75159
76154
~~97492~~

6 Digits
115695
739715
828736
942829

7 Digits
1419694

2586646
4948087
5645235
6029257
6048933
6498877
6817511
7472517

7647885
7776672
7972733
9461031
9877768

13 DIFFICULTY ●●●●●●●●●●○ 30 Minutes

If you like nonograms, this one should suit you!

HOW TO DO A NONOGRAM:

Along each row or column there are numbers that indicate how many blocks of black squares are in a line. For example, "3, 4, 5" indicates that from left to right or top to bottom, there is a group of three black squares, then a group of four black squares, then another group of five black squares.

Each block of black squares on the same line must have at least one white square between it and the next block of black squares. Blocks of black squares may or may not have a number of white squares before and after them.

It is sometimes possible to determine which squares will be black without reference to other lines or columns. It is helpful to put a small dot in a square you know will be empty.

Column clues:

																				2	4		4	2					
					2	3		3	2											3	1		1	3					
	3	2	1	1	3	2	5	2	3	1	1	2	3			1	3	5	5	1	2	13	2	1	5	5	3	1	
	7	6	5	4	8	9	1	9	8	4	5	6	7			7	6	5	4	3	2	1	2	3	4	5	6	7	
15	4	6	7	8	1	2	13	2	1	8	7	6	4	15	15	7	6	5	4	3	2	1	2	3	4	5	6	7	15

Row clues:

				15
	3	5	3	1
	2	3	2	3
	1	1	1	5
	1	1	1	5
		1	1	3
1	1	2	1	2
1	1	4	1	4
		2	2	13
	3		1	
4		2	1	2
		5	5	1
		6	6	3
		7	7	5
				15
				15
		1	7	7
		3	6	6
		5	5	5
		7	4	4
		9	3	3
		11	2	2
		13	1	1
		13	2	2
		13	3	3
		13	4	4
3	1	3	5	5
		3	6	6
		5	7	7
				15

14 DIFFICULTY ✪✪✪✪☆☆☆☆☆☆ ④ Minutes

Each block is equal to the sum of the two numbers beneath it. Find all the missing numbers.

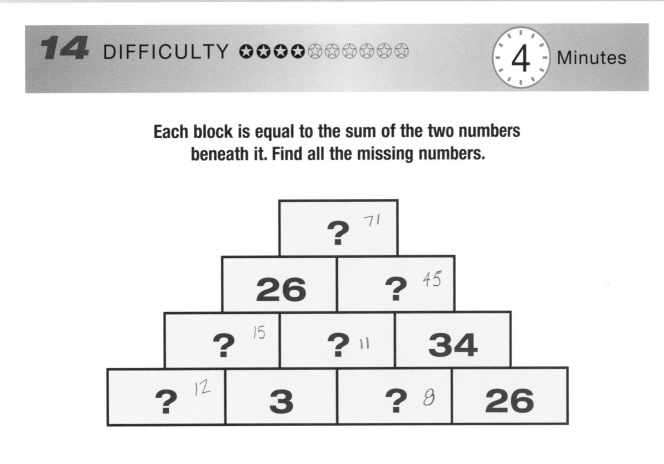

15 DIFFICULTY ✪✪✪✪✪☆☆☆☆☆ ④ Minutes

These four points are the corners of a square. If a has coordinates of (4, 5), and c is at (10, 1), what are the coordinates of b and d?

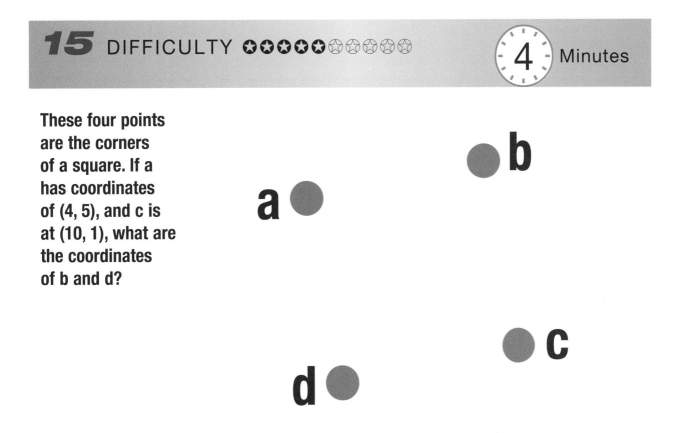

16 DIFFICULTY ●●●●○○○○○○ ③ Minutes

Which is the odd number out?

159, 367, 589, 258, 486, 679

17 DIFFICULTY ●●●●○○○○○○ ④ Minutes

Replace the question marks with mathematical symbols to produce the correct answer. Only the four basic operators (+, −, x, and ÷) are permitted. Perform calculations in strict left to right order. Can you find two possible solutions?

6 ? 2 ? 2 ? 3 ? 7

= 16

18 DIFFICULTY ✪✪✪✪✩✩✩✩✩✩ ④ Minutes √

Can you place the tiles in the grid so that:

★ each row and column contains two squares of each color, and
★ no row or column contains more than one of any number?

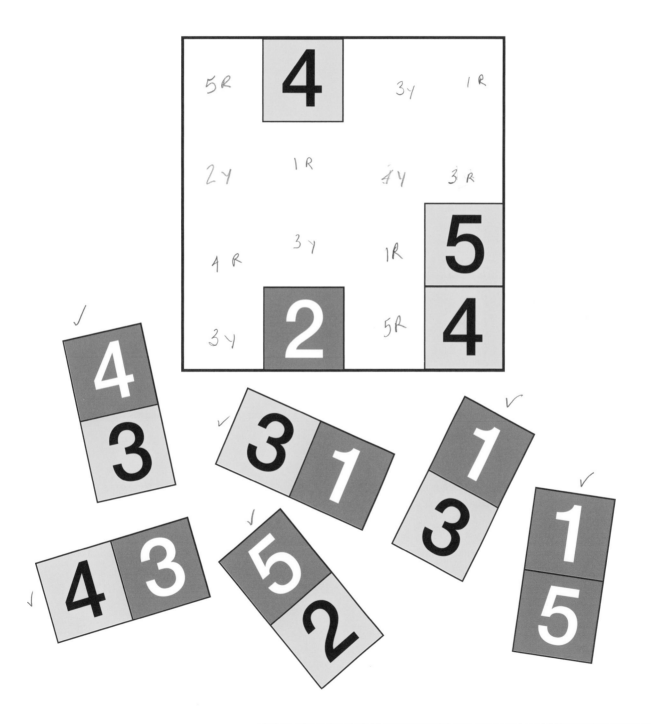

19 DIFFICULTY ●●●●○☆☆☆★☆★☆ — 3 Minutes

Place a number in the middle box that divides into all the other numbers without leaving a remainder. The answer is greater than 1.

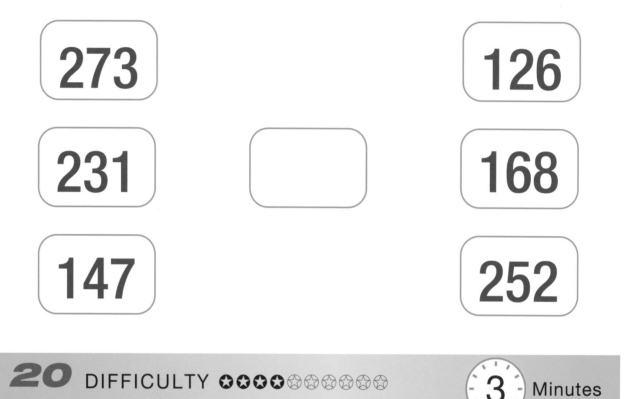

273 126
231 [ ] 168
147 252

20 DIFFICULTY ●●●●●☆☆☆★☆★☆ — 3 Minutes

At a local club, a dice game is played that involves throwing two dice and betting a stake of $5. What are the rules, and how much did Gary Gambler win or lose when he threw a 5, followed by a 2? Study the clues below to discover the answer!

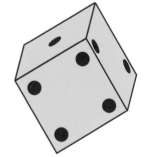

1. Gina threw a 4, followed by a 4, and lost her whole stake. She paid another stake and tried again. This time she threw a 3, followed by a 1, and got $6 back, thus winning $1 on her second try.

2. George threw a 6, followed by a 2, and got $12 back, so won $7.

3. Grant threw a 1, followed by a 3, and got $6 back, so won $1.

21 DIFFICULTY ✪✪✪✪✪✪✪✪☆☆☆    Minutes

Given that scales a and b balance perfectly, how many suns are needed to balance scale c?

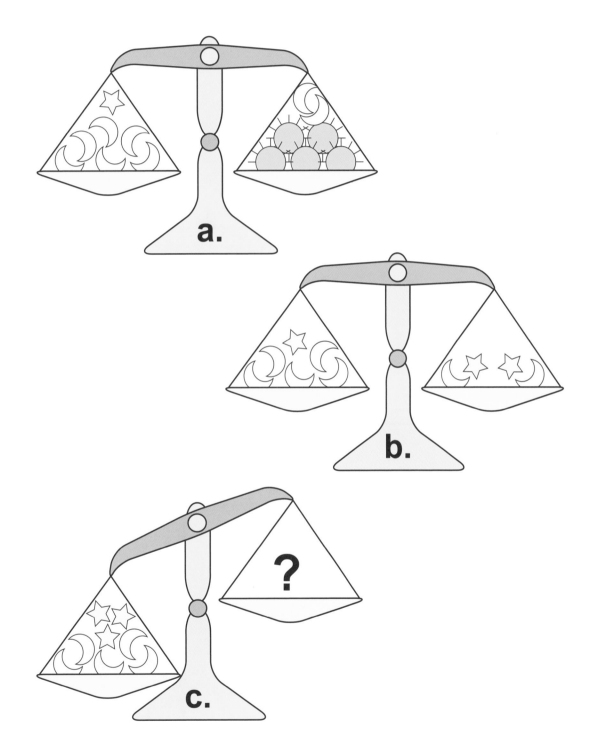

22 DIFFICULTY ✪✪✪✪✩✩✩✩✩ (3) Minutes

What number should replace the question mark in the following sequence?

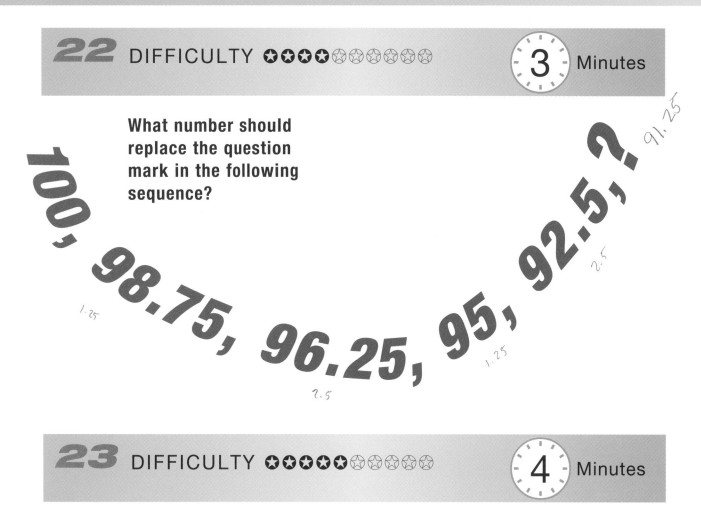

100, 98.75, 96.25, 95, 92.5, ?

1.25 *2.5* *1.25* *2.5* *91.25*

23 DIFFICULTY ✪✪✪✪✪✩✩✩✩ (4) Minutes

Find out the mystery sequence hidden in the dominoes, then decide which number should replace the question mark.

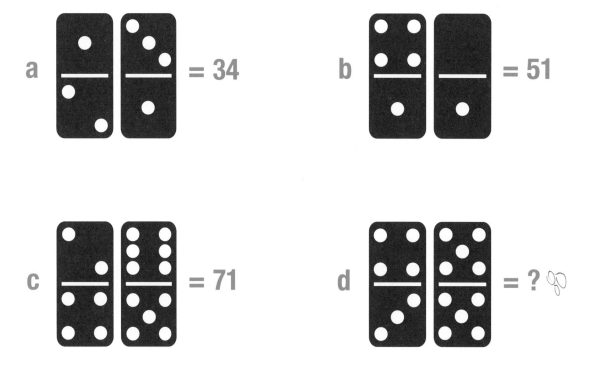

a = 34

b = 51

c = 71

d = ?

24 DIFFICULTY ✪✪✪✪✪✪✩✩✩✩  **6** Minutes

Can you divide this square into four equally shaped parts of nine smaller squares, each containing two different numbers and two different shapes?

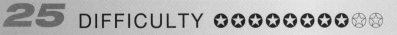

25 DIFFICULTY ✪✪✪✪✪✪✪✪✩✩ **8** Minutes

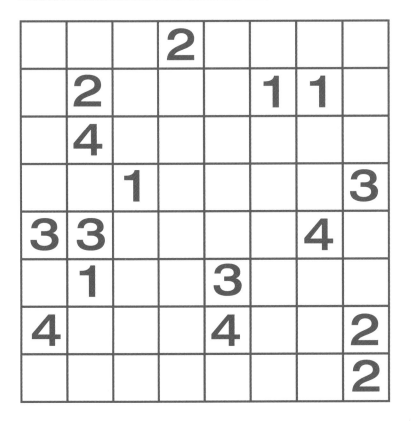

And now can you divide this square into four identical shapes, each composed of sixteen squares, and each containing four different numbers?

26 DIFFICULTY ●●●●○○○○○○ 4 Minutes

Which domino (a, b, c, or d) should fill the empty space?

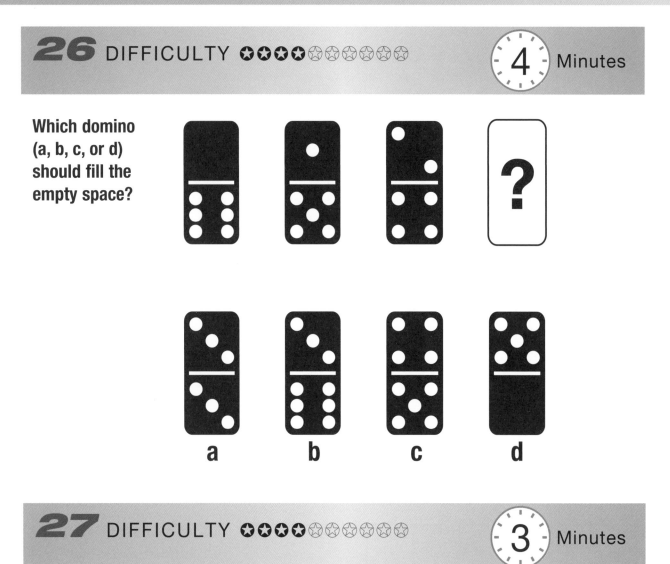

a   b   c   d

27 DIFFICULTY ●●●●○○○○○○ 3 Minutes

Place a number in the middle box that divides into all the other numbers without leaving a remainder. The answer is greater than 1.

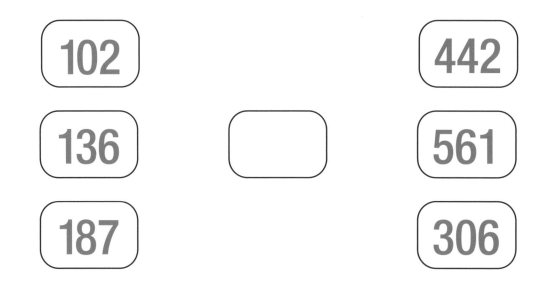

102   442

136   561

187   306

28 DIFFICULTY ✪✪✪✪✪✰✰✰✰✰ ⏱ **5** Minutes

Each block is equal to the sum of the two numbers beneath it.
Find all the missing numbers.

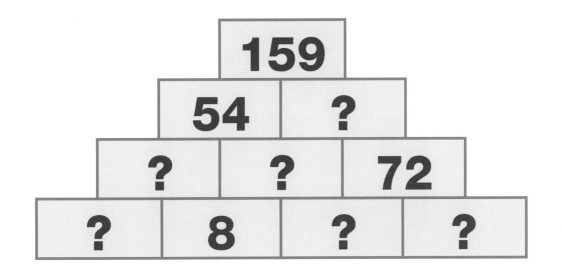

29 DIFFICULTY ✪✪✪✪✰✰✰✰✰✰ ⏱ **3** Minutes

Which is the odd number out?

1,235   2,134

3,145   4,268

5,279   4,569

30 DIFFICULTY ✪✪✪✩✩✩✩✩✩✩   ③ Minutes

What time should come next on clock e?

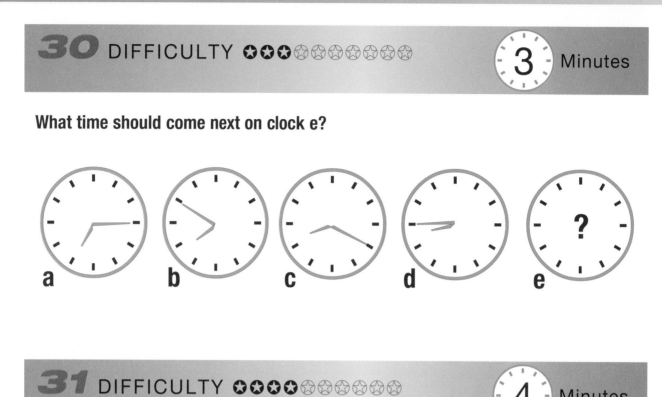

a   b   c   d   e

31 DIFFICULTY ✪✪✪✪✩✩✩✩✩✩   ④ Minutes

Replace the question marks with mathematical symbols to produce the correct answer. Only the four basic operators (+, –, x, and ÷) are permitted. Perform calculations in strict left to right order. Can you find two possible solutions?

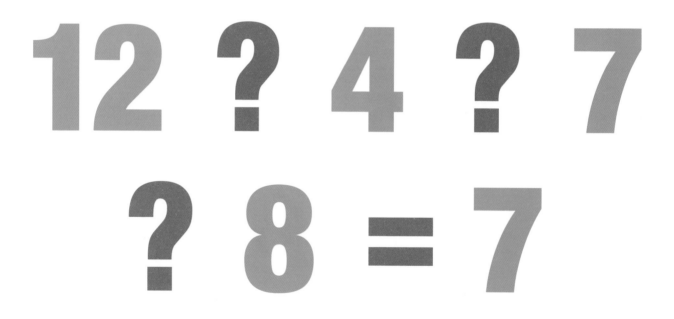

$$12 \, ? \, 4 \, ? \, 7$$

$$? \, 8 = 7$$

32 DIFFICULTY ✪✪✪✪✩✩✩✩✩ **6** Minutes

Can you fit these numbers into the grid? One number has already been given to help you get started.

3 Digits
544
675

4 Digits
2534
3145
4812
4983
5343
6911
7403
9462

5 Digits
20010
~~35041~~
46255
57193
57488

69606
74366
81587
87449
92579

6 Digits
379253
681202

813024
916115

7 Digits
1712470
2041019
3496883
3756076
4099359

4109509
4549428
5179153
6015117
7810067
7895619
8107408
8589334
9264533

33 DIFFICULTY ✪✪✪✪✪✪✪☆☆☆   ⏱ **5** Minutes

Weigh up the symbols below. Given that scales a and
b balance perfectly, how many clubs are needed to
balance scale c?

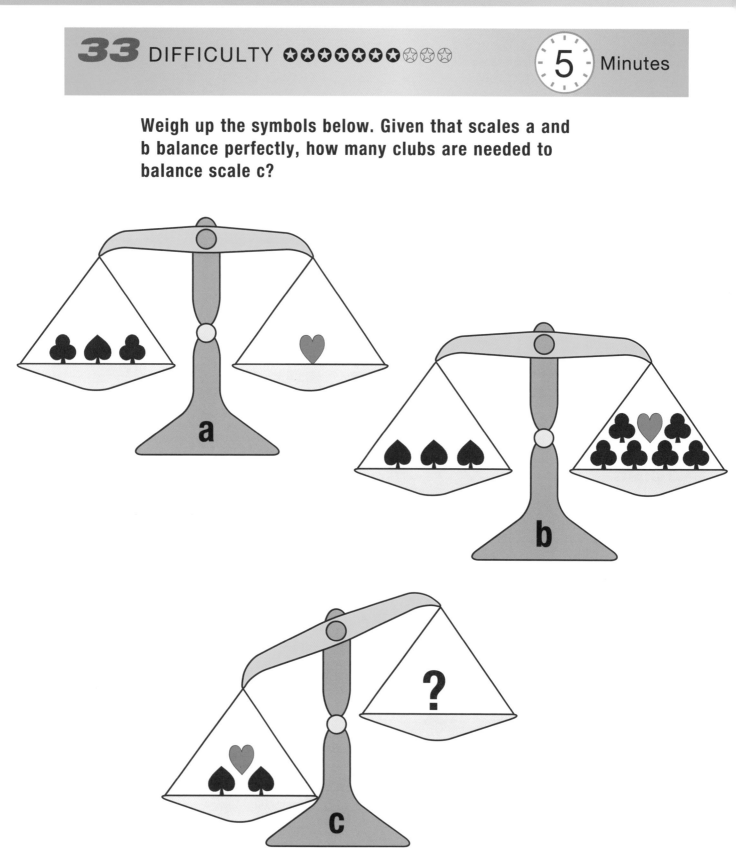

34 DIFFICULTY ✪✪✪✪☆☆☆☆☆☆

3 Minutes

Target time: 3 minutes

Which number is the odd one out?

17 37 61

23 42 59

35 DIFFICULTY ✪✪✪✪☆☆☆☆☆☆

3 Minutes

At the local club, a dice game is played that involves throwing two dice and betting a stake of $12. What are the rules—and how much did Gary Gambler win or lose when he threw a 4, followed by a 5? Study the clues below to discover the answer!

1. Gina threw a 2, followed by a 2, and got $4 back, losing $8.

2. George threw a 6, followed by a 2, and broke even, so got $12 back.

3. Grant threw a 1, followed by a 3, and got $3 back, so lost $9.

36 DIFFICULTY ✪✪✪✪✪✰✰✰✰✰   ⏱ **8** Minutes

Find the answers to the following calculations in the grid, reading up, down, backward, forward, and diagonally.

1. 54,321 – 12,345
2. 15 x 15 x 15
3. 909 + 707
4. 55,000 ÷ 25
5. 11,111 + 12,345
6. 2,727 ÷ 9
7. (6,204 ÷ 2) ÷ 2
8. 10,000 – 4,445
9. 3,108 ÷ 7
10. 5 x 5 x 5 x 5 x 5
11. 15 x 51
12. 999 – 343

2	2	0	0	4	4
3	0	3	1	4	7
6	5	9	4	6	5
1	7	1	5	5	1
6	3	6	5	6	6
1	3	5	2	1	3

37 DIFFICULTY ✪✪✪✪✪✩✩✩✩✩ ④ Minutes

Study these shapes for one minute, then see if you can answer the questions that follow on the next page without checking back.

38 DIFFICULTY ✪✪✪✪✪✪✪✩✩✩ ⑥ Minutes

What theorem do these two diagrams prove?

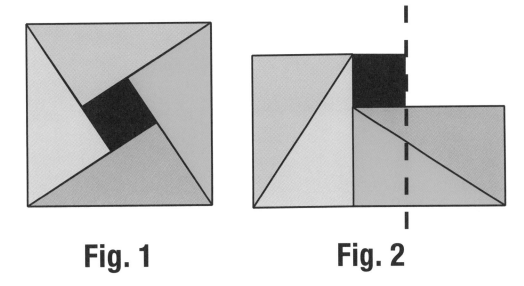

Fig. 1   Fig. 2

[37] DIFFICULTY ✪✪✪✪✪✩✩✩✩✩   ④ Minutes

Can you answer these questions about the puzzle on the previous page without checking back?

1. How many shapes have prime numbers?
2. Which two numbers will total a third number shown?
3. What is the total when you multiply the number on the blue shape by that on the pink shape?
4. Which shapes have odd numbers?
5. Which colors have even numbers?
6. What is the total reached by adding the number on the yellow shape to that on the square, then subtracting this total from the number on the shape on the far right?

39 DIFFICULTY ✪✪✪✩✩✩✩✩✩✩   ③ Minutes

Make a calculation totaling the figure at the bottom using some or all of the numbers in the box with any of the four standard mathematical operators (+, −, x, and ÷).

4 ? 4 ? 6 ?

7 ? 9 ? 10

= 311

The number 1,899,740 appears just once in this number-search grid and occurs in a straight line, running either backward or forward in a horizontal, vertical, or diagonal direction. Can you find it?

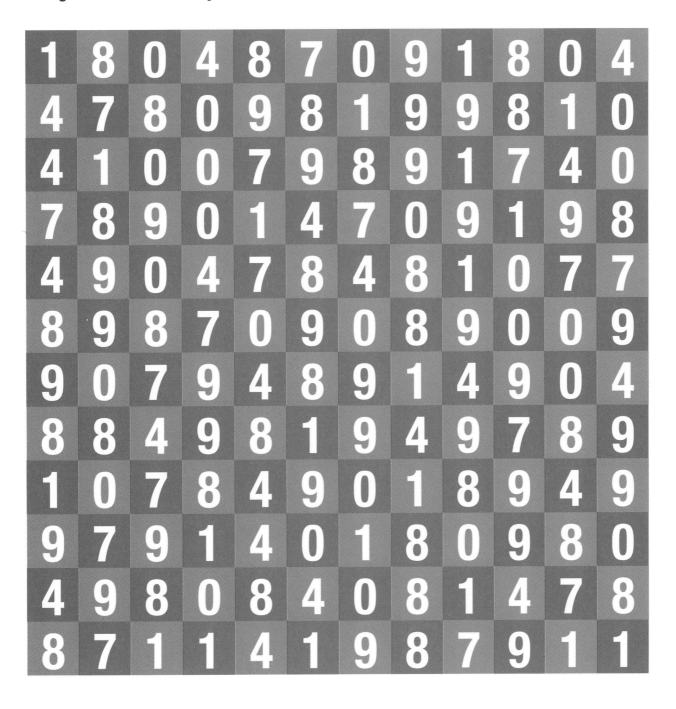

41 DIFFICULTY ✪✪✪✪✪✪✪☆☆

8 Minutes

Can you divide this square into four identical shapes, each composed of sixteen squares, and each containing four different numbers?

			3	3			
		1					
		1		2		1	1
				4	4	2	
2	2						3
	4						3
	4						

42 DIFFICULTY ✪✪✪✪✪✪✪☆☆

6 Minutes

Ten dominoes have been used to build this wall, but seven have been masked out. Can you place the missing dominoes correctly, bearing in mind that each vertical line of four numbers (as well as the two end vertical lines of two numbers) adds up to eight?

43 DIFFICULTY ✪✪✪✪✪☆☆☆☆☆ | ③ Minutes

Place a number in the middle box that divides into all the other numbers without leaving a remainder. The answer is greater than 1.

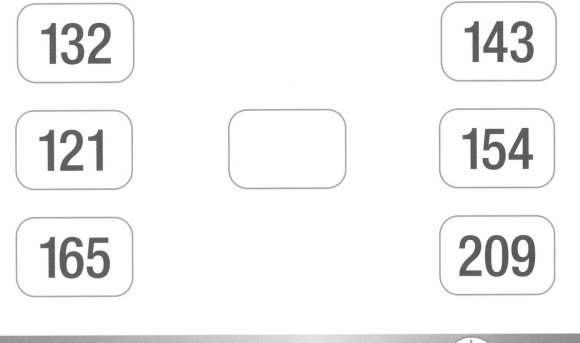

132 143

121 154

165 209

44 DIFFICULTY ✪✪✪✪✪✪☆☆☆☆ | ③ Minutes

Which of these is the odd number out?

17, 71, 88, 88, 176, 671, 846

45 DIFFICULTY ★★★★★★★☆☆ ⓼ Minutes

Traverse this maze from top to bottom (any entry point on the top row may be used). You may only move from a number divisible by 5 to one divisible by 6, from a number divisible by 6 to one divisible by 7, or from one divisible by 7 to one divisible by 5. You may not move diagonally.

66	14	18	65	26	55	19
77	50	21	16	49	24	63
75	33	37	78	40	54	10
96	98	96	25	18	15	36
31	20	36	49	54	50	56
98	48	11	23	91	72	56
20	28	45	78	91	15	72
12	23	54	77	85	95	21
16	25	24	66	14	91	40

46 DIFFICULTY ✪✪✪✪✪✪✪✪✪✪

 30 Minutes

Nonograms make good games. You will be bowled over by this one.
(See puzzle 13 for advice on how to complete a nonogram.)

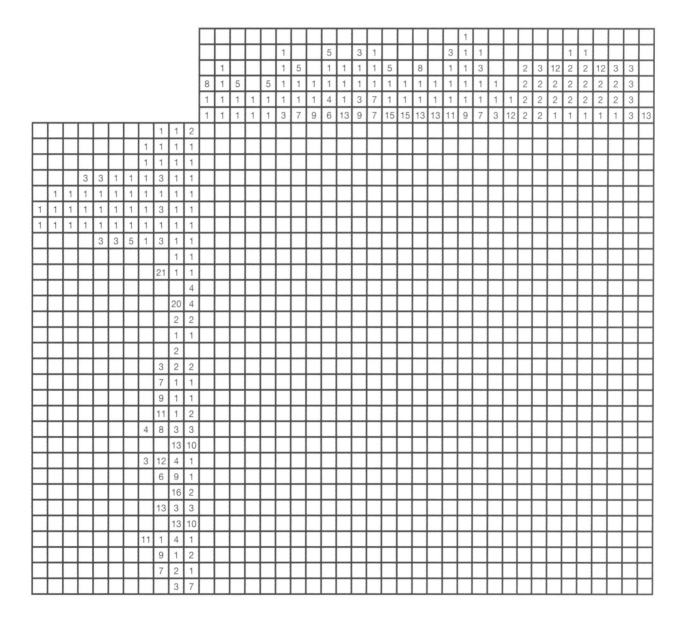

47 DIFFICULTY ★★★★☆☆☆☆☆☆ ⏱ 4 Minutes

Each block is equal to the sum of the two numbers beneath it. Find all the missing numbers.

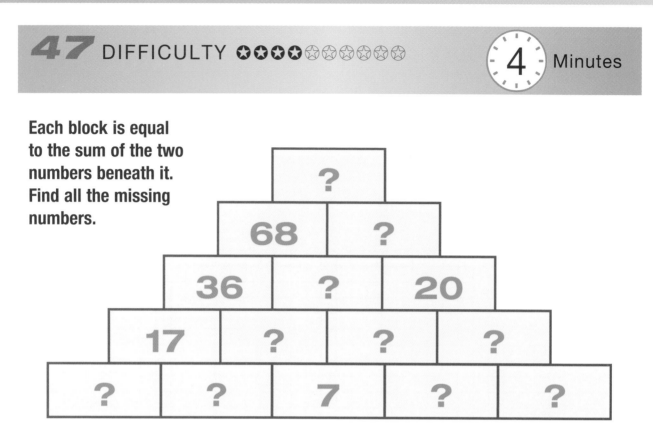

48 DIFFICULTY ★★★★☆☆☆☆☆☆ ⏱ 3 Minutes

Which number should replace the question mark in the following sequence?

10, 5, 12, 6, 16, 9, 22, ?

49 DIFFICULTY ✪✪✪✪✪✪✪✪☆☆   6 Minutes

Place the pieces from a standard set of twenty-eight dominoes into the following grid by matching their numbers with those in the rectangle. It's trickier than you think, so we've placed one in position to give you a start and supplied a checklist on the right that may help!

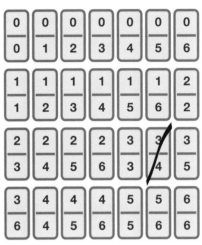

50 DIFFICULTY ✪✪✪✪✪✪☆☆☆☆   6 Minutes
Target time: 6 minutes

Can you divide this square into four identical shapes, each composed of sixteen smaller squares, and each containing five different numbers?

51 DIFFICULTY ✪✪✪✪✪✪✪✪☆☆ ⏱ 5 Minutes

Using three of the four different mathematical operators beneath each of the following three sums, can you achieve the correct totals, as given?

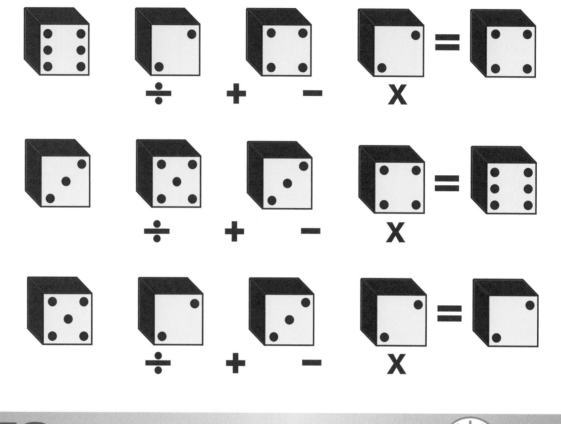

52 DIFFICULTY ✪✪✪✪✪✪☆☆☆☆ ⏱ 3 Minutes

Which is the odd number out?

2,743   **2,917**   **9,461**

9,172   **6,813**   **4,819**

3,724   **1,836**   **9,418**

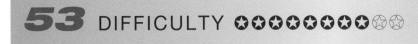 

53 DIFFICULTY ★★★★★★★★☆☆ — 5 Minutes

Fill in the missing number.

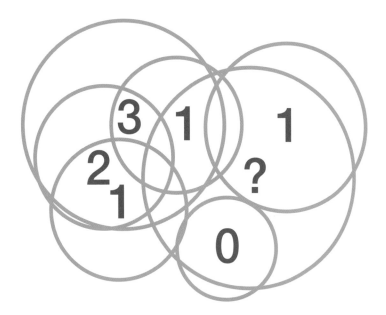

54 DIFFICULTY ★★★★☆☆☆☆☆☆ — 3 Minutes

Place a number in the middle box that divides into all the other numbers without leaving a remainder. The answer is greater than 1.

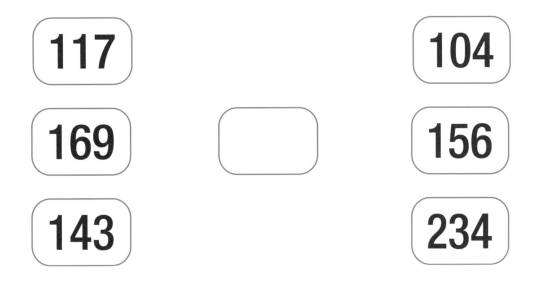

Every row and column contains the same numbers and signs, but they are arranged in a different order each time. Find the correct order to arrive at the final totals shown.

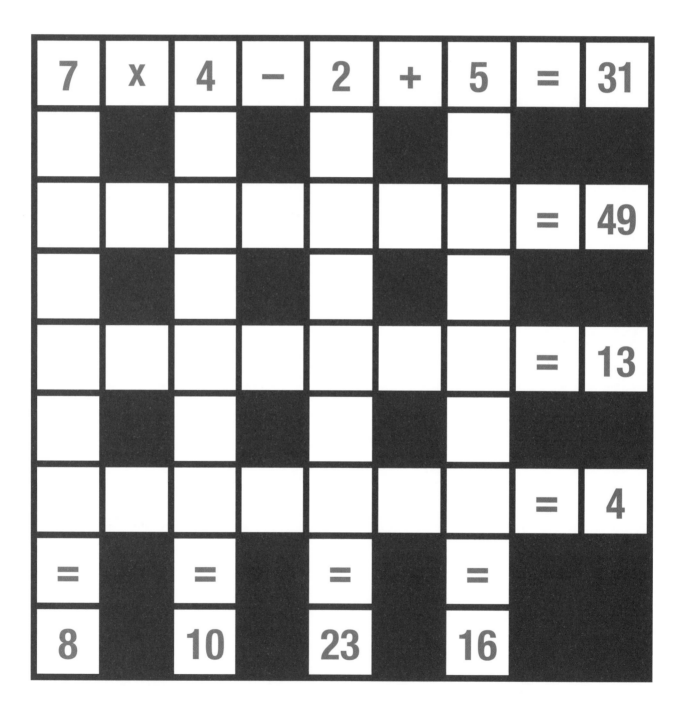

7	x	4	−	2	+	5	=	31
							=	49
							=	13
							=	4
=		=		=		=		
8		10		23		16		

56 DIFFICULTY ✪✪✪✪✪✪✫✫✫✫   6 Minutes

Use one straight line to divide this circle into two sections, each with numbers adding up to the same total. Beware—all is not quite as it appears!

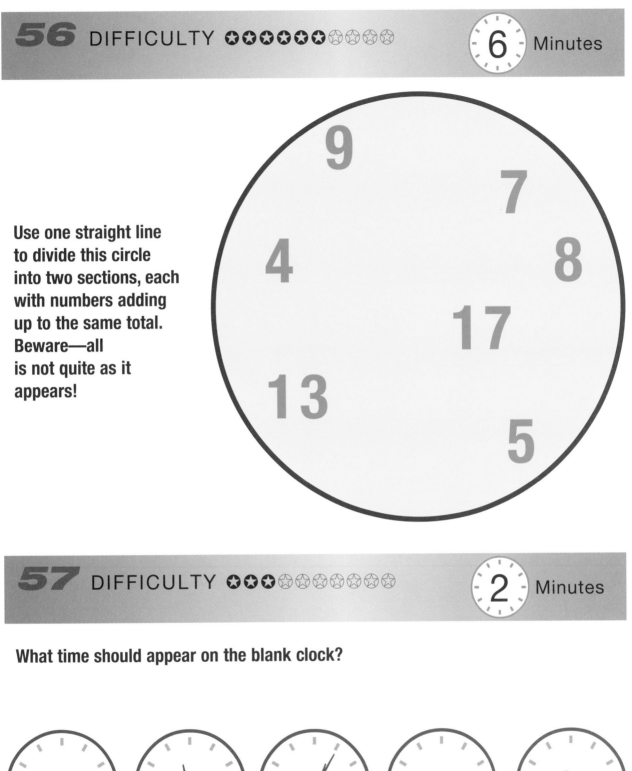

57 DIFFICULTY ✪✪✪✫✫✫✫✫✫✫   2 Minutes

What time should appear on the blank clock?

a   b   c   d   e

58 DIFFICULTY ✪✪✪✪✪✩✩✩✩✩ ⏱ ③ Minutes

Assess the cutlery below; given that scales a and b balance perfectly, how many knives are needed to balance scale c?

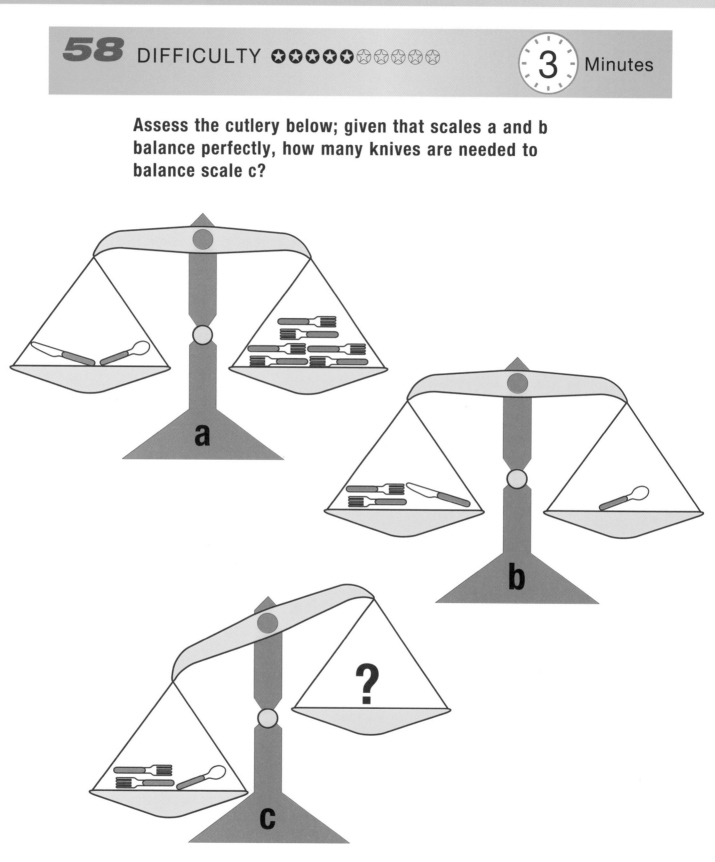

59 DIFFICULTY ★★★★★☆☆☆☆☆  **8** Minutes

Find the answers to the calculations in the grid, looking up, down, backward, forward, and diagonally.

1. 888 + 888
2. 1,111 x 7
3. 21,402 ÷ 2
4. 33 x 333
5. 7 x 7 x 7 x 7
6. 303,030 ÷ 3

7. 1,110 x 9
8. 1,000 − 506
9. 3,434 ÷ 2
10. 101 x 72
11. 88,888 ÷ 2 ÷ 2
12. (2,133 ÷ 3) + 3 + 3

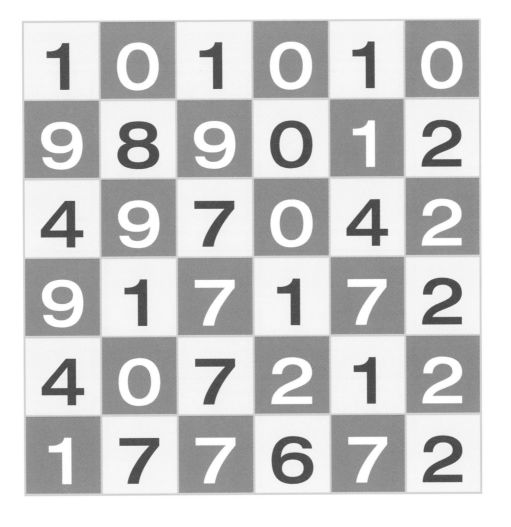

60 DIFFICULTY ✪✪✪✪✪✪✩✩✩✩ ⏲ 8 Minutes

Place the ace, king, queen, and jack of each suit so that:
* no card value appears twice in any row, column, or main diagonal, and
* no suit appears twice in any row, column, or main diagonal.

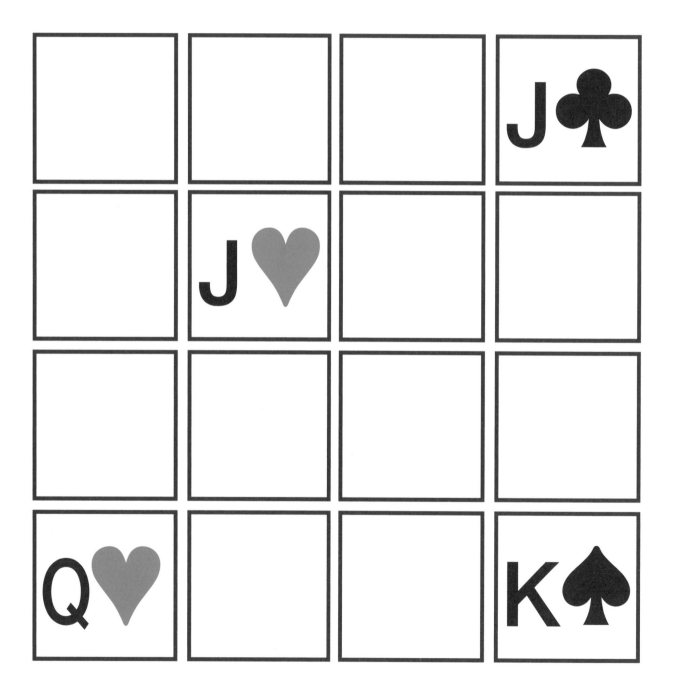

61 DIFFICULTY ⭐⭐⭐✩✩✩✩✩✩✩   3 Minutes

Target time: 3 minutes

Make a calculation totaling the figure below using some or all of the numbers above it and any of the four standard mathematical operators (+, −, x, and ÷).

$$1 \quad 6 \quad 7 \quad 8 \quad 9 \quad 10$$

$$= 476$$

62 DIFFICULTY ⭐⭐⭐⭐✩✩✩✩✩✩   4 Minutes

Replace the question marks with mathematical symbols to produce the correct answer. Only the four basic operators (+, −, x, and ÷) are permitted. Perform calculations in strict left to right order. Can you find two possible solutions?

$$7 \ ? \ 6 \ ? \ 5 \ ? \ 4$$

$$= 2$$

This is a one-player solitaire game. Place two silver coins on spaces 1 and 2, and two pennies on spaces 9 and 10. The aim is to make the coins swap sides by sliding them along the lines.

However, there is a catch. At no point must a silver coin and a penny lie on the same line—for example, your opening move cannot be 2 to 4, because the silver coin at 4 and the penny at 9 would be on the same line. Also, only one coin per space is allowed.

How many moves are there in the shortest solution? One move counts as sliding one coin from one space along a straight line to another space, possibly moving through other spaces along the way, although if you wish to move the same coin along another line in a different direction, it counts as a second move.

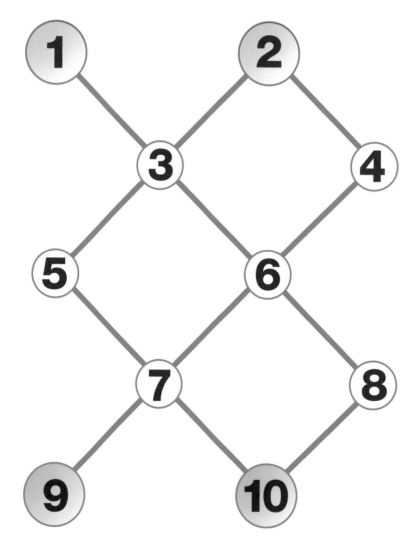

64 DIFFICULTY ✪✪✪✪✪✪✪✩✩ ⏱ **5** Minutes

Given that scales a and b balance perfectly, how many apples are needed to balance scale c?

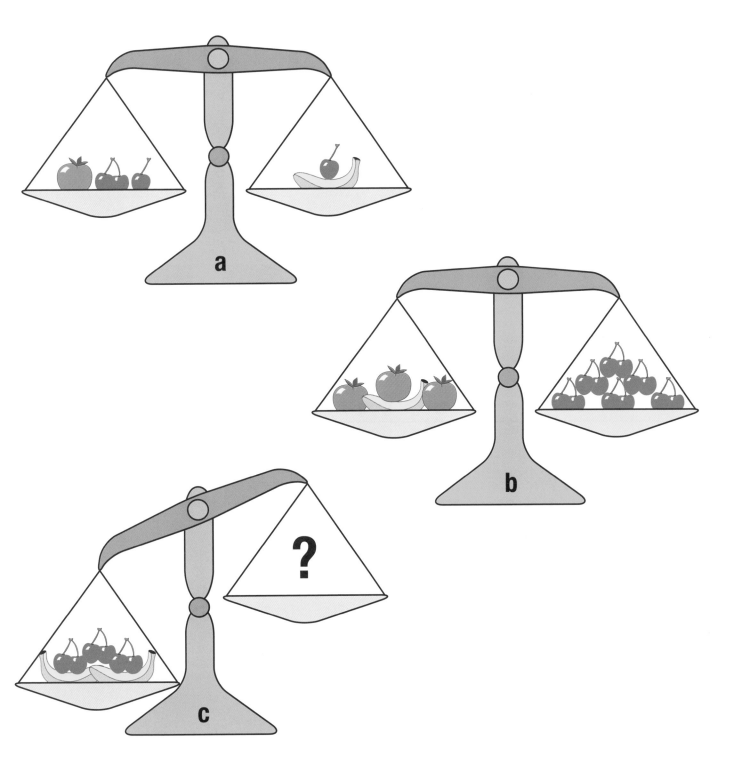

65 DIFFICULTY ✪✪✪✪✪✪✩✩✩✩ ⏱ 10 Minutes

Can you fit these numbers into the grid? One number has already been inserted to help you get started.

3 Digits
323
669

4 Digits
2056
3212
5430
6742
7733
8060
8179
9055

5 Digits
14355
21845

28456
37206
37513
46207
49747
68626
75200
~~89505~~

6 Digits
317861
322009
479351
689083

7 Digits
1636986

2464093
3656016
3778443
4317723
4833109
5207007
5829464
6276067

6569248
7058756
8208754
8757623
9683726

66 DIFFICULTY ✪✪✪✪✪✪✩✩✩✩ ④ Minutes

The number 1,970,157 appears just once in this grid and occurs in a straight line, running either backward or forward in a horizontal, vertical, or diagonal direction. Can you locate it?

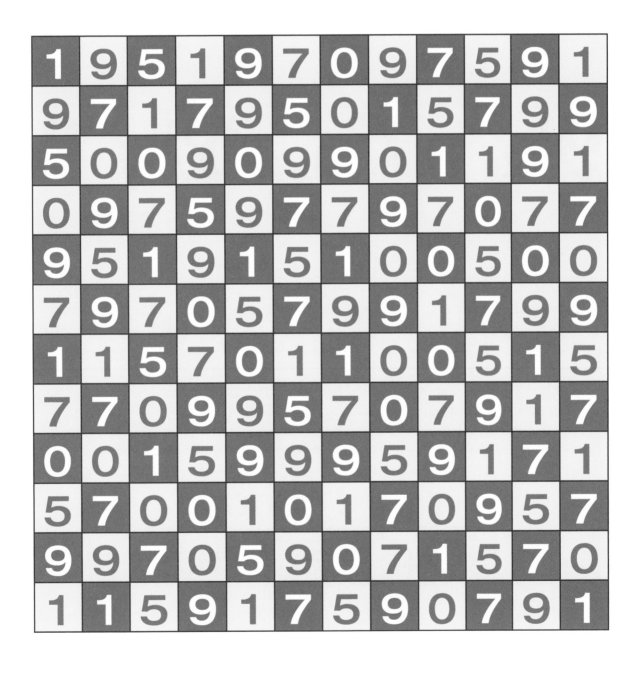

67 DIFFICULTY ✪✪✪✪✪✪✪✪☆☆ — 6 Minutes

Which number comes next?

$$2\tfrac{3}{4}, \quad 13\tfrac{3}{4}, \quad 5\tfrac{1}{4},$$

$$9\tfrac{1}{2}, \quad 7\tfrac{3}{4}, \quad 5\tfrac{1}{4}, \quad ?$$

68 DIFFICULTY ✪✪✪✪☆☆☆☆☆☆ — 4 Minutes

Each block is equal to the sum of the two numbers beneath it.
Find all the missing numbers.

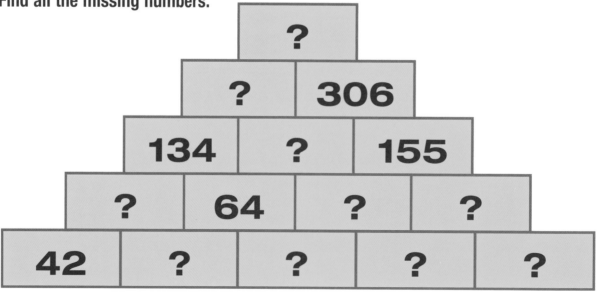

		?		
	?	306		
	134	?	155	
	?	64	?	?
42	?	?	?	?

69 DIFFICULTY ✪✪✪✪✪✪✩✩✩✩  3 Minutes

Which is the odd number out?

3, 8, 15, 24, 29, 35, 48

70 DIFFICULTY ✪✪✪✪✪✪✩✩✩✩ 5 Minutes

Adam and his sister Florence had a pair of standard dice and were playing a game where each needed to throw a double to start. On his very first turn, Adam threw a double six.

1. How likely was Florence to throw a double six on her next throw?

2. How likely was she to throw any double on her next throw?

3. What were the chances of Florence throwing, say, both a one and a six on her next throw?

4. How likely was she to throw her favorite number, four, on either of the die on her next throw?

71 DIFFICULTY ✪✪✪✪✪✪✪☆☆  8 Minutes

Place the ace, king, queen, and jack of each suit so that:
* no card value appears twice in any row, column, or main diagonal, and
* no suit appears twice in any row, column, or main diagonal.

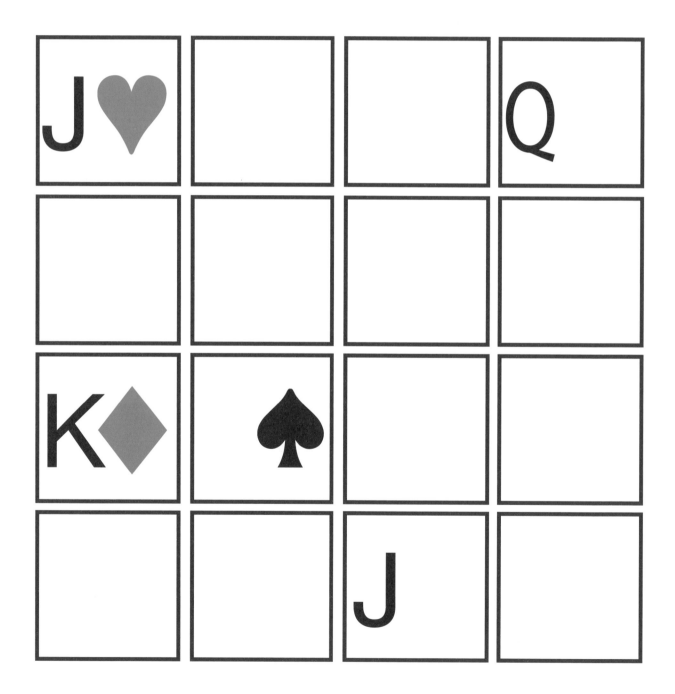

72 DIFFICULTY ✪✪✪✪✪✪✪✪☆☆  8 Minutes

Make a calculation totaling the figure below using some or all of the numbers above it and any of the four standard mathematical operators (+, –, x, and ÷).

2 4 6 7 8 9

= *628*

73 DIFFICULTY ✪✪✪✪✪✪✪✪✪☆ 6 Minutes

The cards on the right are valued as follows: an ace = 1, a jack = 11, a queen = 12, and a king = 13. All the other cards have the same value as their numbers.

Study this card arrangement carefully for one minute, then see if you can answer the questions on the next page without checking back.

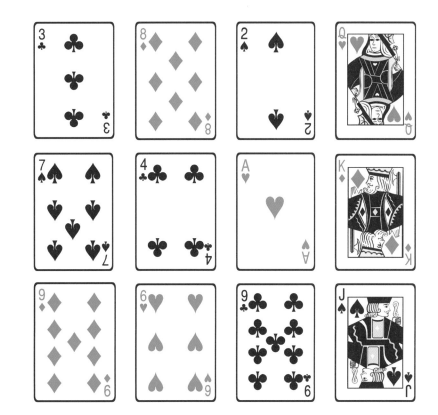

74 DIFFICULTY ✪✪✪✪✪✪✪✪☆☆ | 6 Minutes

Place a number in the middle box that divides into all the other numbers without leaving a remainder. The answer is greater than 1.

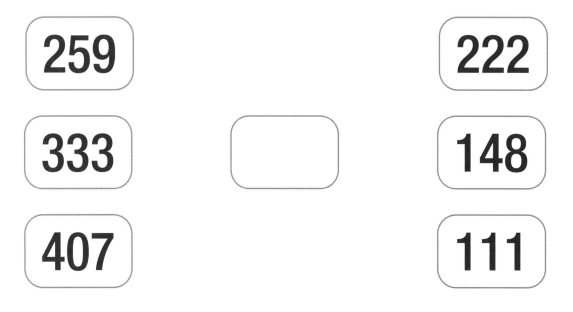

[73] DIFFICULTY ✪✪✪✪✪✪✪✪✪☆ | 6 Minutes

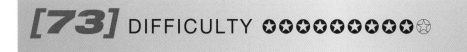

Can you answer these questions about the puzzle on the previous page without having to check back?

1. Which two numbers do not appear?

2. Which is the only pair of identical numbers to appear?

3. What is the highest total value of three cards in a column?

4. Two rows of four cards have the same total. What is this?

5. Which card is in the same column as (and directly below) a diamond, as well as being in the same column as (and directly above) a heart?

6. What is the total value of the four corner cards?

75 DIFFICULTY ✪✪✪✪✪✪✪✩✩ ⏱ 10 Minutes

Can you fit these numbers into the grid? One number has already been inserted to help you get started.

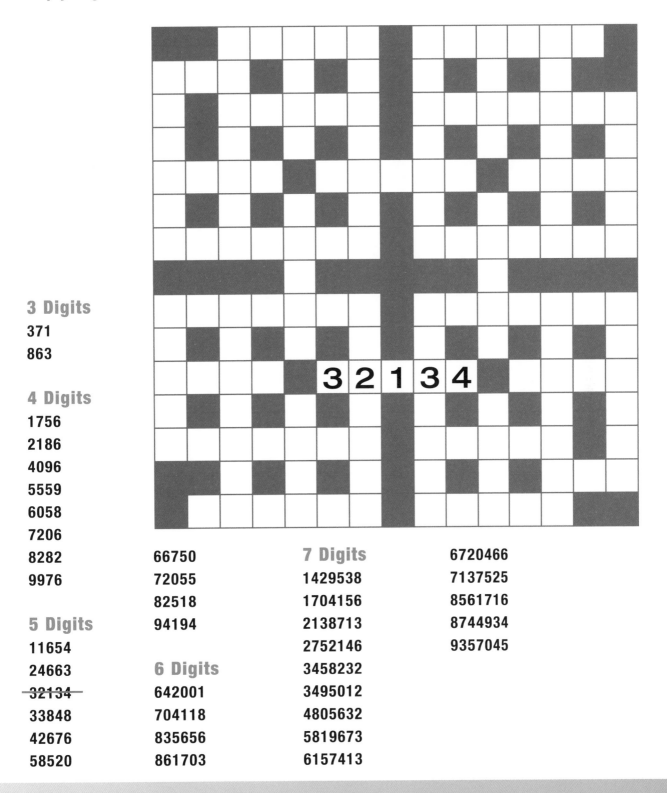

3 Digits
371
863

4 Digits
1756
2186
4096
5559
6058
7206
8282
9976

5 Digits
11654
24663
~~32134~~
33848
42676
58520

66750
72055
82518
94194

6 Digits
642001
704118
835656
861703

7 Digits
1429538
1704156
2138713
2752146
3458232
3495012
4805632
5819673
6157413

6720466
7137525
8561716
8744934
9357045

Assess the symbols below. Given that scales a and b balance perfectly, how many spades are needed to balance scale c?

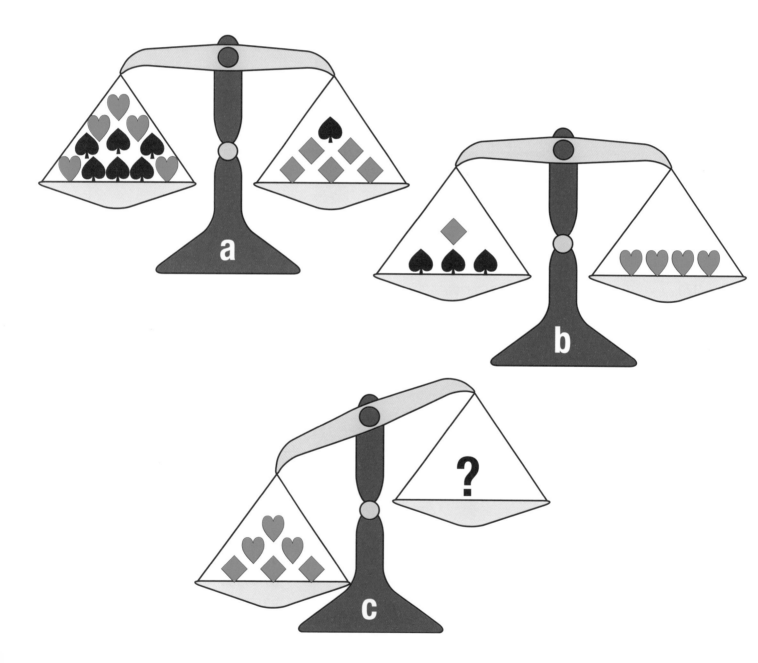

77 DIFFICULTY ⭐⭐⭐⭐⭐⭐⭐☆☆

Target time: 5 minutes

5 Minutes

Consider the celestial bodies below. Given that scales a and b balance perfectly, how many suns are needed to balance scale c?

78 DIFFICULTY ★★★★★☆☆☆☆☆  **8** Minutes

Find the answers to the following calculations in the grid below, reading up, down, backward, forward, and diagonally.

1. 10,000 − 5,454
2. 66 x 99
3. 4,224 x 2
4. 20,000 − 9,912
5. 52,000 ÷ 8
6. 5,555 − 4,321

7. 500 x 120
8. 1,604 x 5
9. 63,636 ÷ 3
10. (7 x 7) x (8 x 8)
11. 6,003 − 2,997
12. 101 x 10 x 9

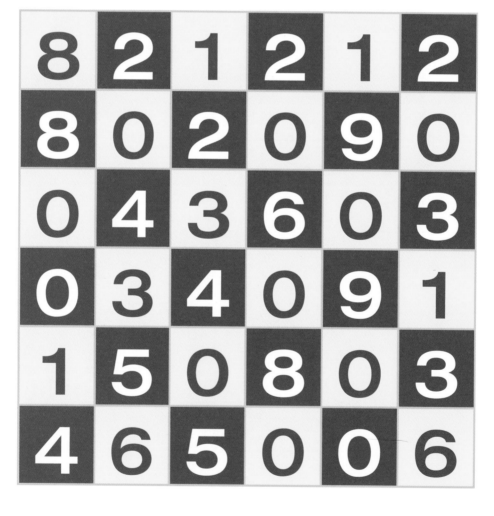

79 DIFFICULTY ✪✪✪✪✫✫✫✫✫✫ ⏲ 3 Minutes

Use two straight lines to divide this clock face into three parts, each containing numbers adding up to the same total.

80 DIFFICULTY ✪✪✪✪✪✪✪✫✫✫✫ ⏲ 5 Minutes

What number comes next in the sequence below?

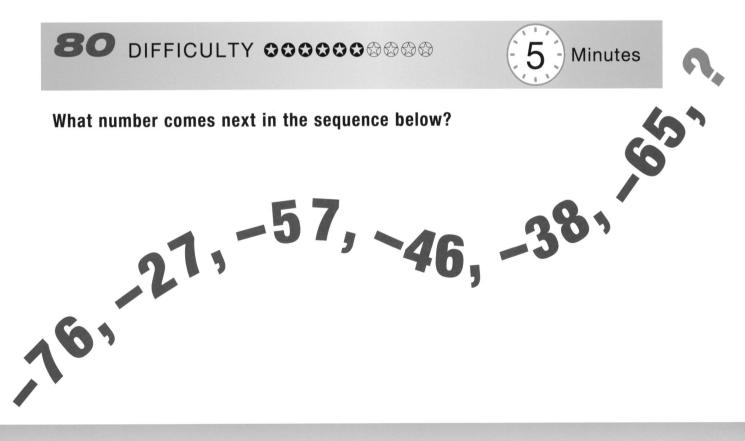

-76, -27, -57, -46, -38, -65, ?

81 DIFFICULTY ✪✪✪✪✪✪✩✩✩✩　6 Minutes

Each block is equal to the sum of the two numbers beneath it.
Find all the missing numbers.

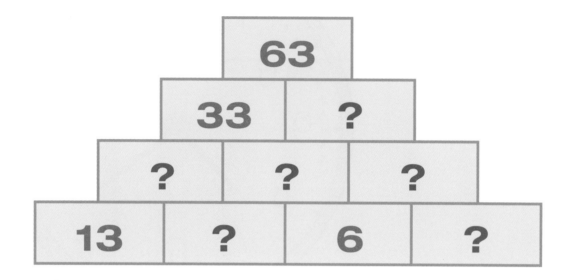

82 DIFFICULTY ✪✪✪✪✪✪✩✩✩✩　3 Minutes

Which number is the odd one out?

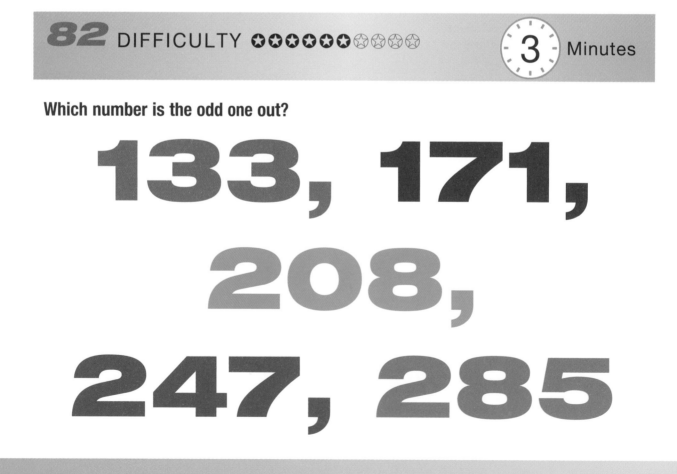

133, 171, 208, 247, 285

83 DIFFICULTY ✪✪✪✪✪✪✩✩✩✩

7 Minutes

Every row and column contains the same numbers and signs, but they are arranged in a different order each time. Find the correct order to arrive at the final totals shown.

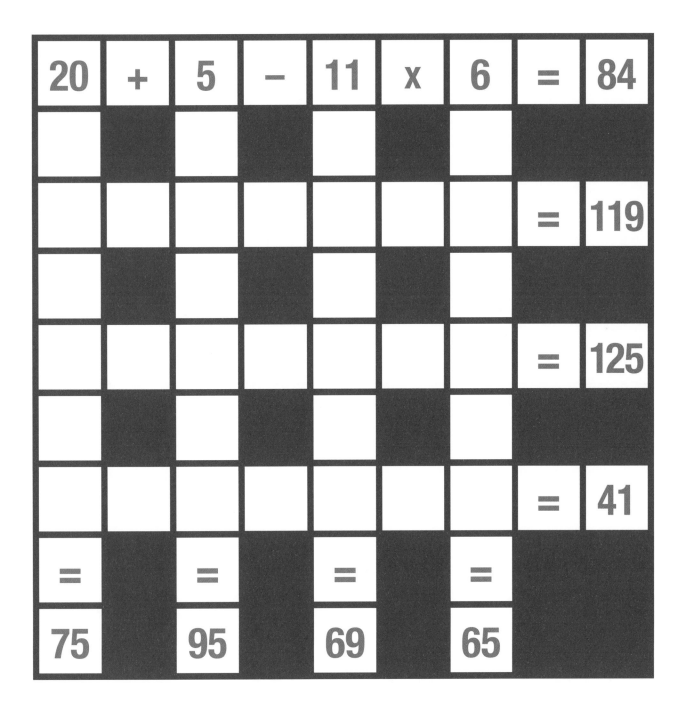

20	+	5	–	11	x	6	=	84
							=	119
							=	125
							=	41
=		=		=		=		
75		95		69		65		

84 DIFFICULTY ✪✪✪✪✪✪☆☆☆☆ ⏰ 6 Minutes

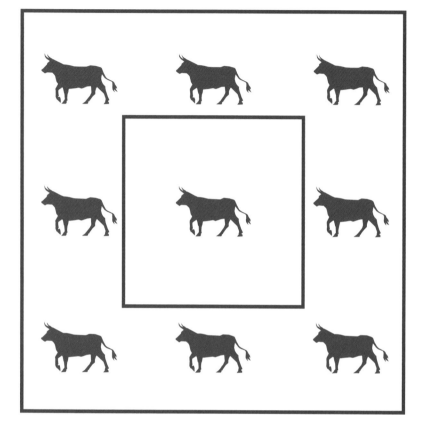

How many more square fences do you need to add so that each bull is separate from all the others?

85 DIFFICULTY ✪✪✪✪✪✪✪✪☆☆ ⏰ 6 Minutes

What number should replace the question mark in the following sequence?

365, 195, 380, 240, 395, 285, 410, ?

86 DIFFICULTY ✪✪✪✪✪✪✪☆☆☆

20 Minutes

Use skill (rather than luck) to solve this nonogram. (See puzzle 13 for advice on how to complete a nonogram.)

87 DIFFICULTY ●●●●●☆☆☆☆☆ — 3 Minutes

What time should it be on clock f?

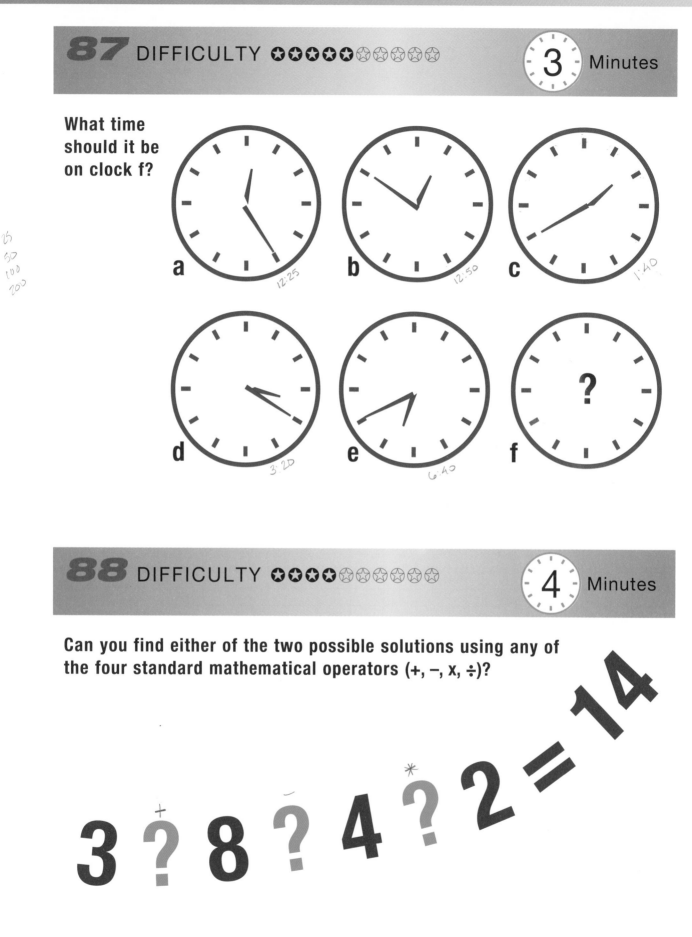

88 DIFFICULTY ●●●●☆☆☆☆☆☆ — 4 Minutes

Can you find either of the two possible solutions using any of the four standard mathematical operators (+, −, x, ÷)?

$$3\ ?\ 8\ ?\ 4\ ?\ 2 = 14$$

89 DIFFICULTY ★★★★★★★☆☆ 8 Minutes

Can you place the tiles in the grid so that:

* the odd numbers sit on the yellow spaces?
* the even numbers sit on the green spaces?
* each row, column, and main diagonal totals 34?

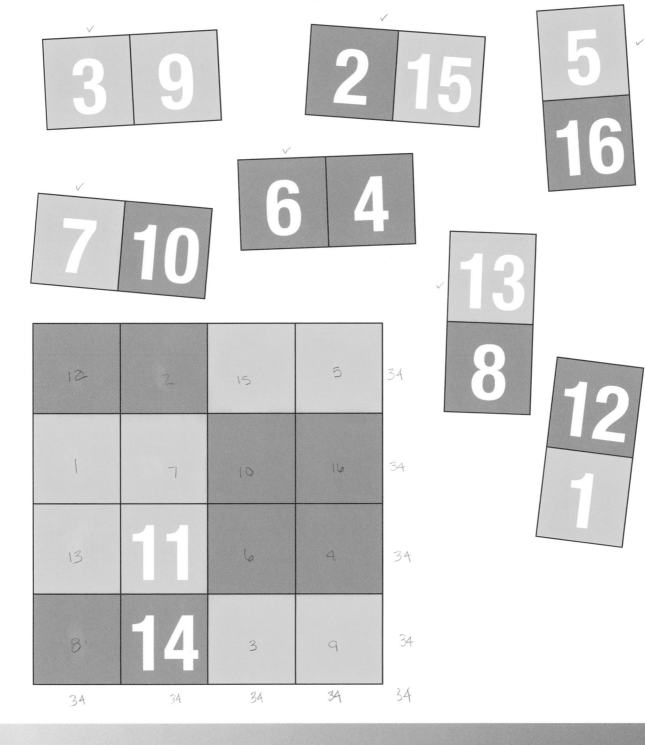

90 DIFFICULTY ★★★★★★★☆☆☆ (10) Minutes

Can you fit these numbers into the grid? One number has already been inserted to help you get started.

3 Digits
770
847

4 Digits
1805
2779
3586
4596
5358
6232
7519
8132

5 0 1 8 2 0 6

5 Digits
14385
23528
38923
46659
50658
61885
77576
82575
91513
92528

6 Digits	**7 Digits**	3199024	6714361
599560	1353745	4505979	7070873
784529	1379963	~~5018206~~	8171539
871625	2455298	5757336	9033244
934069	3129815	6208519	9726708

91 DIFFICULTY ✪✪✪✪✪✪✪☆☆  10 Minutes

The answers to the calculations below can be found in the grid—look up, down, backward, forward, and diagonally!

1. $(999 \div 3) \times 9^2$
2. $(2 + 2)^2 \times (3 + 3)^3$
3. 66×55
4. $(1{,}000{,}000 \div 50) \div 5$
5. $5{,}505.5 \times 2^4$
6. $(13{,}332 \times 2) \div 6$
7. $23 \times 24 \times 25$
8. $6{,}734 \times 3^2$
9. 101×11
10. 176×25
11. $(221 \div 13) + 1{,}717$
12. $163{,}216 \div 404$

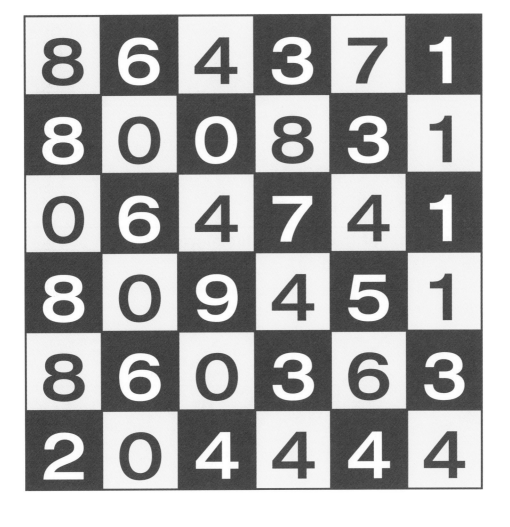

92 DIFFICULTY ✪✪✪✪✪✪✪☆☆

6 Minutes

How many squares on this miniature chess board can the knight visit (using his usual L-shaped move) without visiting a square twice?

93 DIFFICULTY ✪✪✪✪☆☆☆☆☆☆

3 Minutes

What is the sum total of the spots on the eleven hidden sides of these three dice?

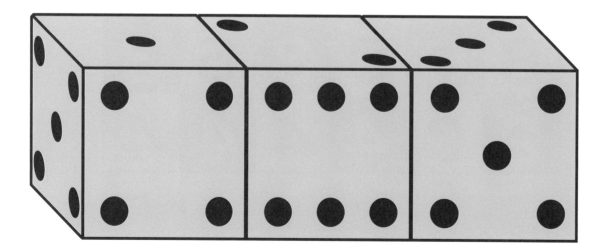

94 DIFFICULTY ✪✪✪✪✪✪✪✪✩✩  6 Minutes

Place a number in the middle box that divides into all the other numbers without leaving a remainder. The answer is greater than 1.

354 649

236 531

413 177

95 DIFFICULTY ✪✪✪✪✪✪✩✩✩✩ 3 Minutes

Which number is the odd one out in this sequence?

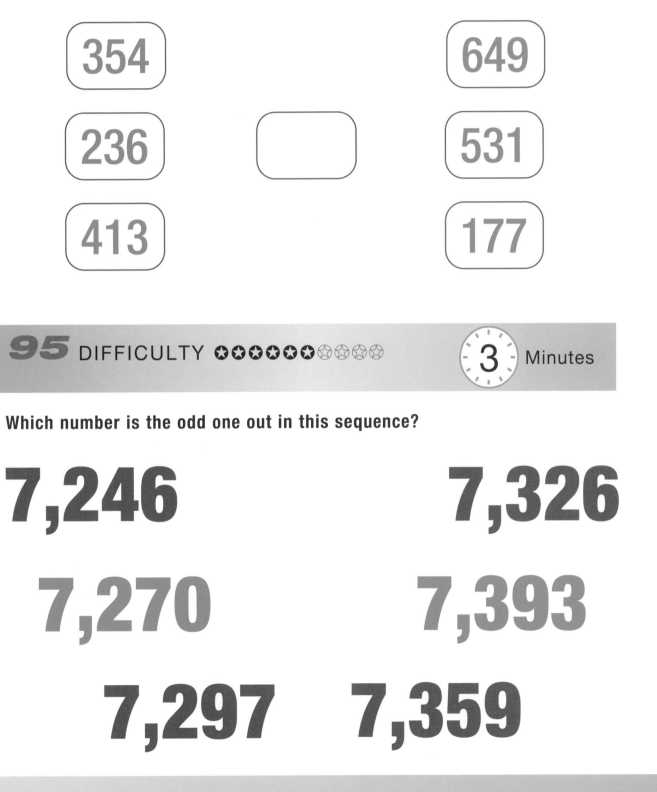

7,246   **7,326**

7,270   **7,393**

7,297   **7,359**

96 DIFFICULTY ★★★★☆☆☆☆☆ | 4 Minutes

Target time: 4 minutes

Replace the question marks with mathematical symbols to produce the correct answer. Only the four basic operators (+, −, x, and ÷) are permitted. Perform calculations in strict left to right order. Can you find all three possible solutions?

$$4 \; ? \; 3 \; ? \; 1 \; ? \; 2 = 9$$

97 DIFFICULTY ★★★★★☆☆☆☆ | 4 Minutes

Can you fit four different dominoes into the shape below, so that each horizontal and vertical line totals fourteen? We've placed two in their correct positions, although we haven't revealed how many dots (if any) should be on the second faces of these dominoes—you'll need to discover this, as well as the locations of the other dominoes, in order to arrive at the solution.

1

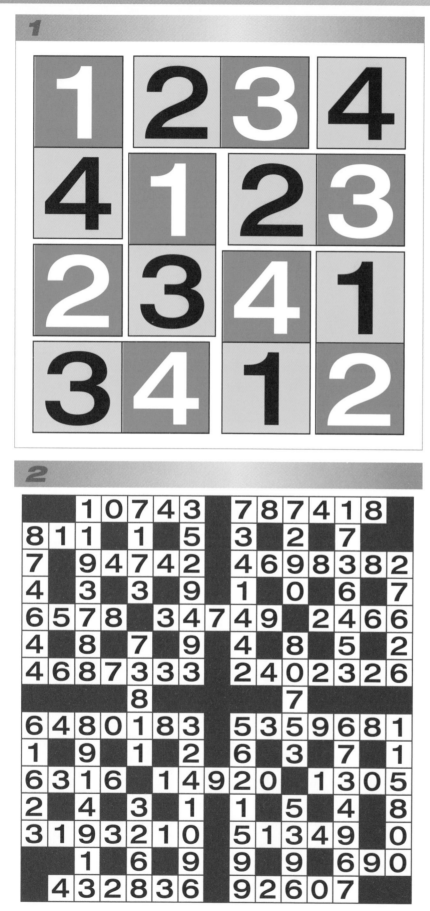

2

3

(25 x 5 x 4) + (9 x 3) = 527
There are ten other
possible solutions.

4

1. 19
2. 1 + 2 + 3 = 6
3. 7
4. Green
5. 2 (1 and 3)
6. 9
7. 4
8. 2

5

b; the other three have
the same angle between
the hands.

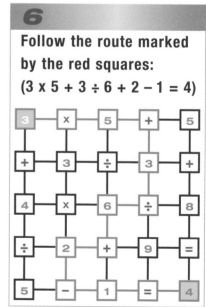

6

Follow the route marked
by the red squares:
(3 x 5 + 3 ÷ 6 + 2 − 1 = 4)

3	x	5	+	5
+	3	÷	3	+
4	x	6	÷	8
÷	2	+	9	=
5	−	1	=	4

7

Three; each apple weighs as much as two oranges, and each banana weighs as much as four oranges. Thus three apples are needed to balance scale c.

8

1. 6,561
2. 2,000
3. 1,232
4. 10,100
5. 352
6. 6,170
7. 2,904
8. 1,000
9. 7,654
10. 1,782
11. 520
12. 30,330
13. 2,260

7	6	5	4	0	2
2	1	4	0	9	2
8	7	1	6	5	6
7	0	2	0	0	0
1	0	3	3	0	3
3	5	2	5	2	0

9

3	+	2	x	6	−	5	=	25
x		x		−		−		
6	−	3	x	5	+	2	=	17
+		+		+		x		
5	+	6	−	2	x	3	=	27
−		−		x		+		
2	+	5	−	3	x	6	=	24
=		=		=		=		
21		7		9		15		

10

Remove one coin from the bottom row to leave five coins remaining. The crux of the problem is the single coin in the top row, and uses logic of odd and even numbers. If your opponent takes it at any stage, make sure your next move leaves the two larger rows equal in coins. Until that happens, ensure that the two larger rows are one coin different (e.g., 2 and 3).

11

5	4	3	7	9	8	7	3	5	4	9	5
9	8	3	5	9	3	7	5	3	4	8	4
3	4	7	5	4	3	5	9	5	3	7	7
4	5	4	9	4	5	8	4	7	3	9	3
5	4	3	7	9	3	3	8	5	9	8	8
9	3	4	8	5	7	9	9	4	9	9	9
4	7	9	4	9	8	9	7	7	3	4	5
8	5	9	5	4	3	5	8	9	8	8	3
7	9	5	3	5	9	8	7	3	4	5	9
5	1	4	7	4	8	7	5	9	7	5	3
8	5	3	5	3	3	4	9	5	8	4	4
9	8	7	3	5	4	5	4	3	9	7	8

12

	7	6	1	5	4		9	4	2	8	2	9	
8	7	7		8		9		4		5		5	
2		7	3	2	1	4		6	4	9	8	7	7
8		6		1		8		1		4		6	1
7	2	6	3		2	0	9	0	1		2	6	8	0
3		7		3		8		3		5		4	4
6	0	2	9	2	5	7		1	4	1	9	6	9	4
				8					2				
7	4	7	2	5	1	7		6	8	1	7	5	1	1
5		9		0		6		0		5		6	1
1	5	7	2		2	4	4	3		7	4	2	5
5		2		2		7		8		9		5	6
9	8	7	7	6	8		9	7	4	9	2		9
	3		5		8		3		8		3	1	5
7	3	9	7	1	5		3	0	4	0	5	

13

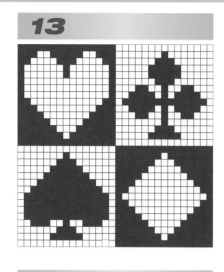

14

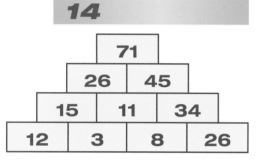

15

b is at (9, 6) and d is at (5, 0).
The secret is to work out
that the average of a and c's
coordinates give the center
of the square as (7, 3).

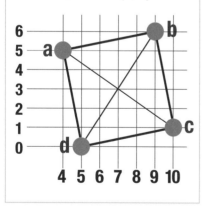

16

486; all the others have
their digits in ascending
order.

17

((6 ÷ 2) x 3) + 7 = 16;   (6 x 2) − 3 + 7 = 16

18

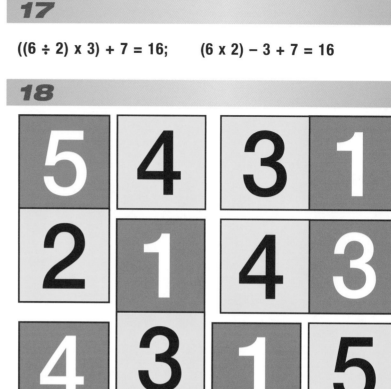

19

21

20

Gary won $4. The total payback is three
times the difference of the number of spots
on the two dice. Thus Gary got back $9:
(5 − 2) x 3 = 9, winning $4.

21

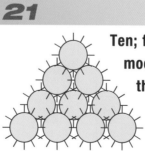

Ten; from b we can infer that three
moons equals one star; from a we can
thus infer that seven moons equals
five suns. If we then convert the
left-hand side of c into moons
we get fourteen moons (because
each star is worth three moons). As we know that seven
moons equals five suns, we can deduce that twice that
will need ten suns to balance scale c.

22

91.25; deduct 1.25, then 2.5 alternately.

23

80; write the points as digits, then add them up in rows:

a.   13 + 21 = 34

b.   40 + 11 = 51

c.   26 + 45 = 71

so d.   45 + 35 = 80

24

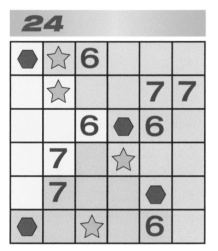

25

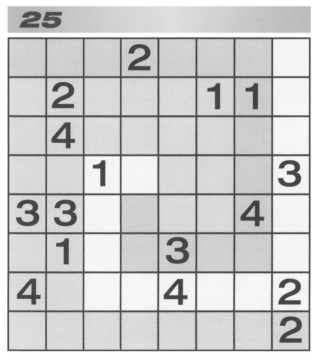

26

a; the dots in the upper part of each domino increase in number by one every time, while those in the lower part decrease by one every time, thus the total number of dots on each domino remains the same every time.

27   28

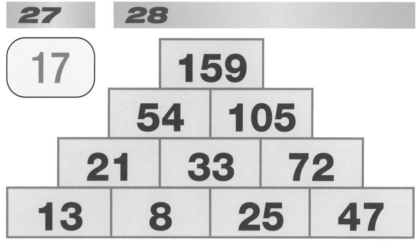

17

159

54   105

21   33   72

13   8   25   47

29

4,569; in all the others the third digit is the sum of the first two digits, and the fourth digit is the sum of the second and third digits.

30

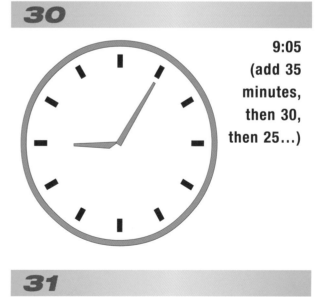

9:05 (add 35 minutes, then 30, then 25...)

31

12 − 4 + 7 − 8 = 7

((12 − 4) x 7) ÷ 8 = 7

32

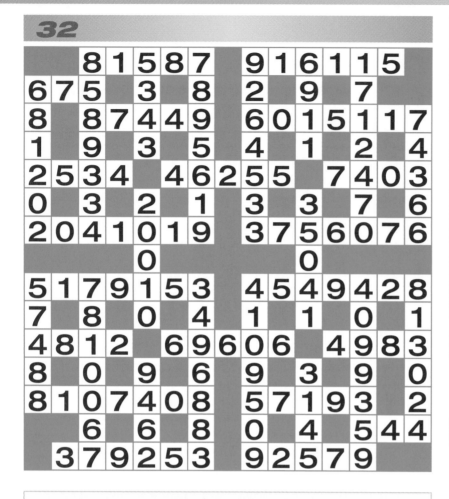

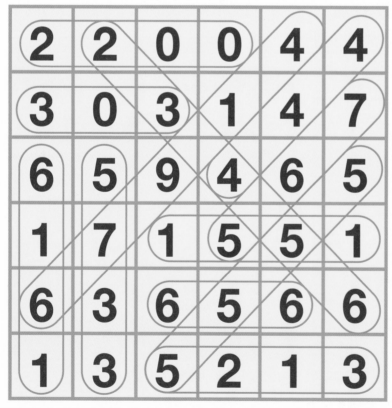

33

Fourteen; one spade weighs as much as four clubs, and one heart weighs as much as six clubs. Thus fourteen clubs are needed to balance scale c.

34

42; all of the others are prime numbers.

35

Gary won $8. The total payback is the number of points on the first die multiplied by the number of points on the second. Thus Gary got back $20 (5 x 4 = 20), winning $8.

36

1. 41,976
2. 3,375
3. 1,616
4. 2,200
5. 23,456
6. 303
7. 1,551
8. 5,555
9. 444
10. 3,125
11. 765
12. 656

37

1. 2; the triangle (7) and pentagon (23)
2. 16 + 7 = 23
3. 4 x 16 = 64
4. Triangle (7) and pentagon (23)
5. Pink (16), blue (4), and lilac (46)
6. 35; 7 + 4 = 11, 46 − 11 = 35

38

The Pythagorean Theorem. Consider Fig. 1. The length of this square's sides is the same as the hypotenuse (longest side) of any of the triangles. In Fig. 2, we have rearranged the same shapes into a different configuration, so the areas must be equal. There are two squares (separated by the dotted line). The left-hand square has sides equivalent to the middle-length side of the triangle, while the sides of the right-hand square are equal to the triangle's shortest side. In other words, the square of the hypotenuse is equal to the sum of the squares of the other two sides, which is the Pythagorean Theorem.

39

$(((7 \times 4) + 4) \times 10) − 9 = 311$. There are thirteen other possible solutions.

40

1	8	0	4	8	7	0	9	1	8	0	4
4	7	8	0	9	8	1	9	9	8	1	0
4	1	0	0	7	9	8	9	1	7	4	0
7	8	9	0	1	4	7	0	9	1	9	8
4	9	0	4	7	8	4	8	1	0	7	7
8	9	8	7	0	9	0	8	9	0	0	9
9	0	7	9	4	8	9	1	4	9	0	4
8	8	4	9	8	1	9	4	9	7	8	9
1	0	7	8	4	9	0	1	8	9	4	9
9	7	9	1	4	0	1	8	0	9	8	0
4	9	8	0	8	4	0	8	1	4	7	8
8	7	1	1	4	1	9	8	7	9	1	1

41

42

43

11

44

846; it should be 847 since each number is reversed then added on to the previous number.

45

Follow the route marked in green.

66	14	18	65	26	55	19
77	50	21	16	49	24	63
75	33	37	78	40	54	10
96	98	96	25	18	15	36
31	20	36	49	54	50	56
98	48	11	23	91	72	56
20	28	45	78	91	15	72
12	23	54	77	85	95	21
16	25	24	66	14	91	40

46

49

3	6	5	5	6	1	3
5	5	0	2	2	4	3
4	4	6	1	0	0	0
1	0	0	1	4	2	5
1	0	1	5	1	4	5
2	3	3	0	2	6	2
6	3	4	2	4	6	3
6	3	4	6	1	2	5

50

			3	1			
3	5				4	5	
	1		2	4		2	
			3		1		
5					4		4
	2	3		5		1	
						2	

47

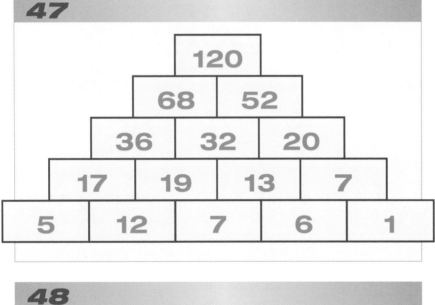

51

((6 x 2) − 4) ÷ 2 = 4
((3 + 5) x 3) ÷ 4 = 6
(5 + 2 − 3) ÷ 2 = 2

52

9,461; the rest can be paired off into anagrams of one another: 2,743–3,724; 9,172–2,917; 6,813–1,836; 4,819–9,418.

48

14; there are two sequences running alternately.
Starting with 10, add 2, 4, 6, etc.
Starting with 5, add 1, 3, 5, etc.
So 9 + 5 = 14.

53

3; because the big circle centered around that number encompasses three of the other numbers (1, 1, and 0). The other big circle has a 3 at the center; it, too, encompasses three numbers (1, 1, and 2).

54

13

55

7	x	4	−	2	+	5	=	31
−		x		+		+		
5	−	2	+	4	x	7	=	49
x		+		x		−		
2	x	7	−	5	+	4	=	13
+		−		−		x		
4	+	5	−	7	x	2	=	4
=		=		=		=		
8		10		23		16		

56

9
7
4
8
17
13
5

57

3:55 (add 1 hour and 25 minutes each time).

58

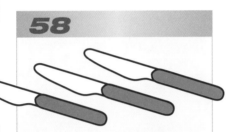

Three; one knife weighs as much as two forks, and two knives weigh as much as one spoon. Thus three knives are needed to balance scale c.

59

1. 1,776
2. 7,777
3. 10,701
4. 10,989
5. 2,401
6. 101,010
7. 9,990
8. 494
9. 1,717
10. 7,272
11. 22,222
12. 717

60

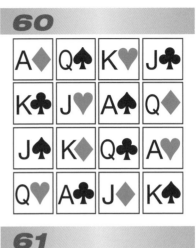

A♦	Q♠	K♥	J♣
K♣	J♥	A♠	Q♦
J♠	K♦	Q♣	A♥
Q♥	A♣	J♦	K♠

61

((10 x 6) + 8) x 7 = 476
There are twenty-three other possible solutions.

62

7 − 6 + 5 − 4 = 2
(7 + 6 − 5) ÷ 4 = 2

63

The shortest solution is eighteen moves: 2 to 3, 9 to 4, 10 to 7, 3 to 8, 4 to 2, 7 to 5, 8 to 6, 5 to 10, 6 to 9, 2 to 5, 1 to 6, 6 to 4, 5 to 3, 10 to 8, 4 to 7, 3 to 2, 8 to 1, and 7 to 10.

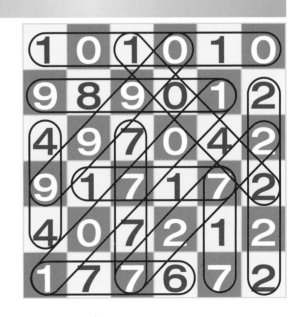

64

Six; two apples weigh as much as five cherries, and nine cherries weigh as much as two bananas. Thus six apples are needed to balance scale c.

65

66

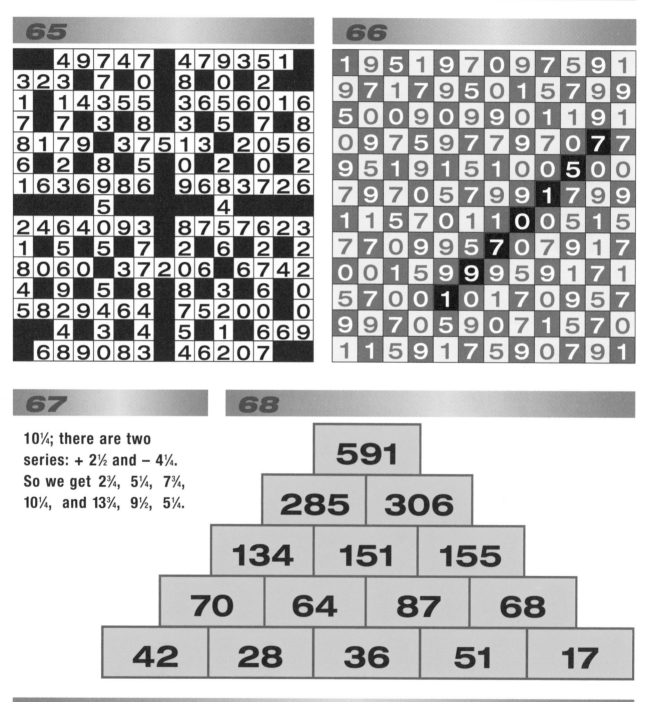

67

10¼; there are two series: + 2½ and − 4¼. So we get 2¾, 5¼, 7¾, 10¼, and 13¾, 9½, 5¼.

68

	591			
	285	306		
	134	151	155	
	70	64	87	68
42	28	36	51	17

69

29; the rest are a sequence of square numbers minus 1, for example, 2² − 1 = 3, 3² − 1 = 8, 4² − 1 = 15, etc.

70

1. There are six faces to each die, which could land any way up, thus the chance of throwing a double six is one in thirty-six.

2. There are six different combinations of doubles, thus the chance of throwing any double is six in thirty-six, i.e., one in six.

3. Bearing in mind that there are two dice, the chance of throwing both a one and a six is two in thirty-six, i.e., one in eighteen.

4. With six faces to each die, the chance of throwing one particular number is eleven in thirty-six. Throwing two dice does not double your chances of throwing a four, because if you have already thrown one, the second throw is irrelevant, so in one of your six tries you don't need to throw again, i.e., only in 5/6 of the times do you add the 1/6 chance, i.e., 1/6 + 5/6 x 1/6. In other words, the chance of NOT throwing a four is 5/6 x 5/6, i.e., 25/36; thus the chance of throwing at least one four is 1 – 25/36, so 11/36.

71

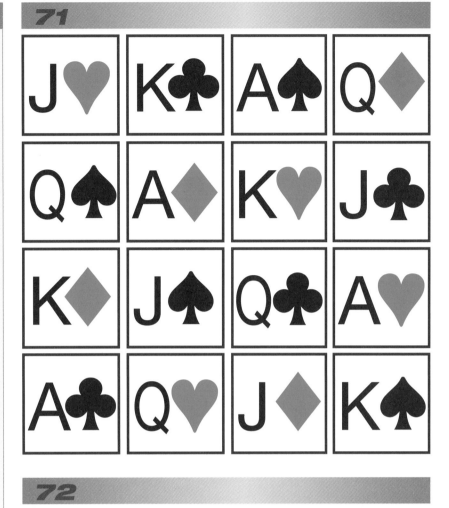

72

$$((6 + 4) \times 9 \times 7) - 2 = 628$$

73

1. 5 and 10
2. a pair of 9s
3. 36; queen (12), king (13), and jack (11)
4. 25; 3 + 8 + 2 + queen (12), and 7 + 4 + ace (1) + king (13)
5. the 4 of clubs
6. 35; 3 + queen (12) + 9 + jack (11)

74

37

75

76

Eleven; four spades weigh as much as three hearts, and seven spades weigh as much as three diamonds. Thus eleven spades are needed to balance scale c.

77

Sixteen; six suns weigh as much as one star, and two suns weigh as much as one moon. Thus sixteen suns are needed to balance scale c.

78

1. 4,546
2. 6,534
3. 8,448
4. 10,088
5. 6,500
6. 1,234
7. 60,000
8. 8,020
9. 21,212
10. 3,136
11. 13,006
12. 9,090

79

80

−19; there are two series (+19) and (−19): −76, −57, −38, and −19, −27, −46, −65.

81

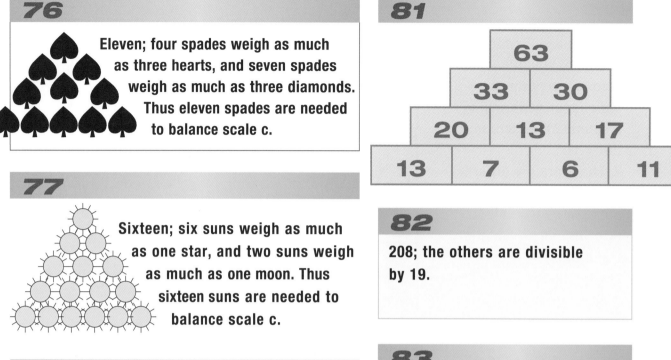

63 / 33 30 / 20 13 17 / 13 7 6 11

82

208; the others are divisible by 19.

83

20	+	5	−	11	x	6	=	84
+		x		x		+		
6	+	20	x	5	−	11	=	119
−		+		+		x		
11	−	6	+	20	x	5	=	125
x		−		−		−		
5	x	11	+	6	−	20	=	41
=		=		=		=		
75		95		69		65		

84

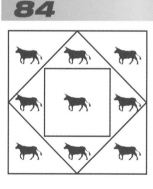

Just one; its four sides run diagonally, connecting the midpoints of each side of the larger fence, just touching the corners of the smaller fence.

85

40; starting with 365, add 15 to obtain alternate numbers (so, 365, 380, 395, 410). Then, arrive at the numbers in between by multiplying the number formed by the last two digits by the first digit. So 3 x 65 = 195, and 3 x 80 = 240, etc.

86

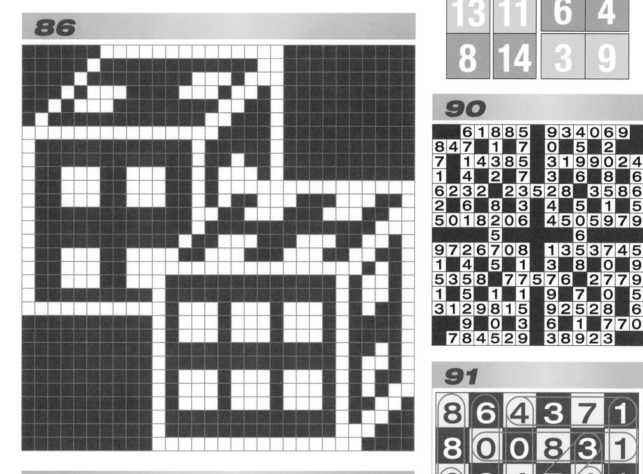

87

1:20; (start at 25 minutes past 12 o'clock, then double the number of minutes past 12 each time—i.e., 50 minutes past, 100 minutes past, 200 minutes past...)

88

((3 x 8) + 4) ÷ 2 = 14;   (3 + 8 − 4) x 2 = 14

89

12	2	15	5
1	7	10	16
13	11	6	4
8	14	3	9

90

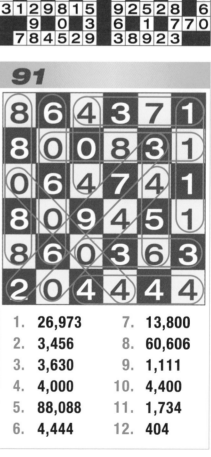

91

8	6	4	3	7	1
8	0	0	8	3	1
0	6	4	7	4	1
8	0	9	4	5	1
8	6	0	3	6	3
2	0	4	4	4	4

1.	26,973	7.	13,800
2.	3,456	8.	60,606
3.	3,630	9.	1,111
4.	4,000	10.	4,400
5.	88,088	11.	1,734
6.	4,444	12.	404

92

A maximum of fourteen (or fifteen if you include the square on which you start); there's no way of visiting the whole board, no matter which route you take.

93

37; there are twenty-one spots on each die, thus a total of sixty-three spots on the three dice. Since twenty-six spots are visible, the total number of spots on the sides that are not visible amounts to thirty-seven.

94

97

95

7,359; each number in the sequence (except the first and the odd one out) is obtained by taking the previous number and adding its two central numbers to it; e.g., 7,246 + 24 = 7,270.

96

(4 x 3) − 1 − 2 = 9
((4 + 3) ÷ 1) + 2 = 9
((4 + 3) x 1) + 2 = 9

Right-brain Puzzles

Perceptual Puzzles is a fun and challenging collection of brainteasers for anyone who wants to get a new angle on their 3-D skills or the geometry behind shape-based games. There is plenty for everyone in this section, as the puzzles require different levels of skill and amounts of time to complete.

Most of the skills you'll be using on these puzzles come from the right-hand side of your brain, which controls the left-hand side of your body. Right-hemisphere skills include gestalt (insight, the ability to see the big picture), 3-D formations, awareness of color and shape, musical talent, imagination, and (believe it or not!) daydreaming.

Our perceptual skills are not as consciously tested as vocabulary or mathematical abilities. Being able to squeeze your car through a tight space or work out which key fits your front door are just two examples of how our everyday unconscious uses visual cognition. Despite the obvious practical applications, there is something unnerving about testing these skills—it seems that without the comfort of words and numbers to help us, we are in a different world where we have to look beyond the obvious. Colors, spacing, lines, corners, directions, and arrangement could all have an effect on the answer—but which ones are relevant?

The trick, therefore, is to look beyond the illustrations and focus on the principles being employed. Don't let the abstract shapes and unfamiliar patterns fool you, for the principle behind each and every puzzle here is relatively straightforward.

Our crack team of puzzle-constructors has carefully crafted a spectacular range of challenges. Not all the obstacles around this course are the same. The star grading assigned to each puzzle in the book tells you what kind of territory to expect—a low number of stars indicates that you're on an easier slope. But if you're tackling an eight-, nine-, or ten-star problem, expect to get your heavy-duty boots and pickax out, for these are the hardest of all to work through. Each puzzle has also been given a time target rating as well, so you've got to keep an eye on the clock. However, keep in mind that both difficulty ratings and target times are based on an average performance, so don't be surprised if you sail through a ten-star puzzle or find yourself struggling with a three-star—everyone is different.

So have fun while rolling dice, completing sets, toppling dominoes, tracking through the mazes, and spotting those differences. If you think help is needed, the answers section is on constant standby. Every question is numbered and has its answer clearly marked in the back of the section. But be sure to try all avenues before resorting to the solutions—things are not always what they seem at first!

With patience and practice, by the end of Perceptual Puzzles, you'll be looking at the world in a whole new light ✪

1 DIFFICULTY ●●●☆☆☆☆☆☆☆   **5** Minutes

Find your way from the front of the house to the back.

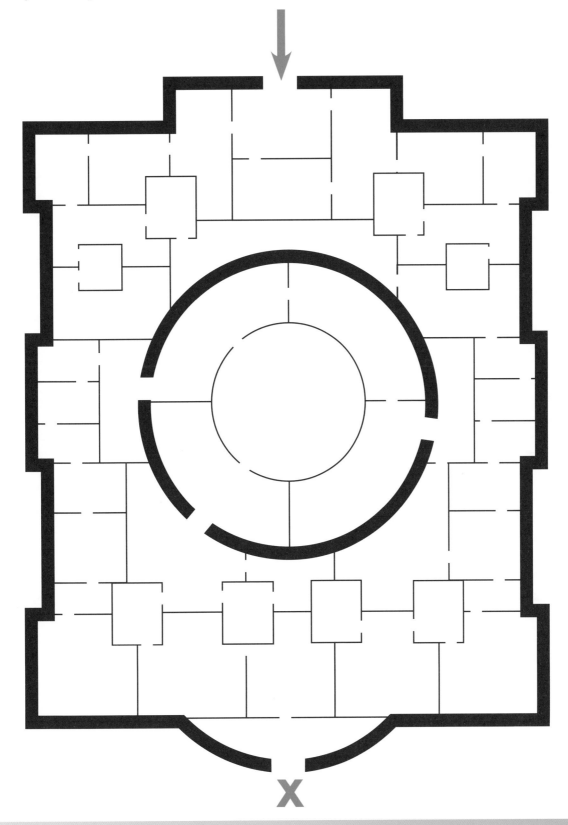

2 DIFFICULTY ✪✪✪✪✪✩✩✩✩✩ ⏱ **5** Minutes

This is a two-player game. Players take turns removing either one coin or two touching coins. The winner is the person who picks up the last coin. Once you've played the game a few times, see if you can work out how to guarantee a win if your opponent plays first.

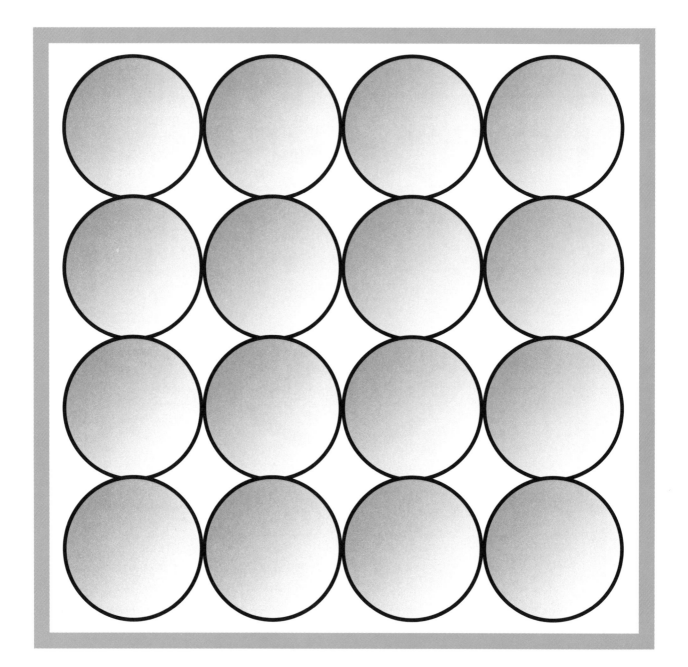

3 DIFFICULTY ✪✪✪✪✪✪✪✩✩✩

5 Minutes

Study the letters below for one minute, then see if you can answer the questions on the next page without checking back.

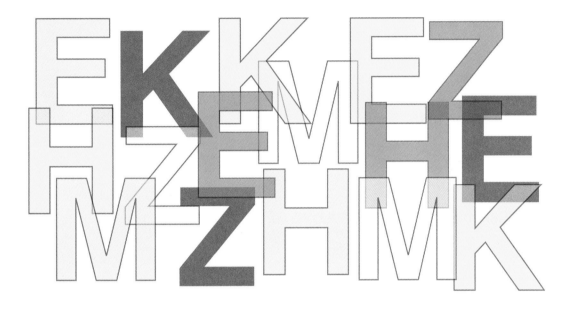

4 DIFFICULTY ✪✪✪✩✩✩✩✩✩✩

3 Minutes

Can you spot the eight differences between these two pictures? Circle them in the drawing on the right.

[3] DIFFICULTY ⭐⭐⭐⭐⭐⭐⭐☆☆☆   5 Minutes

Can you answer these questions about the puzzle on the previous page without checking back?

1. How many Ms are white?

2. How many Es are dark gray?

3. How many Hs are white?

4. How many Ks are purple?

5. How many Ks are there in total?

6. What is the total of yellow Ks plus yellow Es?

7. What is the total of blue Hs plus purple Zs?

8. What is the total of all letters except Es?

5 DIFFICULTY ⭐⭐☆☆☆☆☆☆☆☆   2 Minutes

Three dice were placed on a glass coffee table to amuse baby Adam, crawling underneath. Adam can see only the bottom faces of the dice. If he could count, what is the total number of spots he'd say he can see?

6 DIFFICULTY ✪✪✪✪✪✪✪☆☆☆

30 Minutes

You may want to run as far away as possible from this nonogram!

HOW TO DO A NONOGRAM:

Along each row or column, there are numbers that indicate how many blocks of black squares are in a line. For example, "3, 4, 5" indicates that from left to right or top to bottom, there is a group of three black squares, then a group of four black squares, then another group of five black squares.

Each block of black squares on the same line must have at least one white square between it and the next block of black squares. Blocks of black squares may or may not have a number of white squares before and after them.

It is sometimes possible to determine which squares will be black without reference to other lines or columns.

It is helpful to put a small dot in a square you know will be empty.

Row clues:

10
4 3
2 5 2
2 8 1
1 11 1
1 11 1
1 12 1
1 5 6 1
1 4 4 1
1 4 4 1
1 3 3 1
4 3 2 1
4 3 2 2
2 3 1 3
1 3 4 5
1 5 3 7
9 9 2
11 8
26
27
27
24
22
20
20
19
4 3 7
3 2 2 2
3 3 2 3
4 3

7 DIFFICULTY ⭐⭐⭐⭐⭐☆☆☆☆☆   **6** Minutes

Find your way to the center of the maze.

8 DIFFICULTY ✪✪✪✪✩✩✩✩✩✩  **3** Minutes

Which of the four boxed figures completes the set?

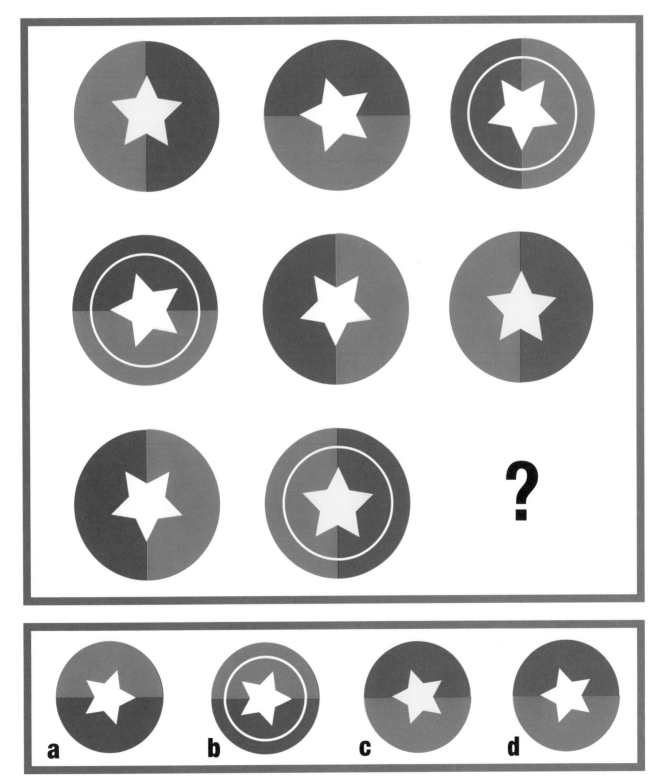

9 DIFFICULTY ⭐⭐⭐⭐⭐⭐☆☆☆

10 Minutes

There is only one place in which Pattern a can be found in the grid. The pattern may be rotated but not reflected. Can you find it? Similarly, there are three places in which Pattern b is hidden in the grid. Find them, too.

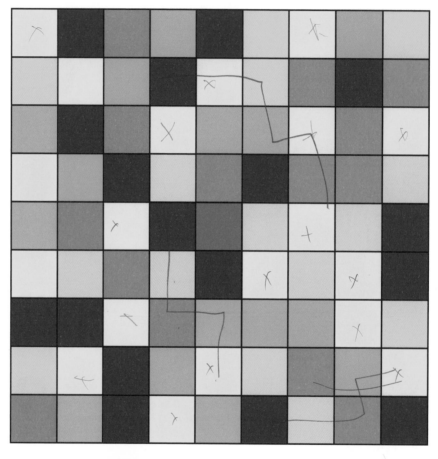

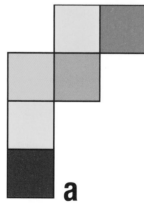

a

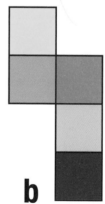

b

10 DIFFICULTY ✪✪✪✪✪✩✩✩✩✩  **4** Minutes

Cinderella (not pictured here!) has two identical ugly stepsisters. Can you identify them? They might even be reflections of one another, so look carefully.

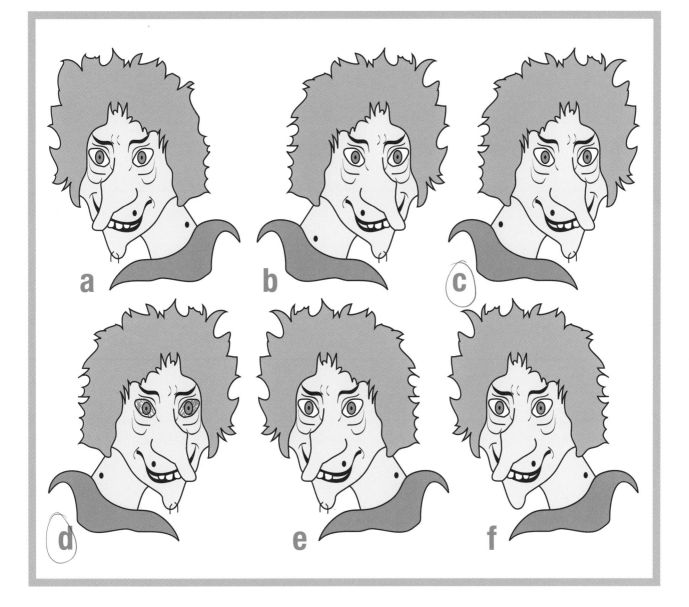

When the figure below is folded to form a cube, which one of the following (a, b, c, d, or e) can be reproduced?

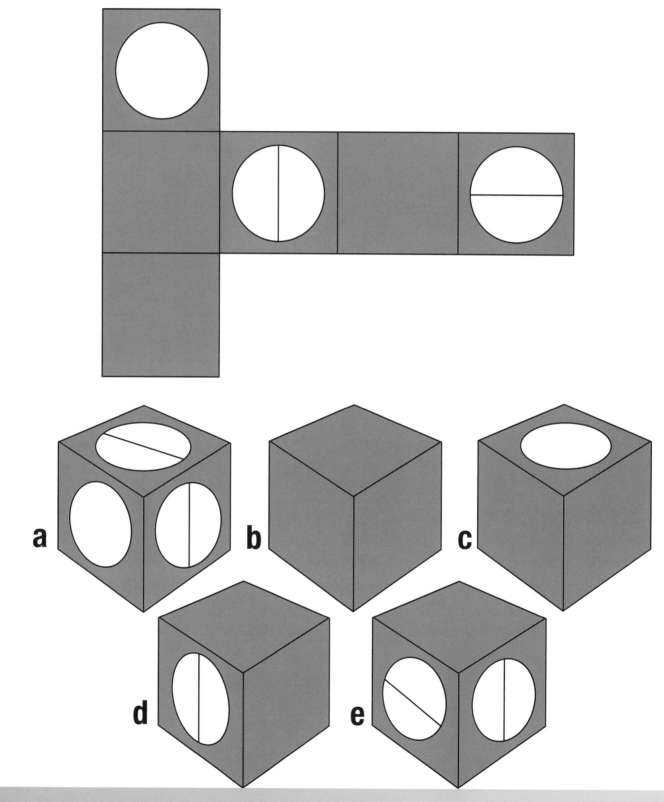

12 DIFFICULTY ⭐⭐⭐⭐⭐☆☆☆☆☆ ③ Minutes

Which domino (a, b, c, or d) should fill the empty space?

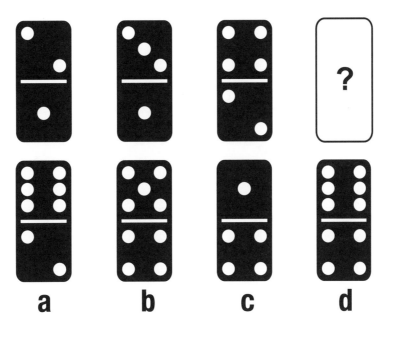

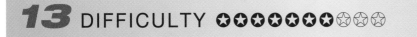

a   **b**   **c**   **d**

13 DIFFICULTY ⭐⭐⭐⭐⭐⭐⭐☆☆☆ ⑤ Minutes

Juliette has lined up these three dice on her coffee table. She can see the same seven faces that you can see. Angelica (her friend, sitting opposite) can see the top three faces of the dice, as well as a further four faces you and Juliette cannot see. None of you can see the bottom three faces of these dice. What is the total number of spots on all the faces of the dice that Angelica can see, given that there aren't six spots visible to anyone on the die furthest right from your point of view as you look at the diagram?

14 DIFFICULTY ✪✪✪✪✪✪☆☆☆☆   ⑥ Minutes

Should the central circle be a  or a ⚫ ?

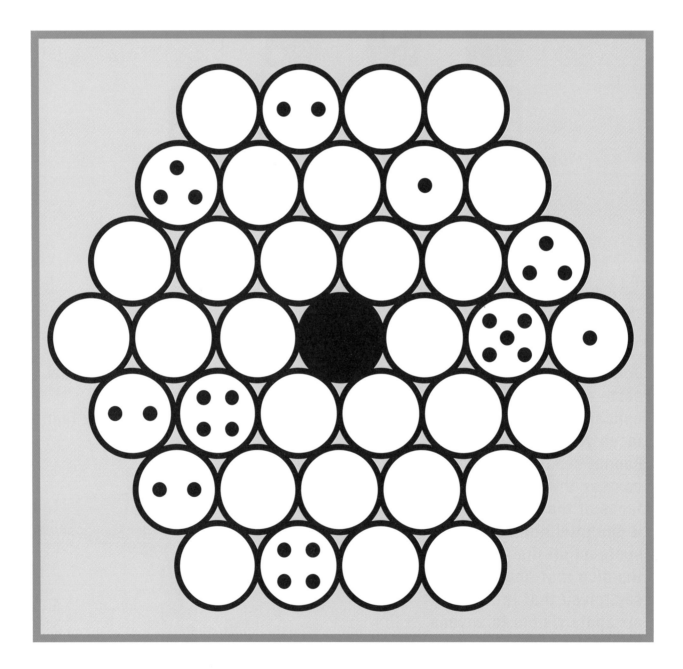

15 DIFFICULTY ✪✪✪✪☆☆☆☆☆☆  **4** Minutes

Carefully study the pens below. Which is different from the rest?

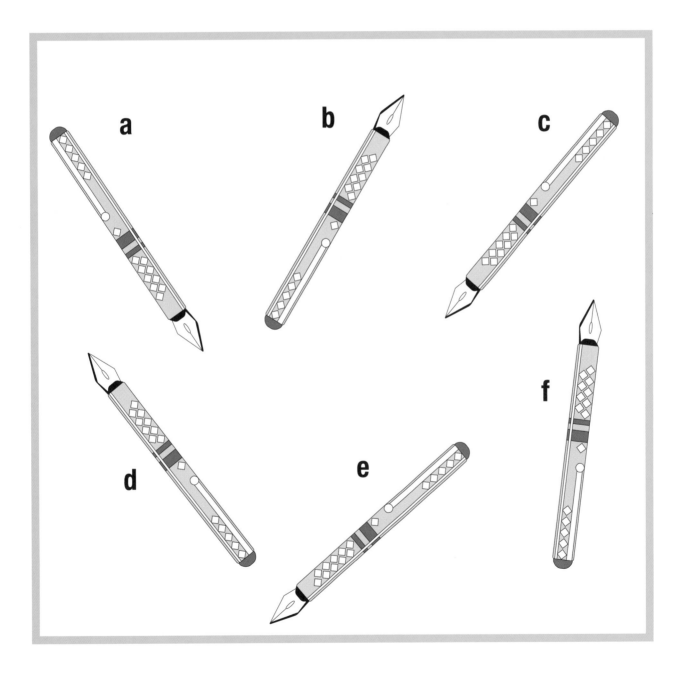

16 DIFFICULTY ★★★☆☆☆☆☆☆☆ | ③ Minutes

Color in the shape below. Can you find the minimum number of different colors needed so that no two touching areas are the same color?

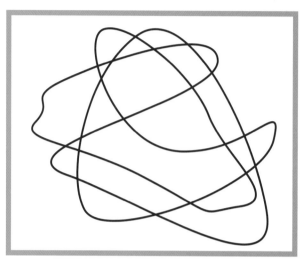

17 DIFFICULTY ★★★☆☆☆☆☆☆☆ | ③ Minutes

Pat the dog has laid out his bones for your inspection. Can you deduce the order in which he placed them on the pile?

18 DIFFICULTY ●●●☆☆☆☆☆☆☆   5 Minutes

Get your automobile to the garage, marked with an X, avoiding the potholes as you go.

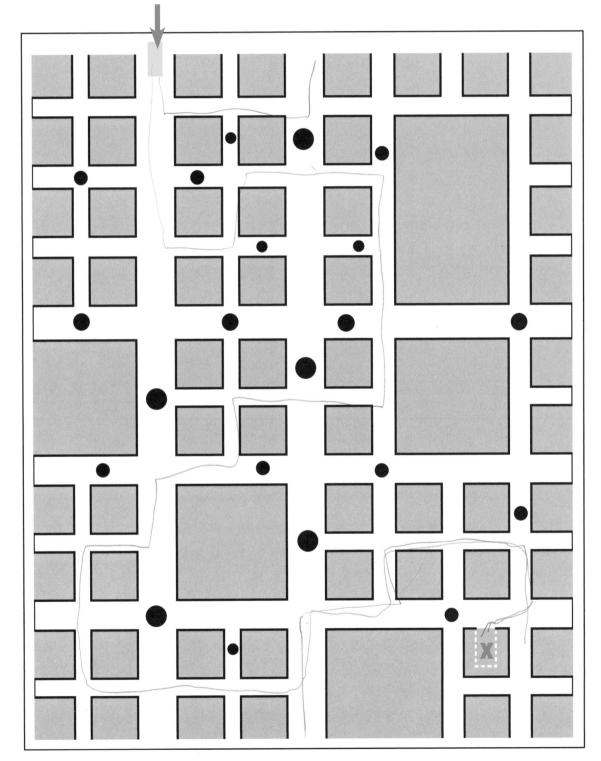

19

A tangram is an ancient Chinese puzzle. To make your own tangram, take a piece of cardboard (the thicker the better) and draw a 4 x 4 grid pattern on it. Then cut out seven pieces, as indicated by this diagram.

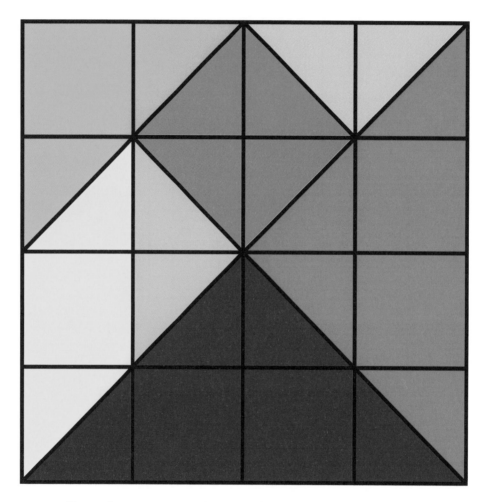

Now rearrange the shapes to make the images on the facing page. You must use all seven pieces each time, and overlapping the pieces is not allowed. We've done one for you, below.

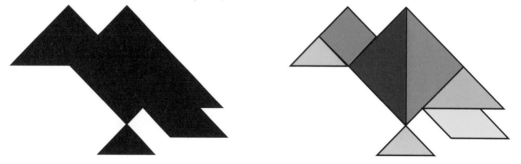

a DIFFICULTY
★★★☆☆☆☆☆☆☆
Target time: 3 minutes

Sleeping cat

b DIFFICULTY
★★★☆☆☆☆☆☆☆
Target time: 3 minutes

Candle

c DIFFICULTY
★★★★★☆☆☆☆☆
Target time: 5 minutes

Man in the hat

d DIFFICULTY
★★★★★☆☆☆☆☆
Target time: 5 minutes

Curious arrow

e DIFFICULTY
★★★★★★★★☆☆
Target time: 8 minutes

Paradoxical square

f DIFFICULTY
★★★★★★★★☆☆
Target time: 8 minutes

Mountains into molehills

20 DIFFICULTY ✪✪✪✪✪✪✪✪✪✫   ⏱ **8** Minutes

When the shape below is folded to form a cube, which one of the following (a, b, c, d, or e) can be produced?

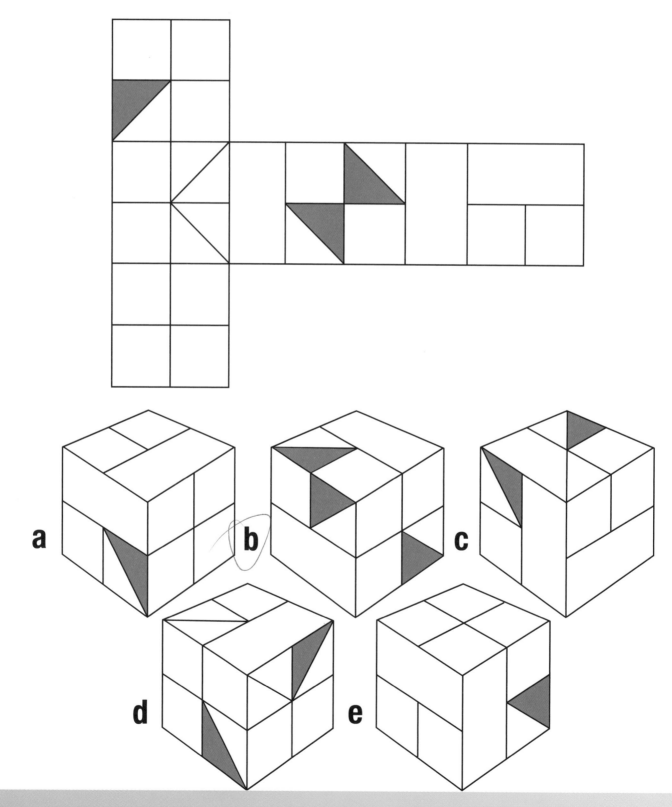

21 DIFFICULTY ✪✪✫✫✫✫✫✫✫✫  (2) Minutes

Which of the four boxed figures at the bottom completes the set above it?

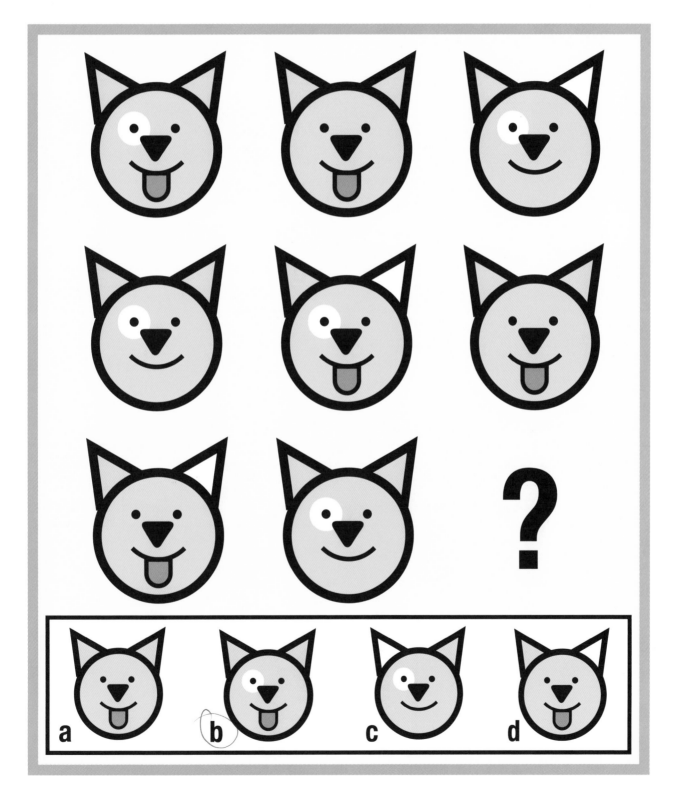

22 DIFFICULTY ⭐⭐⭐⭐⭐⭐✩✩✩✩✩
s

⏱ **3** Minutes

Which two pieces will fit together perfectly to form a purple copy of this white shape? Pieces may be rotated, but not flipped over.

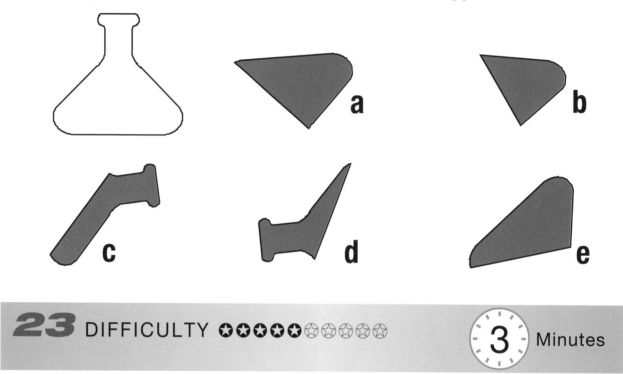

23 DIFFICULTY ⭐⭐⭐⭐⭐✩✩✩✩✩

⏱ **3** Minutes

Which domino (a, b, c, or d) should fill the empty space?

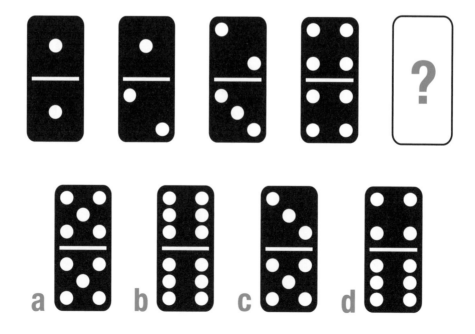

24 DIFFICULTY ★★★★★☆☆☆☆☆  **5** Minutes

Carefully study the pictures below. Which crane is different from the rest?

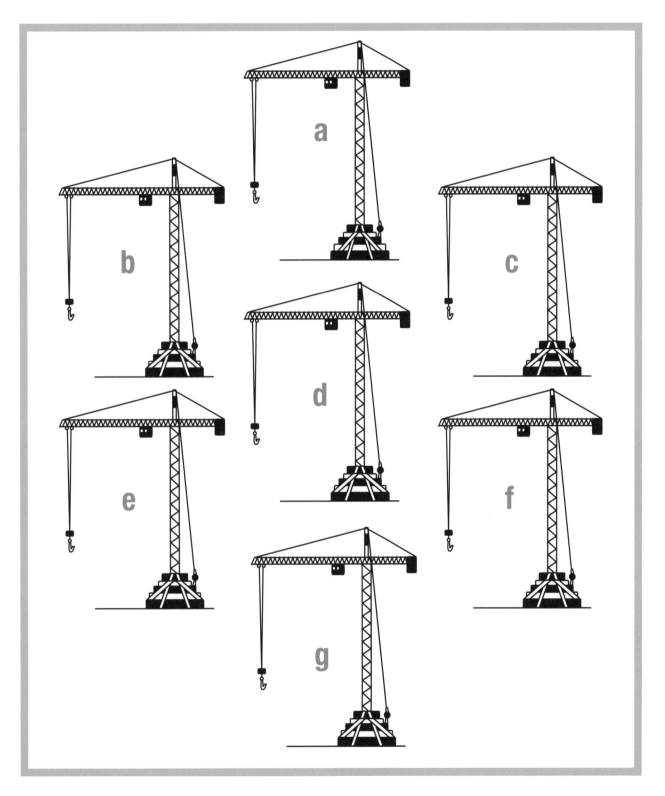

25 DIFFICULTY ⭐⭐⭐⭐⭐⭐⭐☆☆☆ ⏱ 7 Minutes

What shape should be in the center square? (If you need a clue to help you work out the answer, the colors you see are red, blue, green, yellow, and apricot.)

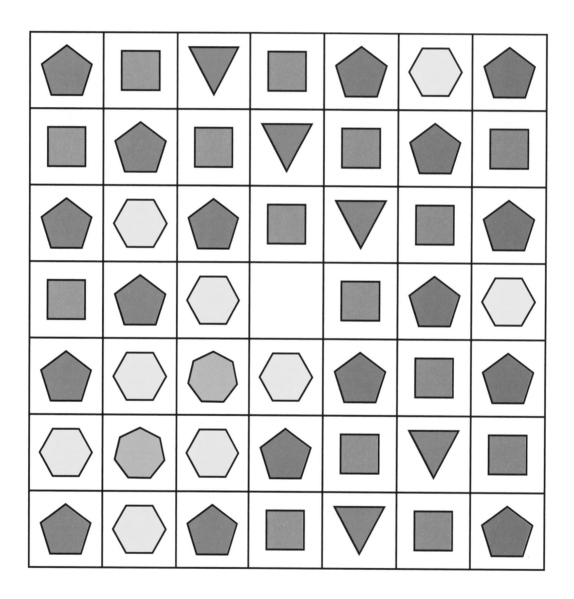

26 DIFFICULTY ★★★★★★★★☆☆   **30** Minutes

This nonogram is ripe for solving. (See puzzle 6 for advice on how to complete a nonogram.)

Column clues (top):

C1	C2	C3	C4	C5	C6	C7	C8	C9	C10	C11	C12	C13	C14	C15	C16	C17	C18	C19	C20	C21	C22	C23	C24	C25	C26	C27	C28	C29	C30
																3								2	2	1			
						1										2	1	3	2	2	2		3	2	2	2			
		3	2	4	5	2	1				3					2	2	3	4	2	2	2	1	1	1	2	3	3	3
		3	3	3	4	4	3	3	3	3	3	1	2	3	1	7	4	3	3	3	3	3		3	2	3	3	2	6
4	1	2	3	4	8	4	7	8	10	18	15	15	13	12	10	4	8	4	7	8	10	16	30	15	13	12	10	7	4

Row clues (left):

		4	1	2	1	1	3
3	2	1	2	2	1	2	1
3	4	2	2	3	1	1	2
3	3	2	2	3	1	1	2
		3	4	8	1	3	
			2	4	1	6	
		1	4	4	2	1	
			5	6	2	2	
				8	2	3	
			3	6	1	4	
		3	6	3	1	3	
		2	8	2	2	3	
			2	10	3	3	
			2	11	4	2	
		2	11	2	2	1	
				14	4	4	
				12	6	3	
				12	8	1	
				10	3	6	
				8	3	6	
				4	2	8	
					2	10	
					2	11	
					2	11	
						14	
						12	
						12	
						10	
						8	
						4	

27 DIFFICULTY ⚫⚫⚫⚫✪✪✪✪✪✪

 **5** Minutes

Divide this picture by drawing three straight lines to produce five sections, each containing five different shapes in five different colors.

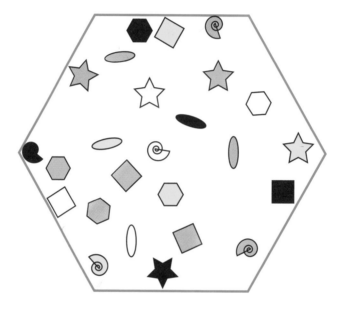

28 DIFFICULTY ⚫⚫⚫⚫⚫✪✪✪✪✪

5 Minutes

What is the minimum number of different colors needed to color in this honeycomb pattern (including the background) in such a way that no two touching areas are the same color?

4

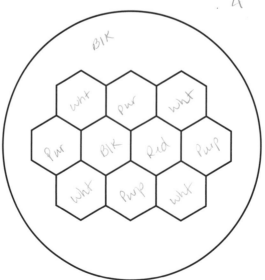

29 DIFFICULTY ✪✪✪✪☆☆☆☆☆  **4** Minutes

Maggie's magic mirror reflects very strangely! Can you match each jug to its correct (although misplaced and somewhat distorted) image in the mirror on the right?

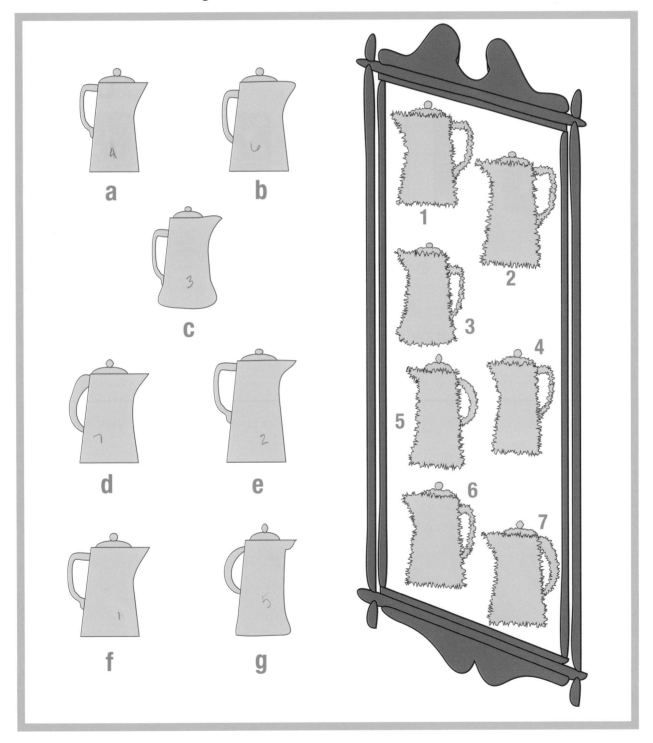

30 DIFFICULTY ✪✪✪✪✪✪✪✪✪✰ — 8 Minutes

Dominoes can be arranged into square "picture frames"—this example shows such a frame, where every side adds up to eighteen.

Can you arrange the eight dominoes below into two square frames, each made of four pieces, so that all the sides of both frames add up to nine?

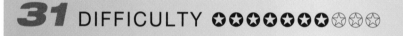

31 DIFFICULTY ✪✪✪✪✪✪✪✰✰✰ — 7 Minutes

Divide this picture by drawing two straight lines to produce three sections, each containing two butterflies, four caterpillars, and five larvae.

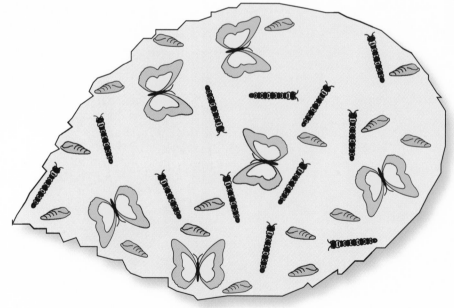

32 DIFFICULTY ✪✪✪✪✪✪✪☆☆☆ ⏱ **5** Minutes

Study these cupcakes for one minute, then see if you can answer the questions on the next page without checking back.

[32] DIFFICULTY ✪✪✪✪✪✪✪✩✩✩   5 Minutes

Can you answer these questions about the puzzle on the previous page without checking back?

1. What color is the frosting on cupcake c?

2. What color is the case containing cupcake g?

3. How many cupcake cases are blue?

4. How many plates have blue trim?

5. How many of the cherries on cupcake f have a leaf?

6. How many cupcakes are in white cases?

7. How many cupcakes have white frosting?

8. How many cherries does cupcake e have?

33 DIFFICULTY ✪✪✪✪✪✩✩✩✩✩   5 Minutes

Can you spot the eight differences between these two pictures? Circle them in the drawing on the right.

34 DIFFICULTY ✪✪✪✪✪☆☆☆☆☆ ③ Minutes

Which of the four boxed figures at the bottom completes the set?

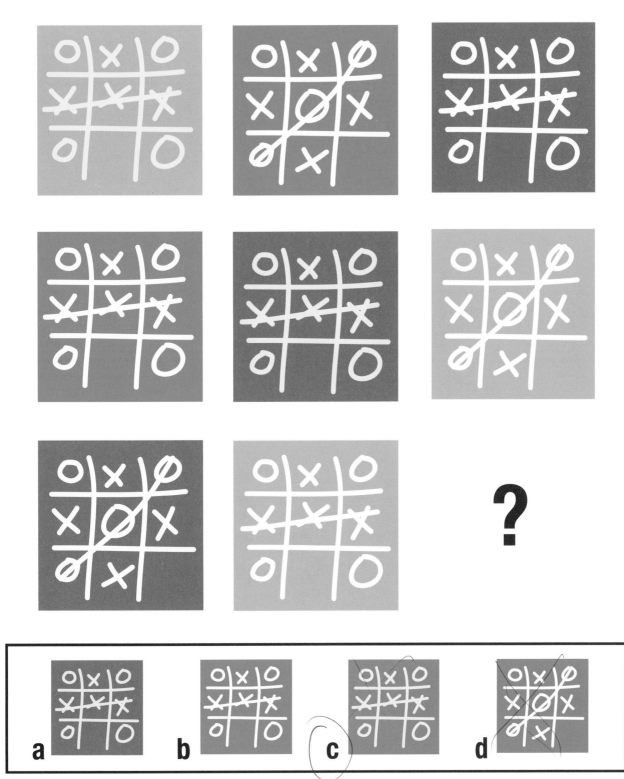

When the shape below is folded to form a cube, which one of the following (a, b, c, d, or e) can be produced?

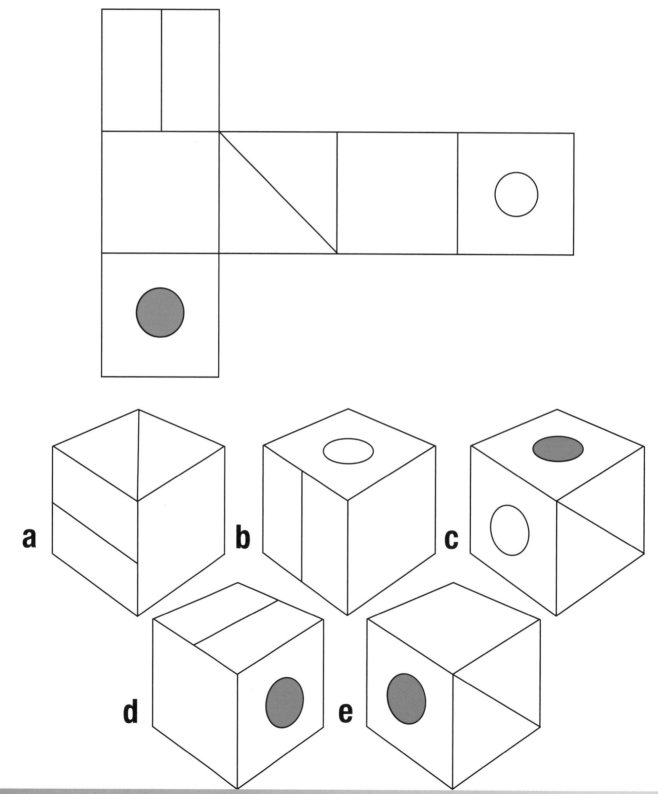

36 DIFFICULTY ✪✪✪✪✪✩✩✩✩✩ ⏱ 3 Minutes

Which two pieces will fit together perfectly to form a green copy of this white shape? Pieces may be rotated, but not flipped over.

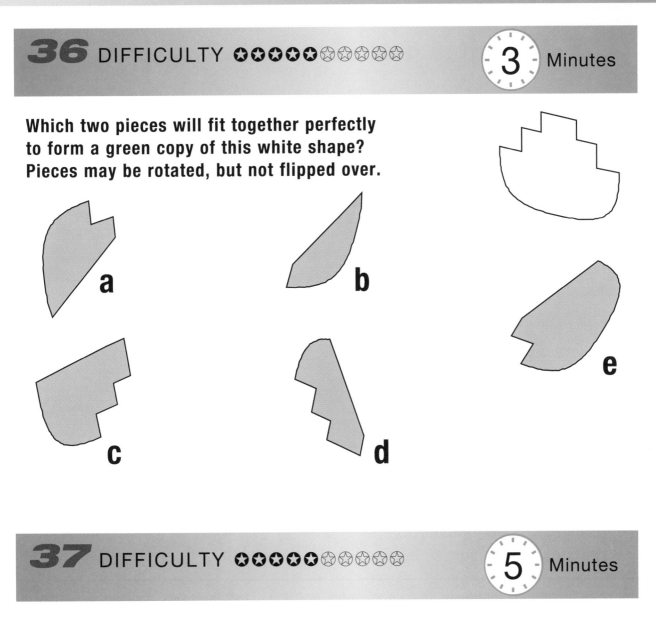

37 DIFFICULTY ✪✪✪✪✪✩✩✩✩✩ ⏱ 5 Minutes

Starting with the top row of coins, move any two adjacent coins four times, separating the heads from the tails, to end up with the bottom row.

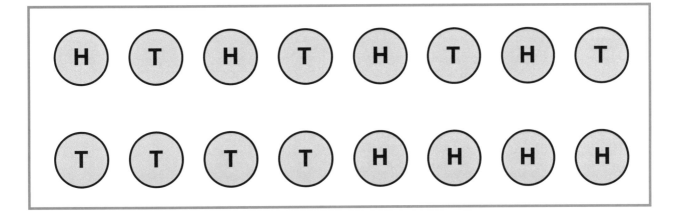

38 DIFFICULTY ✪✪✪✪✪✪✪✪✪✪  10 Minutes

The square below contains exactly one of each of thirty-six faces from six standard dice. In each horizontal row of six smaller squares, each vertical column of six smaller squares, and both diagonal lines of six smaller squares, there are faces with different numbers of spots.

We've placed a few to give you a start, but can you provide the rest using only the given clues?

1. The face of the die in square 3 has the same number of spots as that in square 32.
2. The face of the die in square 14 has the same number of spots as that in square 31.
3. The face of the die in square 25 has the same number of spots as that in square 36.

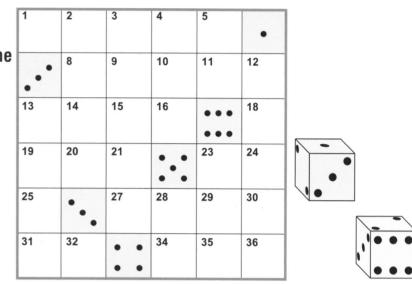

39 DIFFICULTY ✪✪✪✪✪✪✪✪☆☆  5 Minutes

Here are five clocks. Four are perfect, but the fifth was damaged. Can you determine the time on clock e?

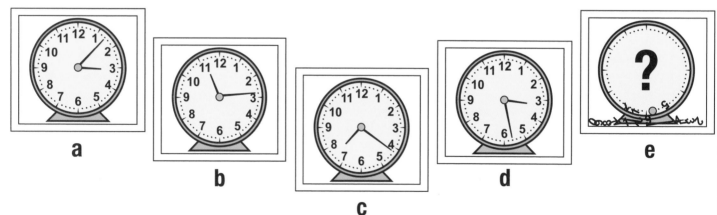

40 DIFFICULTY ✪✪✪✪✪✪✪☆☆☆

Target time: 7 minutes

7 Minutes

Carefully study the diagrams below. Which is different from the rest?

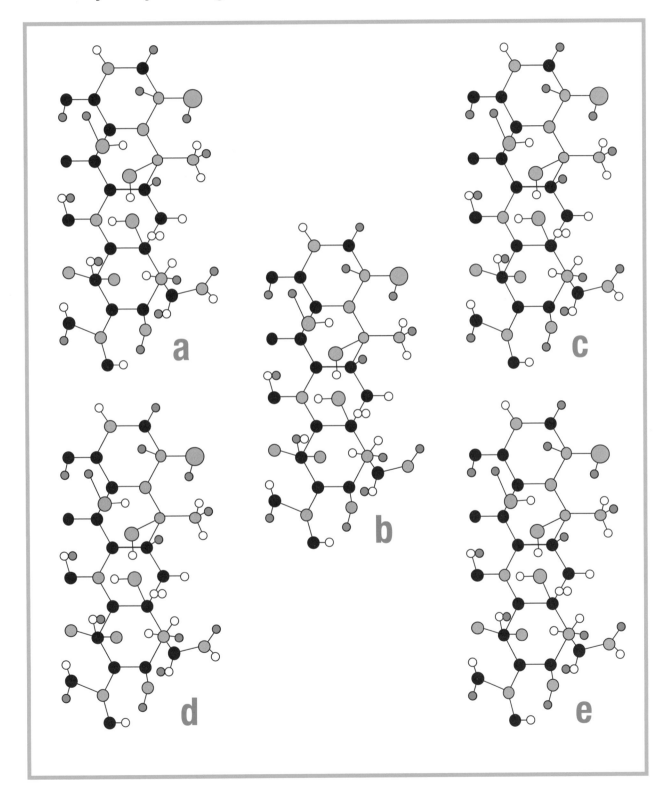

41 DIFFICULTY ✪✪✪✪✪☆☆☆☆☆   (6) Minutes

Find your way through the woods from the cabin at the top to the picnic table marked with an X.

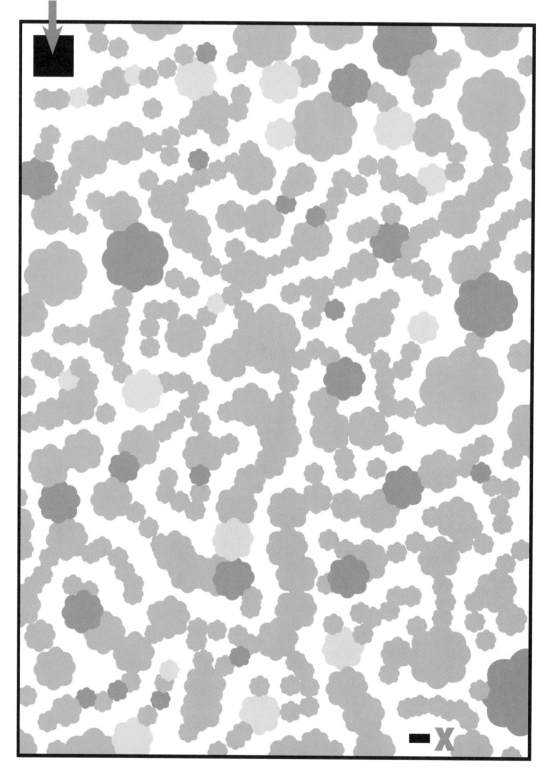

42 DIFFICULTY ✪✪✪✪✪✩✩✩✩✩
Target time: 6 minutes

6 Minutes

Find a route from the top to the bottom down through the pipes, avoiding any blockages.

43 DIFFICULTY ⭐⭐⭐⭐⭐✩✩✩✩✩ — 5 Minutes

Can you deduce the minimum number of different colors needed to color in the diagram in such a way that no two touching areas are the same?

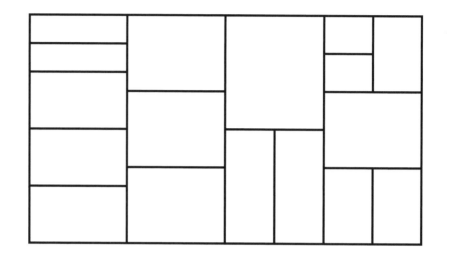

44 DIFFICULTY ⭐⭐⭐⭐⭐⭐⭐⭐⭐⭐ — 10 Minutes

The square below contains one of each of thirty-six faces from six standard dice. In each horizontal row of six smaller squares and each vertical column of six smaller squares, there are faces with different numbers of spots. Also in the long diagonal line of six smaller squares from top left to bottom right, there are faces with different numbers of spots. In the long diagonal line from top right to bottom left, however, no face has four spots, but there are faces with five different numbers. We've placed a few to give you a start. Given that the total number of spots on the four corner dice equals fourteen, can you place the rest?

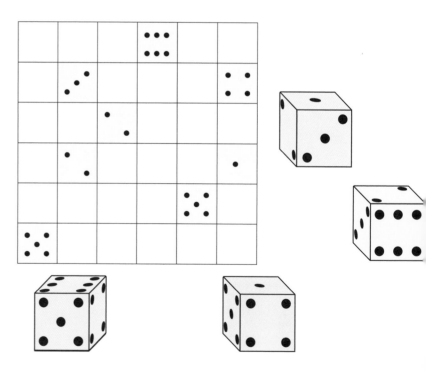

45 DIFFICULTY ✪✪✪✪✪✪✪☆☆   12 Minutes

1. There is only one place in which Pattern a can be found in the grid. The pattern may be rotated but not reflected. Can you find it?
2. Similarly, there are six places in which Pattern b is hidden in the grid. Can you find them?

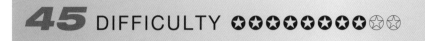

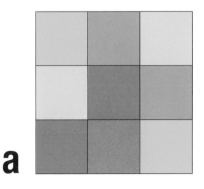

a

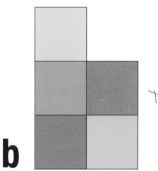

b

46 DIFFICULTY ●●●☆☆☆☆☆☆☆ 3 Minutes

Can you spot the six differences between these two pictures?
Circle them in the drawing on the right.

47 DIFFICULTY ●●●●●●☆☆☆☆ 6 Minutes

Can you divide
this square on
the right into
four identical
shapes, each
composed of
sixteen smaller
squares, and
each containing
four different
shapes?

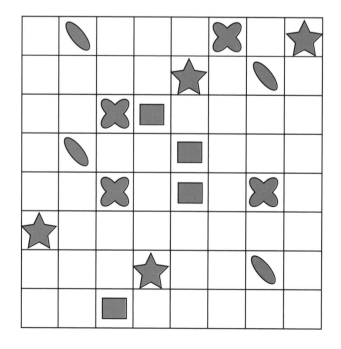

48 DIFFICULTY ✪✪✪✪✪☆☆☆☆☆ ③ Minutes

Which two pieces will fit together perfectly to form a red copy of this white star? Pieces may be rotated, but not flipped over.

49 DIFFICULTY ✪✪✪✪✪✪✪☆☆☆ ⑥ Minutes

Dominoes can be arranged into square picture frames. This example shows a frame where every side adds up to eighteen. Can you arrange the eight dominoes below into two square frames made of four pieces each, so that all the sides of both frames add up to ten?

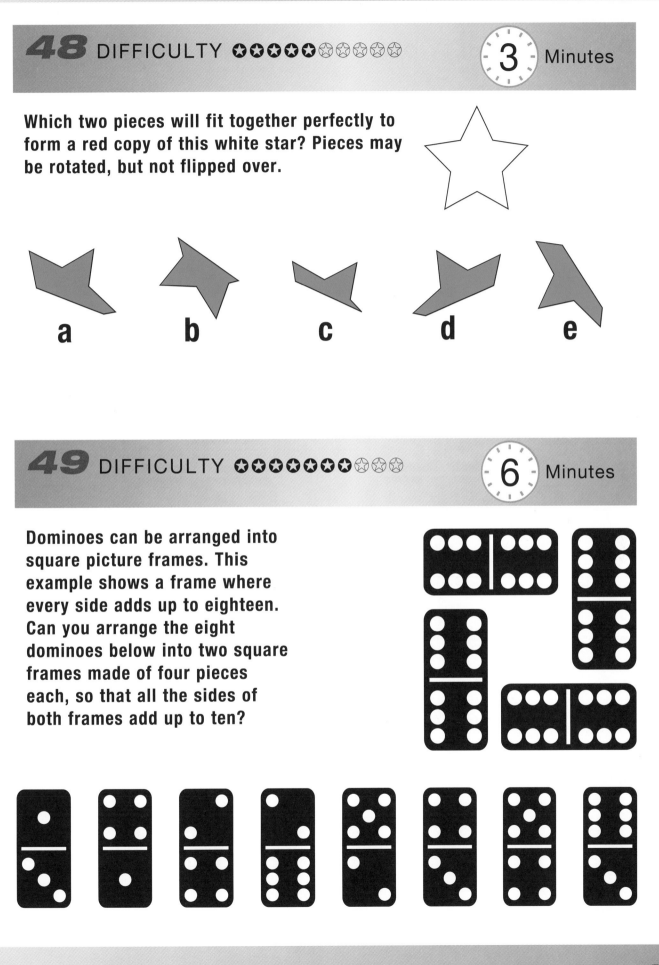

Slide one of the dominoes marked by an arrow into the center to complete the hidden pattern. Which one of the four should it be?

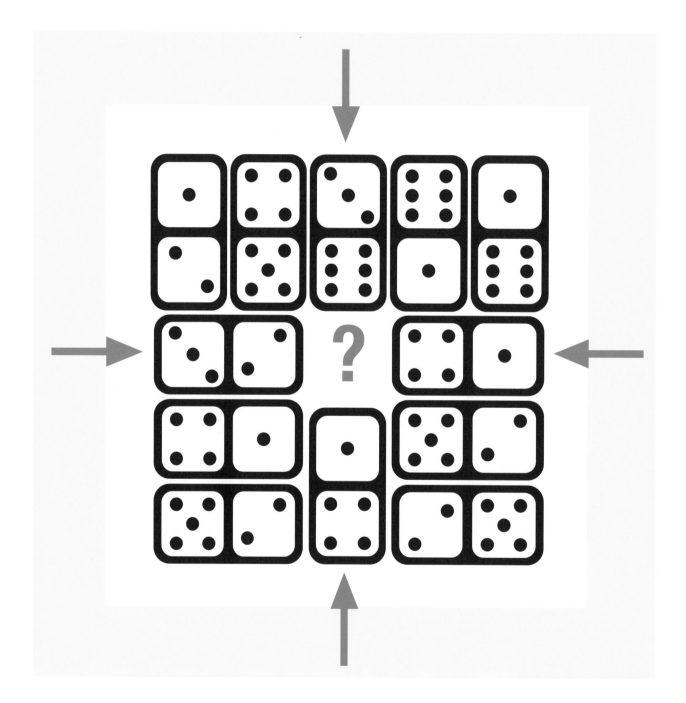

51 DIFFICULTY ✪✪✪✪✪✪✪☆☆☆

7 Minutes

Only two of these vases of flowers are the same. Can you identify them? They might even be reflections of one another, so look closely!

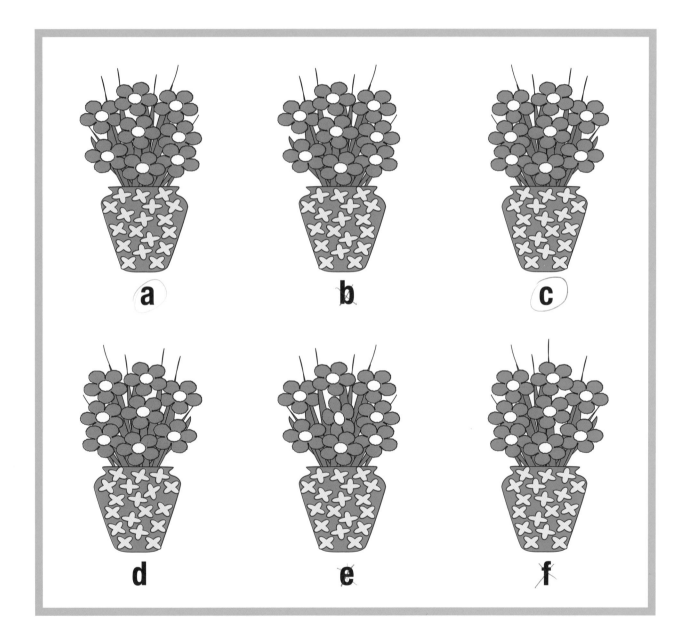

52 DIFFICULTY ✪✪✪✪✪✪✪✪✪✪ ⏱ 15 Minutes

This is a one-player solitaire game. Place four silver coins on spaces 1 to 4, and four pennies on spaces 5 to 8. The aim is to make the coins swap sides by sliding them from circle to circle. Only one coin per space is allowed, and coins must not jump one another.

How many moves are there in the shortest solution? One move counts as sliding one coin from one space to another in a straight line, moving through any number of unoccupied spaces along the way.

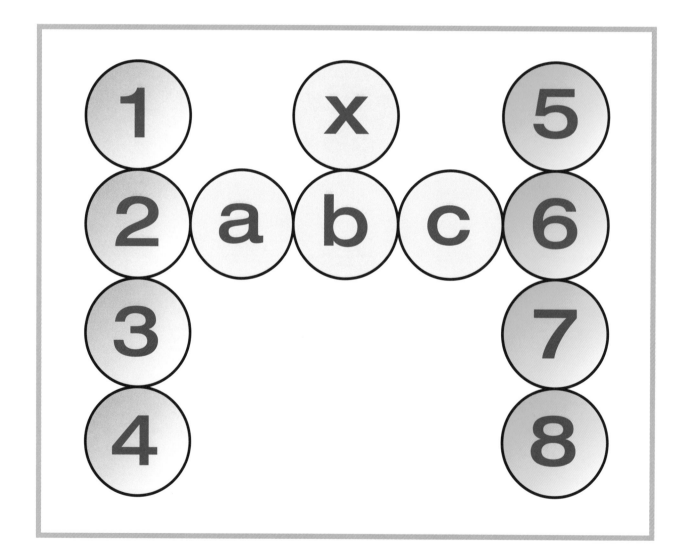

53 DIFFICULTY ✪✪✪✪✪✪✪☆☆☆

30 Minutes

Don't be scared by this nonogram! (See puzzle 6 for advice on how to complete a nonogram.)

Column clues (top):

```
                                  1
                              1 1 3
                              1 3 1
                        4 2 2 4          1       1
              4 3 2 2 4 5 4 2 6          1     2 1     1
              1 2 2 3 2 1 1 3 2       6     2 1 2 1 1 2 2 2 2 4 4 5 7 12
          10 6 5 4 5 4 3 1 2 3 1 7 7 19 12 4 9 2 8 4 2 1 4 3 1 2 1 1 1 1
          11 9 10 2 2 2 1 1 1 1 1 1 1 16 1 1 12 1 13 1 1 2 1 1 1 2 2 2 3 7 11
```

Row clues (left):

```
          11 11
           8  8
        5  3  5
     4  1  2  5
        3  4  3
     2  5  2  2
        1  8  2
        1  5  1
        1  6  1
        1  7  1
        2  3  1
        1  1  1
              7
             12
        8  3
     4  7  2  5
        5  8  4
        6 13
        6 10
        1 10  1
        1 17  1
        8  8  1
        7  9  1
        6  9  2
  3  1  3  1  1  2
     3  3  1  1  2
        3  2  2  2
     3  1  3  3  3
        6  6
       11  9
```

54 DIFFICULTY ✪✪✪✪✪✪✩✩✩✩ — 6 Minutes

In the sequence below, which of the lettered alternatives (a, b, c, or d) should replace the question mark?

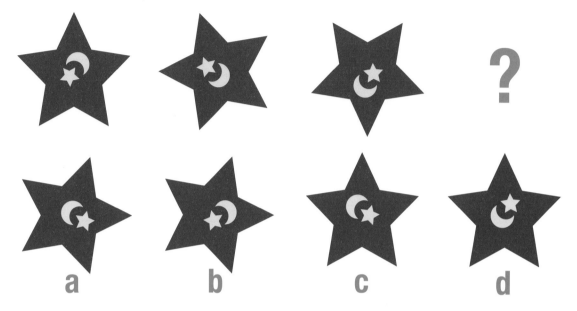

55 DIFFICULTY ✪✪✪✪✪✪✩✩✩✩ — 6 Minutes

Can you spot the eight differences between these two pictures? Circle them in the drawing on the right.

56 DIFFICULTY ●●●☆☆☆☆☆☆☆

2 Minutes

Which domino (a, b, c, or d) should fill the empty space?

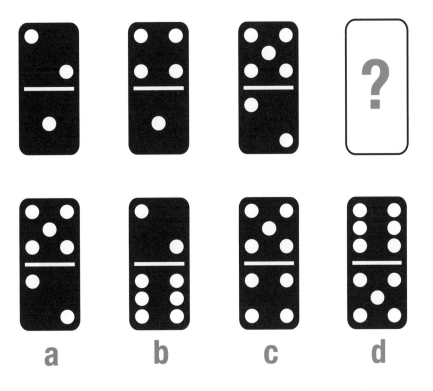

57 DIFFICULTY ●●●●●●●☆☆☆

5 Minutes

You may well need a break after decid-
ing which two pieces fit together perfectly
to form a mirror image copy of this teacup.
Pieces may be rotated, but not flipped over.

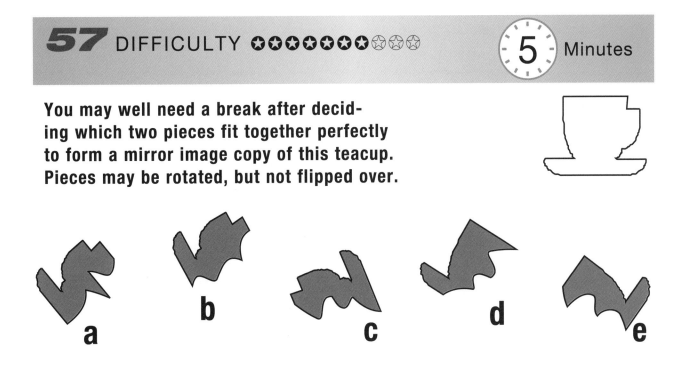

58 DIFFICULTY ✪✪✪✪✪✪✪☆☆☆

⏱ 7 Minutes

At first glance, these diggers may look the same, but only two are identical. They might even be reflections of one another. How quickly can you decide which two are the same?

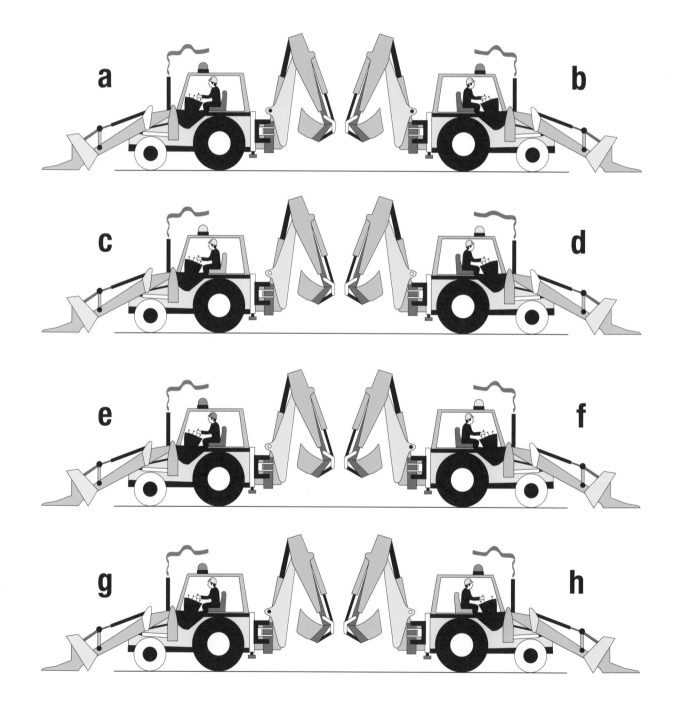

59 DIFFICULTY ✪✪✪✪✪✪✩✩✩✩✩    **4** Minutes

Which of the four boxed figures (a, b, c, or d) completes the set?

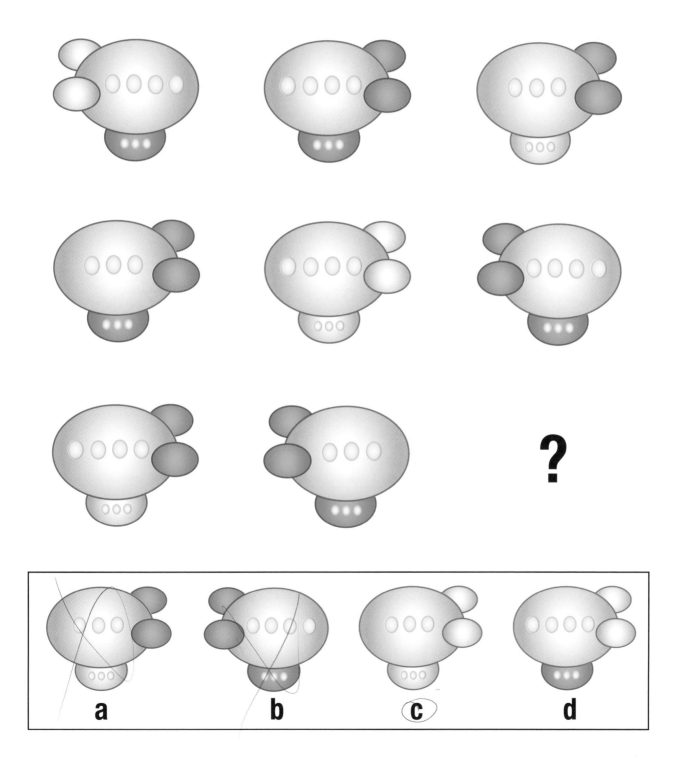

60 DIFFICULTY ✪✪✪✪✪✪✪✩✩✩

5 Minutes

Change all the rows either to all heads or all tails, without touching more than ONE coin.

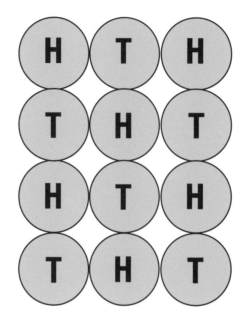

61 DIFFICULTY ✪✪✪✪✪✪✪✩✩✩

7 Minutes

Can you divide this square into four identical shapes, each composed of sixteen squares, and each containing five different chess pieces?

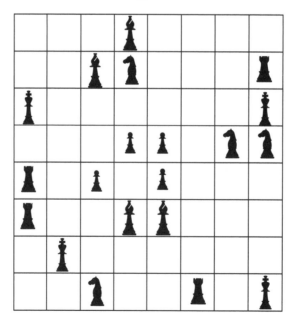

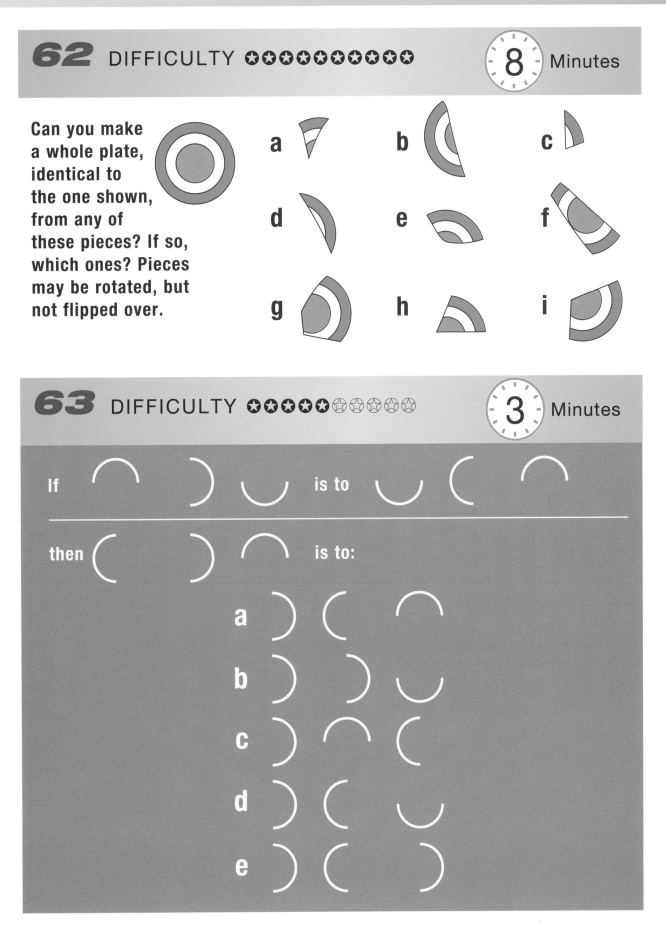

64 DIFFICULTY ✪✪✪✪✪☆☆☆☆☆ ⏱ **6** Minutes

Find your way through the maze. X marks the exit.

65 DIFFICULTY ✪✪✪✪✪✪✪✪☆☆

6 Minutes

Study these nine sets of chairs, lamps, and tables for one minute, then see if you can answer the questions on the next page.

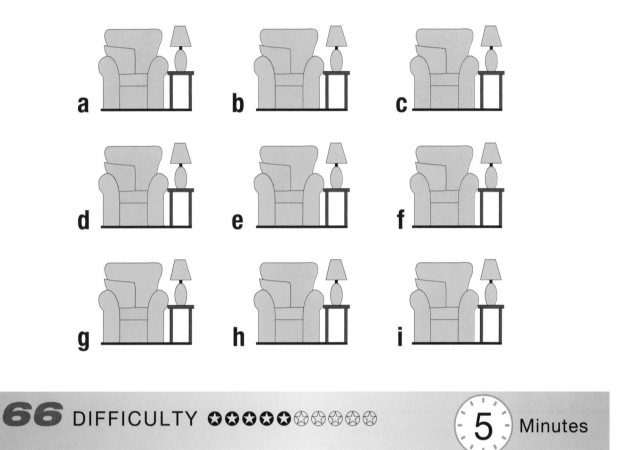

66 DIFFICULTY ✪✪✪✪✪✪☆☆☆☆

5 Minutes

Can you spot the eight differences between these two pictures? Circle them in the picture on the right.

ꚙ꒒ꞁꞁꞁ

[65] DIFFICULTY ✪✪✪✪✪✪✪✩✩ 6 Minutes

Can you answer these questions about the puzzle on the previous page without checking back?

1. What color is the cushion on chair f?

2. What color are the arms of chair g?

3. How many lamps have both an orange shade and an orange base?

4. How many chairs have both a green cushion and a green seat?

5. How many chairs have both an orange back and a green seat?

6. How many lamps have both a green shade and a green base?

7. How many lamps have both an orange shade and a green base?

8. What color is the shade on the lamp next to chair h?

67 DIFFICULTY ✪✪✪✪✪✪✪✪✩ 8 Minutes

Ten dominoes have been used to build this wall, but seven have been masked out. Can you place the missing dominoes in the correct places, bearing in mind that each vertical line of four numbers (as well as the two end vertical lines of two numbers) adds up to ten; the second horizontal row of dominoes has dots totaling sixteen, and the third horizontal row of dominoes has dots totaling ten?

68 DIFFICULTY ✪✪✪✪✫✫✫✫✫✫ ④ Minutes

Carefully study the clowns below. Which one is different from the rest?

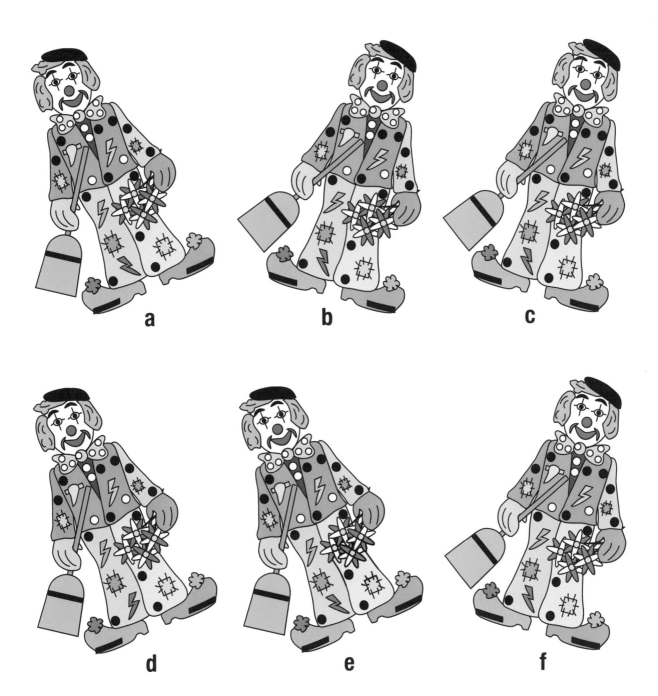

When the shape below is folded to form a cube, which one of the following (a, b, c, d, or e) is produced?

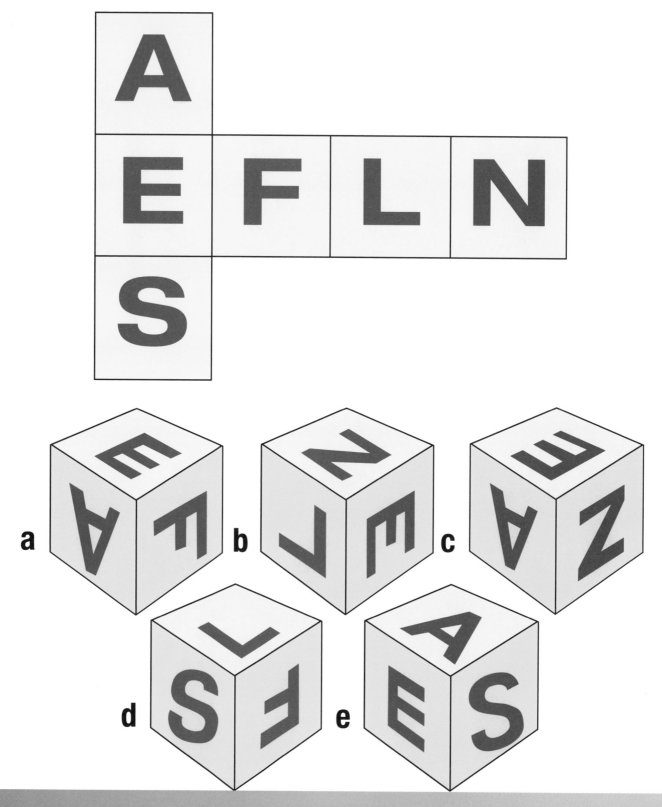

70 DIFFICULTY ✪✪✪✪✪✪✩✩✩✩ — 6 Minutes

Place the pieces from a standard set of twenty-eight dominoes into the following grid by matching their numbers with those in the rectangle. It's trickier than you might think, so we've placed one in position and supplied a checklist, which may help!

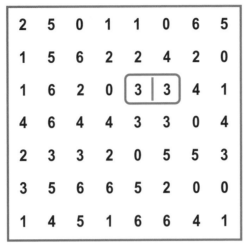

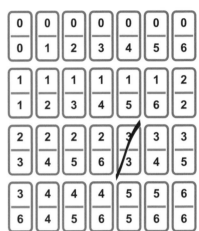

71 DIFFICULTY ✪✪✪✪✪✩✩✩✩✩ — 4 Minutes

Match the arrow flights with the correct arrowheads. If you pick the correct five, a name will be spelled out.

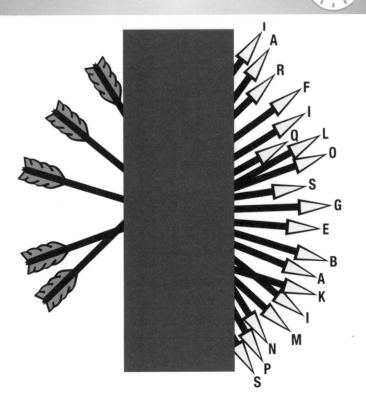

72 DIFFICULTY ✪✪✪✪✪✪✪☆☆☆

7 Minutes

At first glance, these dresses may look the same, but only two are identical. Can you determine which two?

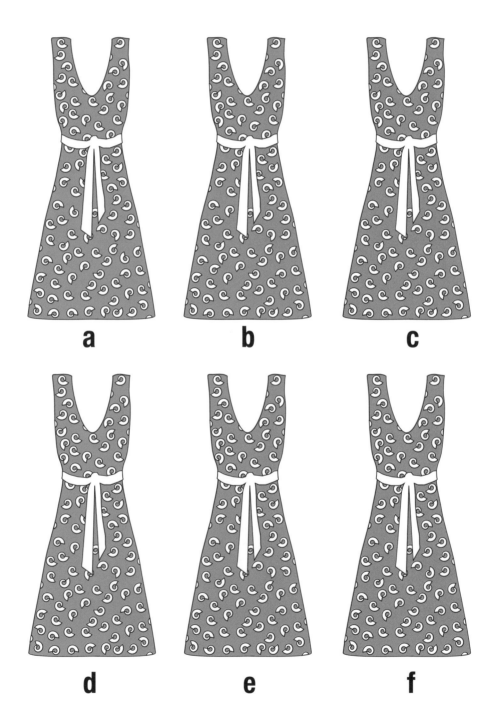

a

b

c

d

e

f

73 DIFFICULTY ✪✪✪☆☆☆☆☆☆☆ ⏱ 2 Minutes

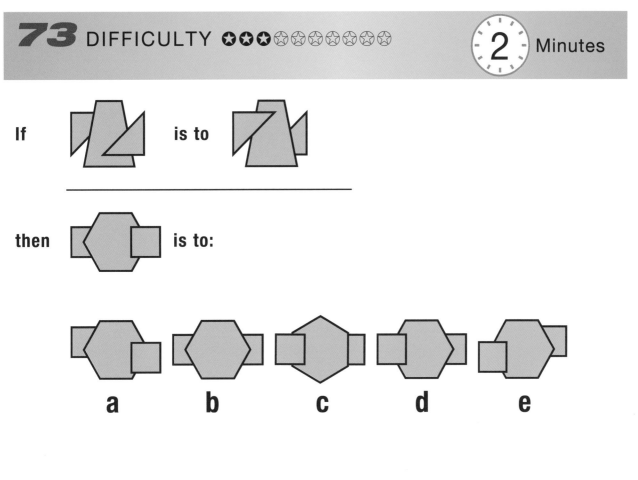

If ▨ is to ▨

then ⬡ is to:

a   b   c   d   e

74 DIFFICULTY ✪✪✪✪✪☆☆☆☆☆ ⏱ 5 Minutes

Can you color in this simplified version of a map of the U.S. so that no two touching areas are the same, using just four colors? You may use colored pens.

75 DIFFICULTY ✪✪✪✪✪✪✫✫✫✫ ④ Minutes

Which of the four boxed figures (a, b, c, or d) completes the set?

76 DIFFICULTY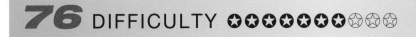

A little bird has told us that this nonogram is waiting to be solved. (See puzzle 6 for advice on how to complete a nonogram.)

77 DIFFICULTY ✪✪✪✪✪✪✪☆☆☆ | 5 Minutes

Peter enjoys selling his wares at the local market on Saturdays. One day he decided to play a little game with his regular customers. Five customers agreed to play and each threw two dice. Their throws and rewards are shown on the right—except Mary's, where you can see only the dice she threw. Can you determine exactly how Peter determined how many loaves and fish each customer should get, and precisely what quantity of loaves and fish he awarded to Mary?

Andrew = 8 loaves and 2 fish

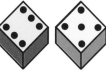

John = 4 loaves and 2 fish

Elizabeth = 6 loaves and 12 fish

James = 8 loaves and 6 fish

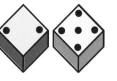

Mary = ? loaves and ? fish

78 DIFFICULTY ✪✪✪✪✪✪✪☆☆☆ | 5 Minutes

Can you spot the eight differences between these two pictures? Circle them in the drawing on the right.

JEANNE'S DRESS SHOP — SALE NOW ON — MASSIVE REDUCTIONS

JOANNE'S DRESS SHOP — SALE NOW ON — MASSIVE REDUCTIONS

79 DIFFICULTY  5 Minutes

A table has been set for a children's party. Study the seating plan for one minute, then see if you can answer the questions on the next page without checking back.

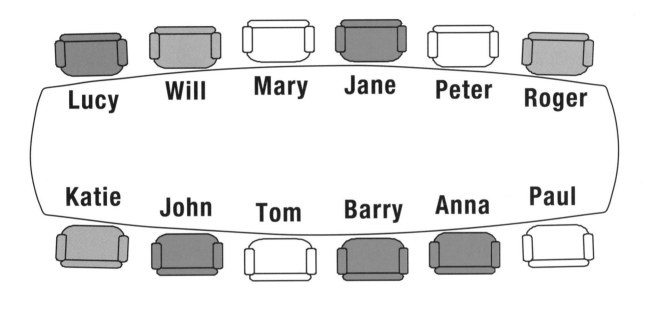

80 DIFFICULTY 5 Minutes

Study these vases of flowers for one minute, then see if you can answer the questions on the next page without checking back.

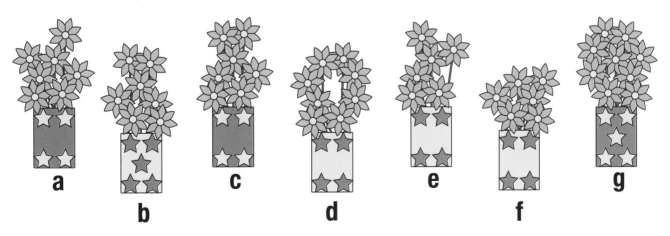

[79] DIFFICULTY ⭐⭐⭐⭐⭐✩✩✩✩✩ 5 Minutes

Can you answer these questions about the puzzle on the previous page (top) without checking back?

1. Who will sit between Tom and Anna?

2. Who will sit directly opposite Paul?

3. Which boy has the shortest name?

4. What color is Mary's seat?

5. How many chairs are red?

6. How many chairs are white?

7. How many children have names ending in a, e, i, o, or u?

8. How many children will sit directly between (and on the same side of the table as) Lucy and Peter?

[80] DIFFICULTY ⭐⭐⭐⭐⭐✩✩✩✩✩ 5 Minutes

Can you answer these questions about the puzzle on the previous page (bottom) without checking back?

1. Which two vases have six flowers each?

2. Which vase has the greatest number of flowers?

3. How many vases are green with yellow stars?

4. How many green vases have five yellow stars?

5. How many yellow vases hold seven flowers?

6. How many petals does each flower have?

7. How many vases have eight flowers each?

8. What is the total number of stars on all of the vases combined?

81 DIFFICULTY ✪✪✪✪✪✪✪☆☆  **8** Minutes

Find a route from left to right through the maze.

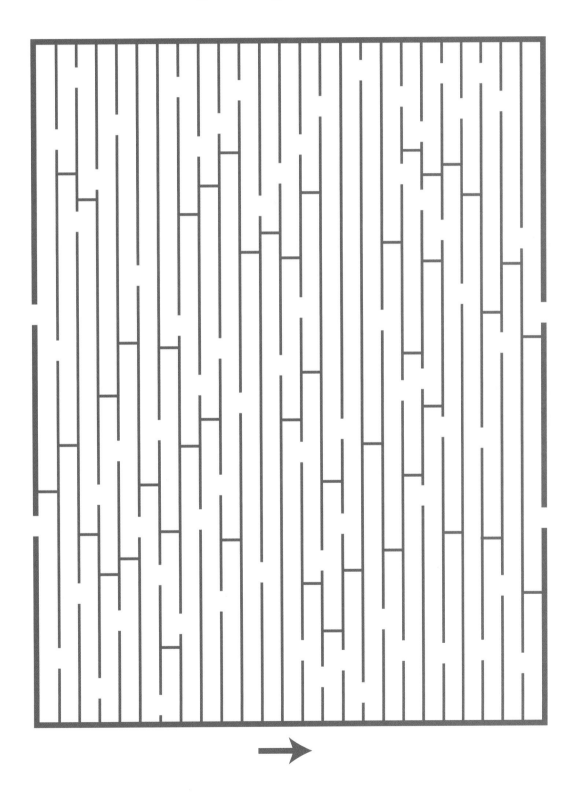

82 DIFFICULTY ✪✪✪✪✪✪✪✪✪☆

 12 Minutes

How many times can you find Pattern a in the hexagonal grid? The pattern may be rotated but not reflected. Pattern b can be found in only one place in the grid. Can you find it?

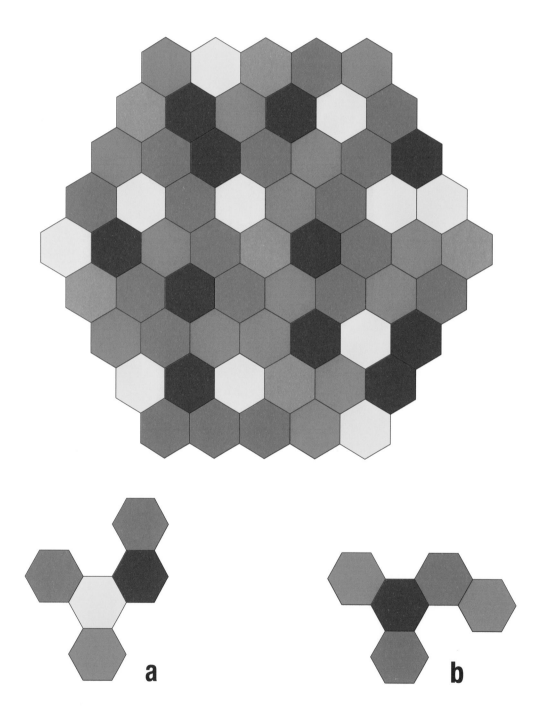

a

b

83 DIFFICULTY ✪✪✪✪✪✪✪☆☆☆   ⏱ **7** Minutes

One of these piles of mail differs in some way from the others—which is it?

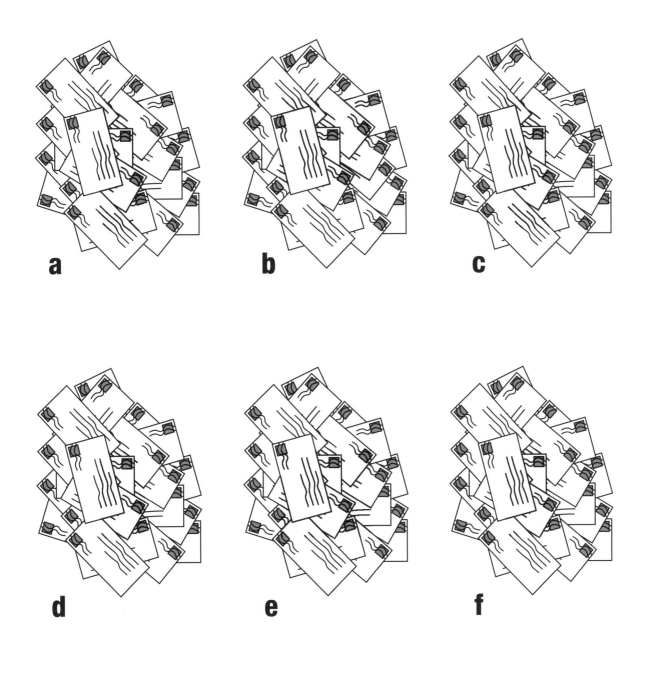

a   b   c

d   e   f

84 DIFFICULTY ✪✪✪✪✪✪✪☆☆  30 Minutes

Aren't you just burning with curiosity to find the solution to this nonogram? (See puzzle 6 for advice on how to complete a nonogram.)

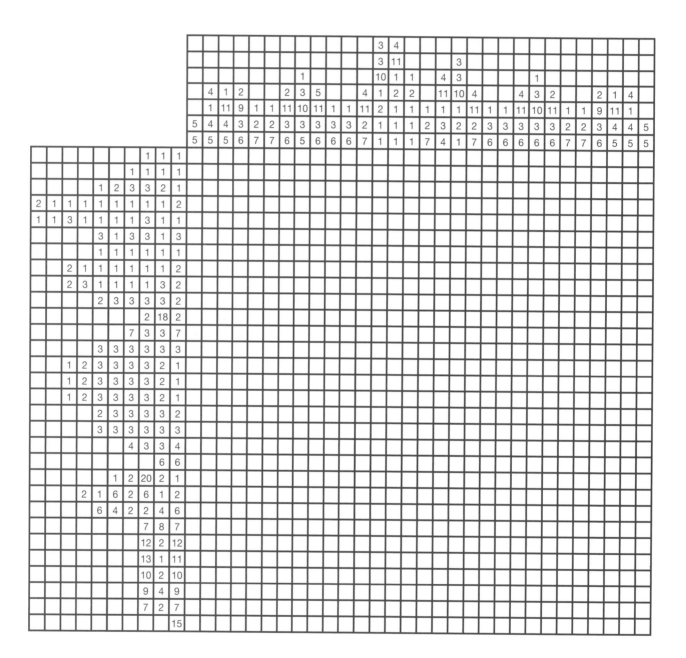

When the shape below is folded to form a cube, which one of the following (a, b, c, d, or e) is produced?

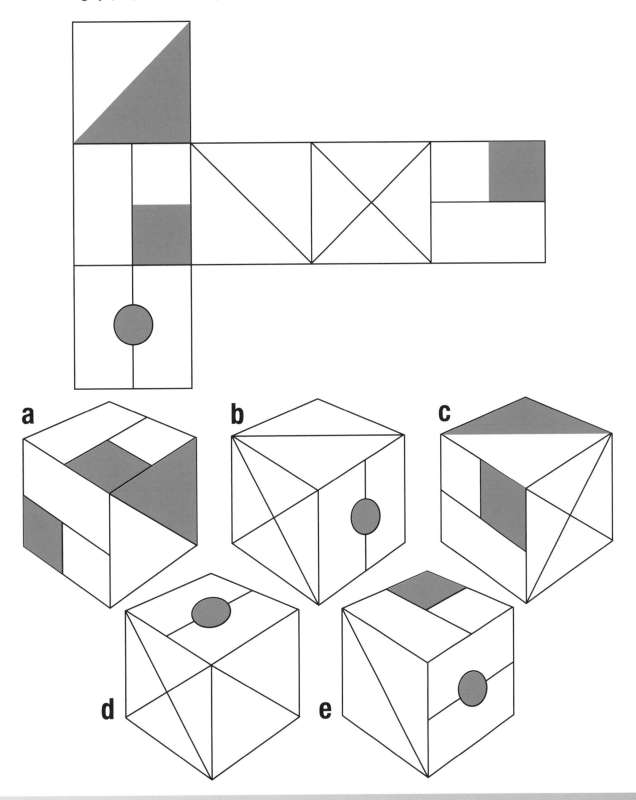

86 DIFFICULTY ✪✪✪✪✪✪✪✪☆☆

⏱ **7** Minutes

Florence played a game of Snakes and Ladders with her brother Tom. He threw the first 6, so he started first, placing his playing piece on square 6. After that, every time it was Florence's turn, her die followed the sequence 6, 5, 4, 3, 2, 1; so her first move was to square 6, then to square 11, etc. After his first turn when he threw the 6, Tom's die followed the sequence 1, 2, 3, 4, 5, 6 each time, so his second move was to square 7, his third was to 9, etc. The normal rules of the game were followed, so whenever someone landed on a square that had the foot of a ladder, the piece was moved to the top of the ladder. Whenever someone landed on a square that had the head of a snake, the piece was moved to the tail of the snake. The number thrown to end the game didn't necessarily matter, since the first person to move a piece completely off the board won. Who won the game—Florence or Tom?

87 DIFFICULTY ✪✪✪✪✪✪☆☆☆☆   ⏱ 6 Minutes

What color should be in the central triangle?

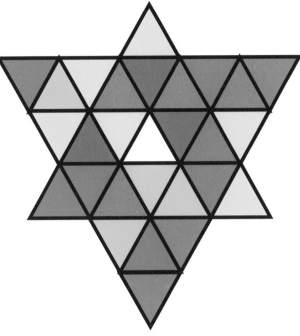

88 DIFFICULTY ✪✪✪✪✪✪✪☆☆☆   ⏱ 7 Minutes
Target time: 7 minutes

It's impossible to color in this shape so that no two colors touch without using four different colors. What is the LEAST number of times in which you have to resort to using the fourth color (i.e., on how many areas)?

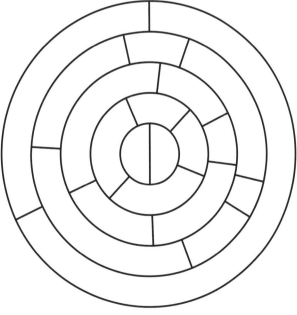

89 DIFFICULTY ✪✪✪✪✪☆☆☆☆☆ 4 Minutes

In the puzzle below, which of the lettered squares (a, b, c, or d) fits into the empty space?

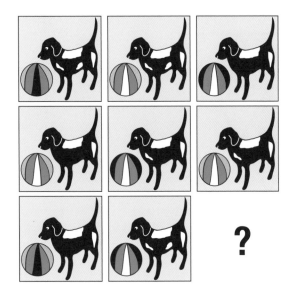

?

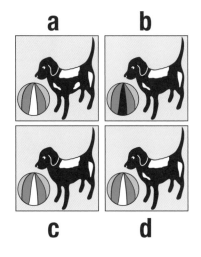

a   b

c   d

90 DIFFICULTY ✪✪✪✪☆☆☆☆☆☆ 4 Minutes

Move one coin to make two rows of four in any direction.

1

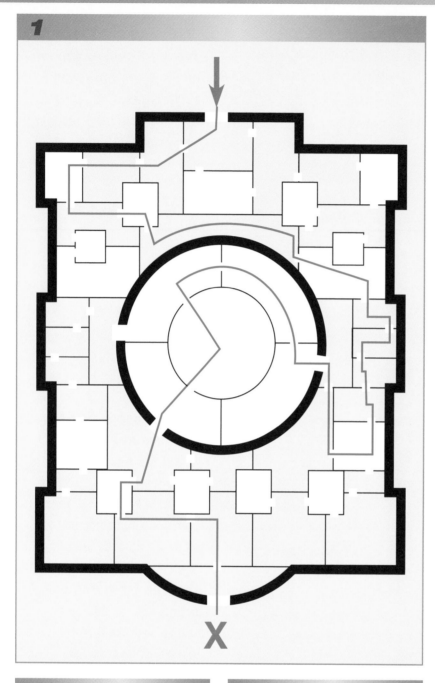

2

Whatever move your opponent performs, make the diametrically opposite move on your next turn. For example, if your opponent takes the coin in the top left corner, you take the coin in the bottom right corner.

3

1. 2
2. 1
3. 0
4. 0
5. 3
6. 2 + 1 = 3
7. 1 + 1 = 2
8. 12

4

5

Twelve; the opposite sides of a die add up to seven, so the bottom three faces are (from left to right) two spots, four spots, and six spots, thus a total of twelve.

6

7

8

d; each line contains two white stars and a yellow star, and each line also has a circled star. Each line contains a red and blue halved circle that has been turned through 0 degrees, 90 degrees, and 180 degrees (resulting in two lines running from top to bottom and one line from side to side).

The missing image should contain a white star and a circle that has been turned through 90 degrees (i.e., runs from side to side).

9

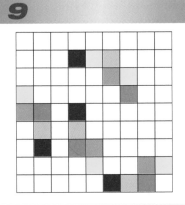

10

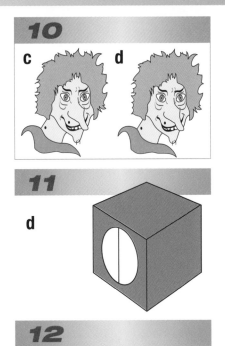

c   d

11

d

12

a; the top number of each is the sum of the previous top and bottom numbers, the bottom number is the difference between the top and bottom numbers on the previous domino, as well as being the difference between the total number of dots on both dominoes.

13

Twenty-three; Angelica can see the top faces of all three dice, thus a total of twelve spots. The opposite sides of a die add up to seven. On the furthest left die, the side face Angelica can see has two spots. On the central die, the side face Angelica can see has three spots. On the furthest right die, the side face Angelica can see has five spots. On the bottom face of the furthest right die, there are four spots, and the end face of this die (invisible to you) doesn't have six spots (intro), so must have one. Thus Angelica can see a total of twelve spots on the top faces, ten spots on the side faces and one on the end face, so a combined total of twenty-three spots.

14

One spot. ⊙
To determine why, look at each row, either going from side to side or on a diagonal from right to left or left to right. In each of these three possible directions, the row must contain all odd-numbered circles or all even-numbered circles. Going from right to left (or vice versa) the row in which the middle circle appears contains a five spot and a one spot, so it follows that the middle circle must contain another odd spot (in this case a one). Similarly, from bottom right to top left, the row contains a one, another odd number.

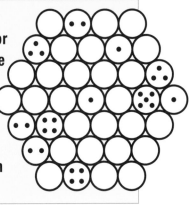

15

e; (it has more diamonds toward the nib of the pen).

16

Two colors

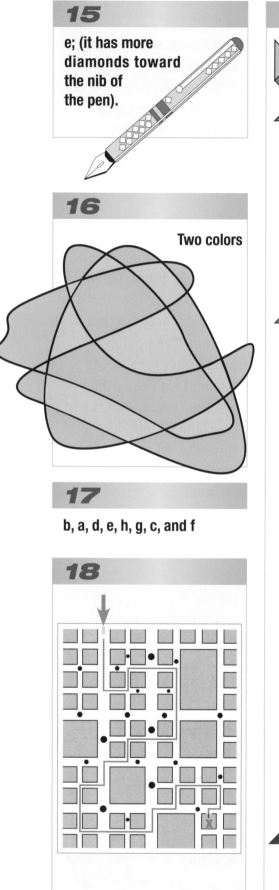

17

b, a, d, e, h, g, c, and f

18

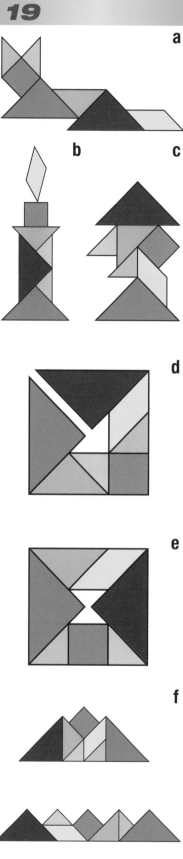

19

a

b

c

d

e

f

20

b

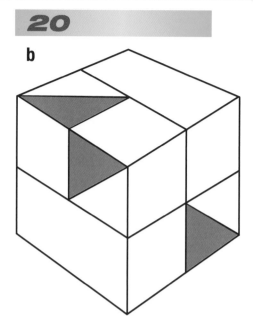

21

b; each line contains one dog with a white ear, two dogs with a patched eye, and two dogs with their tongues out. The missing image must have a white patched eye, no white ear, and its tongue hanging out.

22

a and c

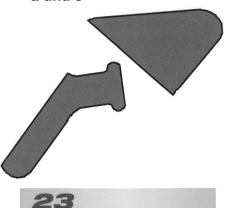

23

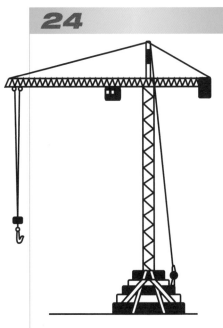

b; the total number of dots increases in number first by one, then by two, then by three, and finally by four, so the final number of dots must equal twelve.

24

a; the struts at the base are closer together and do not extend to the outside edge of the base.

25

Each square contains a symbol with one side more or one side less than its immediate neighbor (above, below, left, right). Each symbol is also a color with one letter in its name more or one letter less than its immediate neighbor, e.g., red, blue, green, yellow, apricot.

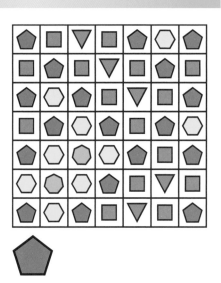

26

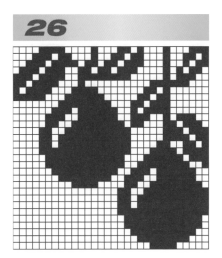

27

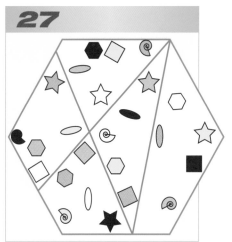

28

Four colors are needed.

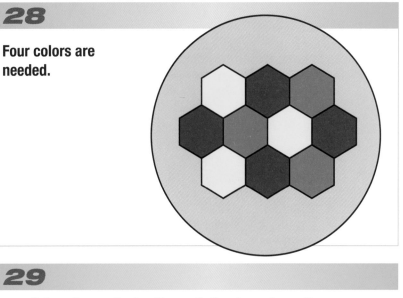

29

a = 4, b = 6, c = 3, d = 7, e = 2, f = 1, and g = 5

30

Domino 3/3 must be used with a 3 at the other corner and since there is only one other 3 (attached to a 1, totaling 4), the next corner is a 5. There is only one 5 (attached to a 2), so the corner is 2. Since the remaining corner of this side is a 3, this must be domino 2/4. Thus (similarly any rotation or reflection):

Domino 1/2 must be used with a 6 at the corner. This is attached to the 2, which requires a corner domino of 1, so 1/4. The corner of this side must be 4, part of domino 4/4, so this is next to corner 1, part of domino 1/2. Thus (similarly any rotation or reflection):

31

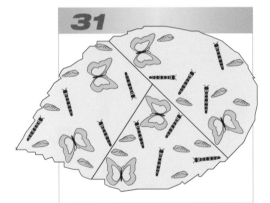

32

1. Pink
2. Red
3. 3
4. 3
5. 1
6. 2
7. 3
8. 4

33

34

c; each line contains two tic-tac-toe games where Xs win and one where Os win.
Each line contains a pink, an orange, and a blue square.
Each line contains two white games and a yellow game.
The winning game must therefore have an X win, a pink square, and a yellow game.

35

a

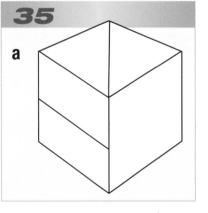

36

a and d

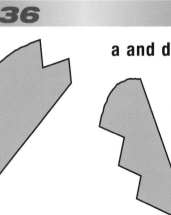

37

Start: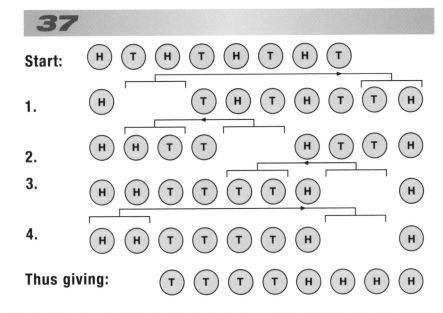

1.

2.

3.

4.

Thus giving: T T T T H H H H

38

The number in square 31 isn't 6 (clue 2), so in diagonal 6–31, square 21 = 6. Square 36 isn't 3 (clue 3), so in diagonal 1–36, square 15 = 3; and in 6–36, 24 = 3. Square 31 is 5 or 2 (2) as is 32 (1), so 36 is neither, thus 36 = 6 and 25 = 6 (3). Square 8 isn't 6 (diagonal), so in 2–32, square 2 = 6; thus 10 = 6. In 13–18, the 1 isn't in 14 (2), so must be in 13. Since there's a 5 in 22, there isn't a 5 in 1 or 19, so in 1–31, 31 = 5; so 14 = 5 (2), 32 = 2, and 3 = 2 (1). By elimination, 1 = 4, 8 = 1, 19 = 2, 20 = 4, 9 = 5, 27 = 1, 29 = 2 (diagonal), 11 = 4 (diagonal), 16 = 2, 28 = 4, 30 = 5, 4 = 3, 5 = 5, 12 = 2, 18 = 4, 23 = 1, 35 = 3, and 34 = 1.

4	6	2	3	5	1
3	1	5	6	4	2
1	5	3	2	6	4
2	4	6	5	1	3
6	3	1	4	2	5
5	2	4	1	3	6

39

11:35; the hour hand moves back by four hours (or forward by eight hours) and the minute hand moves forward by seven minutes each time.

40

b

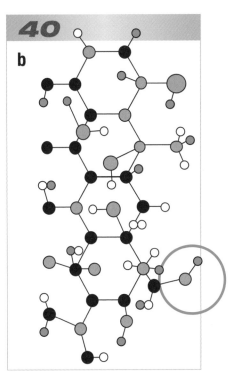

41

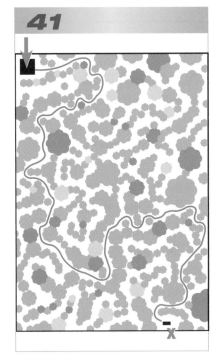

42

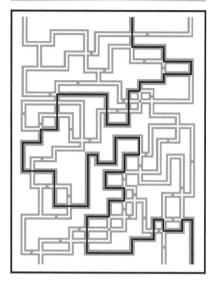

43

It is possible to do with three colors.

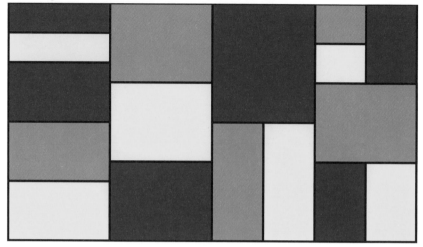

44

1	5	4	6	3	2
2	3	6	5	1	4
6	1	2	3	4	5
3	2	5	4	6	1
4	6	1	2	5	3
5	4	3	1	2	6

The number in row four, column four cannot be 1 or 2 (horizontal) or 3 or 5 (diagonal) or 6 (vertical), so it must be 4. Similarly, row six, column six cannot be 1, 2, 3, 4, or 5, so it must be 6. To complete the diagonal column one, row one must be 1. In row four, the 5 cannot be in column one or five, so it must be column three. The total of the four corner spots is 14 (intro) so row one, column six is 2. The top right to bottom left

diagonal contains five different numbers and no 4, so row three, column four is not 2, 4, 5, or 6 so it must be 1 or 3. As neither row five, column two nor row two, column five can be a 3, row three, column four must be 3. Column six, row three must be 5, and row five 3. In row one, the 5 cannot be in column three or five, so it must be in column two. In column five, the 2 cannot be in rows one, three, or four so it must be in row six. In row six, the 3 cannot be in columns two or four so must be in column three, the 4 cannot be in column four so must be in column two, which leaves 1 in column four. The 5 in column four cannot be in row five, so it must be in row two, and

the 2 in row five. In row two, the 2 cannot be in column three or five so it must be in column one. In column one, the 3 cannot be in rows three or five, so it must be in row four. Thus row four, column five is 6. In row one, the 3 is not in column three, so it must be in column five, and the 4 in column three. In row two the 6 is not in column five so it must be in column three, and the 1 in column five. Column five is thus completed by a 4 in row three. In row three, the 1 is not in column one, so it must be in column two, and the 6 in column one. Thus column one is completed by a 4, column two by a 6, and column three by a 1.

45

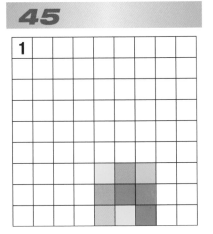

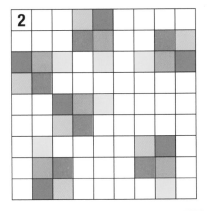

46

47

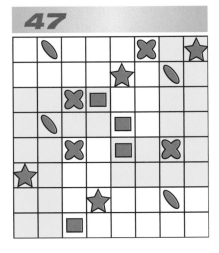

48

b and e

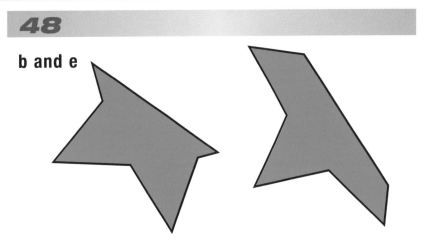

49

Two dominoes each total 9 (5/4 and 6/3). For these sides to total 10, both 1s must be corner numbers. Two dominoes each total 7 (5/2 and 4/3). They must each have 3 as a corner number, thus 3/4 and 3/6 (as 3/1 has a corner of 1, as described above). So one square has domino 3/4 with the 3 as a corner and the 3 of 3/6 as its other corner to total 10. Domino 3/6 must have 1 at its corner. If the 1 domino is 1/3, the corner is 6, thus 6/2 (6/3 has been used) but the final side would then total 11, which is incorrect. So the domino is 1/4, with 5 at the corner, hence 5/2 to make the correct total (see image below left).

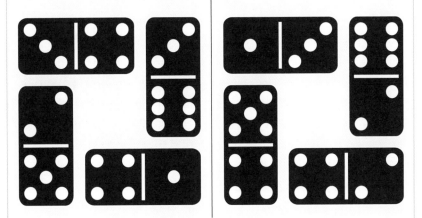

The remaining dominoes form a square with domino 5/4 and a corner of 1, part of domino 1/3. To total 10, 1/3 has a corner of 6 from domino 6/2. which in turn has a corner of 2 from domino 2/4 (see image above right).

50

The bottom one. This results in the domino squares alternating between odd and even in rows and columns (except the fifth row, which is now incomplete).

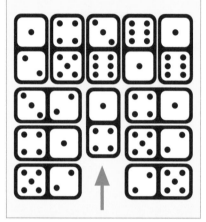

51

a and c

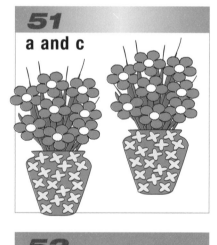

52

The shortest route is thirty moves, as follows: 2 to x, 6 to 2, 5 to a, x to 5, a to 6, 2 to c, 1 to x, c to 1, 6 to 2, 7 to a, 8 to b, 5 to 8, b to 5, x to 7, a to 6, 2 to c, 3 to x, 4 to b, 1 to 4, b to 1, c to 3, 6 to 2, 5 to a, x to 5, a to 6, 2 to c, 1 to x, c to 1, 6 to 2, x to 6.

53

54

a; the large star rotates by a quarter turn counterclockwise, and the smaller shapes within it by a quarter turn clockwise every time.

55

56

c; the total number of dots increases in number by two every time.

57

c and d

58

a and g are the same.

59

1d; each line contains two airships with red fins and one with blue fins. Each line contains two airships with red gondolas underneath and one with a blue gondola. Each line contains two airships facing left and one facing right. Each line contains two airships with four lights on the balloon and one with three lights. The missing image therefore has blue fins, a red gondola, faces left, and has four lights on the balloon, so it must be d.

60

Push the middle row up by moving the top coin to the bottom and using it to push up the whole column.

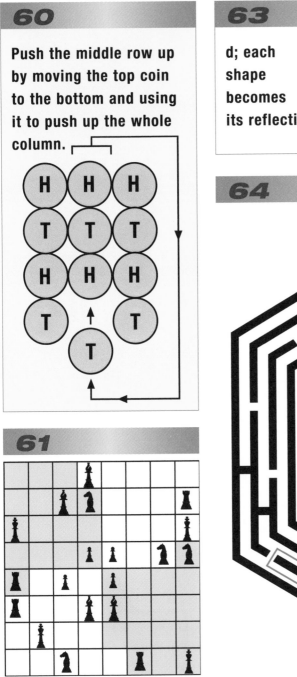

63

d; each shape becomes its reflection.

64

61

62

a c

b g

65

1. Orange
2. Orange
3. 2
4. 3
5. 3
6. 2
7. 3
8. Orange

66

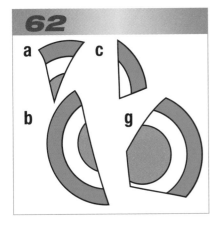

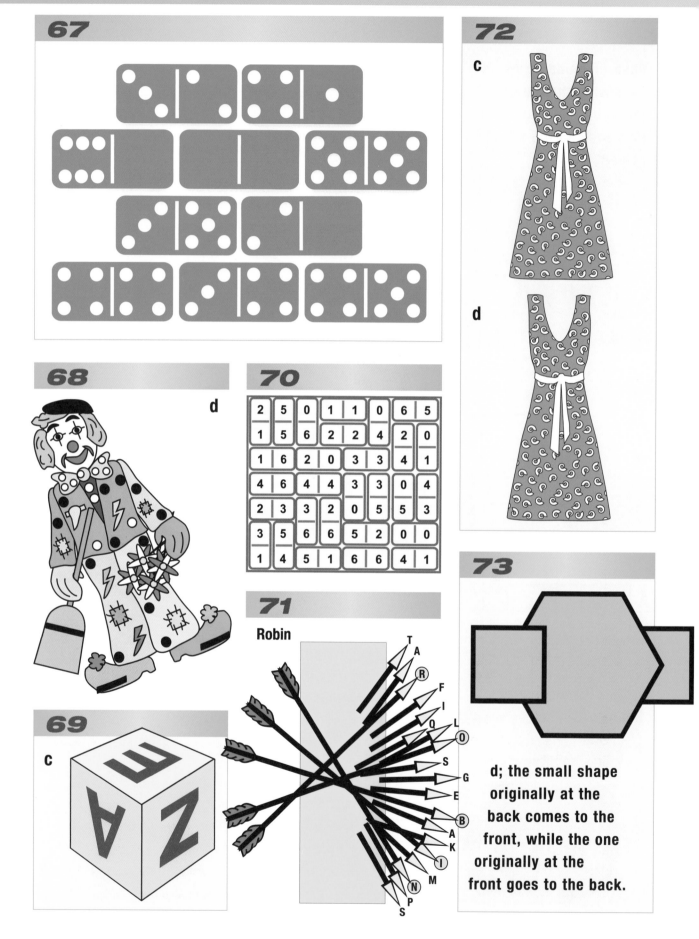

67

68

69
C

70

71
Robin

72
c

d

73
d; the small shape
originally at the
back comes to the
front, while the one
originally at the
front goes to the back.

74

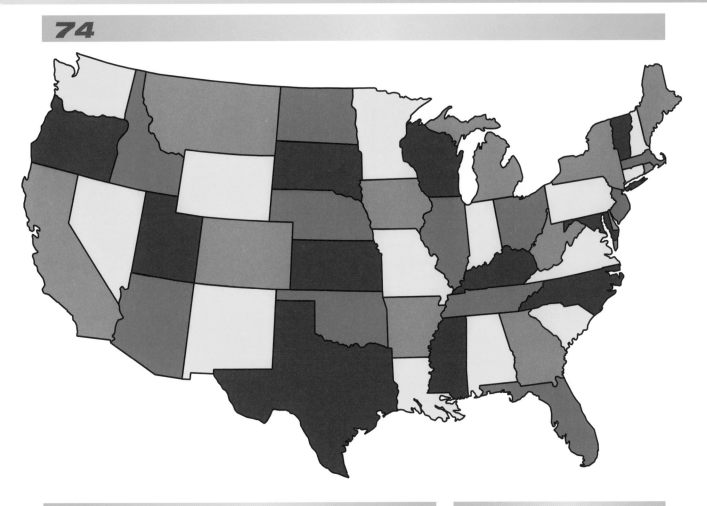

75

a; each line contains two signs that are right-side up, and one that is upside-down. Each line contains two "STOP"s with an exclamation point and one without. Each line contains one red "FILTERED" and two black. On each line the steam is colored white twice and yellow once. The missing image should be right-side up. "STOP" should have an exclamation point. "FILTERED" should be in black. The steam on the cup should be yellow, so it must be a.

76

77

Since the opposite two sides of a die have spots totaling seven, Peter gave double the quantity of the number of spots that appear on the opposite side of the die. The yellow die relates to the quantity of loaves, and the blue to the quantity of fish. Thus Mary was awarded four loaves and ten fish.

78

82

Pattern a can be found six times.

a   b

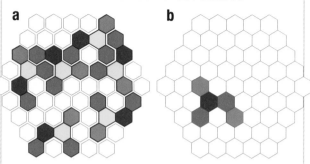

79

1. Barry	7. 3
2. Roger	(Katie, Jane,
3. Tom	and Anna)
4. White	8. 3
5. 5	(Will, Mary,
6. 4	and Jane)

80

1. e	6. 8
and f	7. 1
2. g	8. 30
3. 3	
4. 1	
5. 1	

83

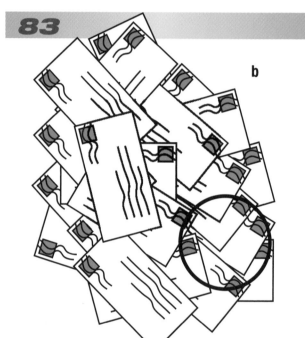

b

81

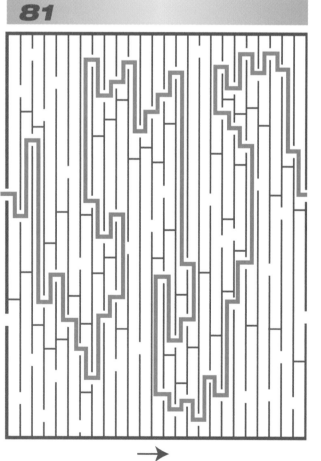

→

84

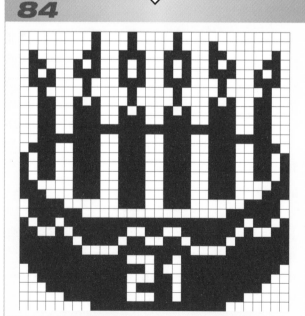

85

d

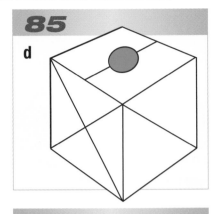

86

Tom

87

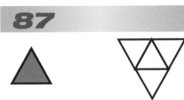

Green. Each set of four triangles has 3 colors.

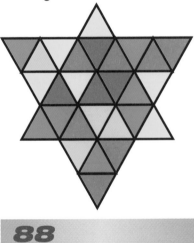

88

You need to resort to using it only once.

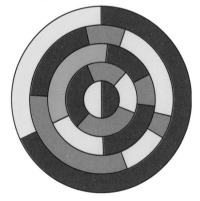

89

b; each different dog and each different ball appears three times. Thus the missing dog has three white spots and a ball with two green stripes, two red stripes, and one black stripe.

90

One answer is to place the topmost coin on top of the one at the center of the cross.

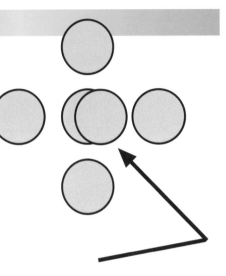

In this section of Spatial Puzzles we'll be improving your perception skills in both two and three dimensions and hopefully having fun along the way.

The ability to perceive things in three dimensions is becoming more important in our everyday lives. Computer programs are now able to take a two-dimensional image, such as a photograph, and apply it to a three-dimensional model so that a full-perspective image of a human face can be rendered. This technology can be used to help catch criminals or to see your face on the main character in a computer game! 3-D-style images such as holograms now play an important part in security and forgery protection.

One type of spatial skill is called "perceptual constancy." This means that, even though we see a car close to us in the street, we would know how that object would behave if we saw it again in the distance or on television. This also explains why our senses can become easily confused. When we go into a hall of mirrors at the fair or look at an optical illusion, our previous experience works against us and provides confusing yet amusing results. It is also the basis of some visual comedy and fun vacation photo snaps, where objects can appear out of scale.

Perceptions also have their place in aiding our experience of art. For instance, in Bridget Riley's artwork in the op art movement, where flat paintings give the impression of a 3D surface. There are also of course the classic engravings and woodcuts of the Dutch graphic artist M. C. Escher (1898–1972), with his impossible— looking staircases.

So, before you dive headlong into this section, here's a few words of advice. All the puzzles have a time limit as a guide, but if you'd prefer to proceed at your own pace . . . who's to know?! You can just open a random page and find a puzzle that looks interesting. However, as that doesn't narrow it down much, be sure to pay attention to our special star grading system. Easier puzzles have one, two, or three stars. Eight, nine, or (ouch) ten stars means you're in danger of going boggle—eyed. You have been warned.

Every question is numbered and has its answer clearly marked in the back of the section. But be sure to try all avenues before resorting to the solutions—things are not always what they seem at first!

Our perception is that you're going to get a lot of enjoyment out of the puzzles within, so we won't delay you a moment more. Have fun! ✪

1 DIFFICULTY ●●●●●●○○○○○   ③ Minutes

Travel from one star's center to the other's center without crossing any lines.

2 DIFFICULTY ✪✪✪✪✪✪✪✪☆☆

5 Minutes

Using only straight lines, can you divide this rectangle into eight sections, each of identical shape and size, and each with four red circles?

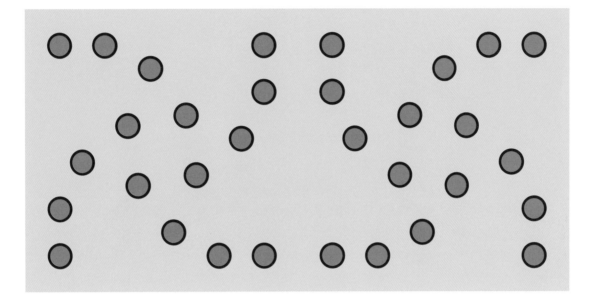

3 DIFFICULTY ✪✪✪✪✪☆☆☆☆☆

2 Minutes

Here are four matches. Can you move one match to leave two?

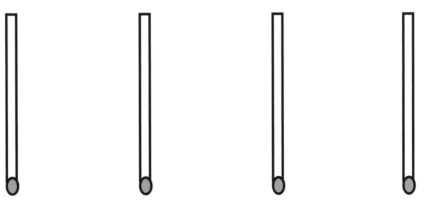

4 DIFFICULTY ✪✪✪✪✩✩✩✩✩✩ | ④ Minutes

Can you pair this stamp with its correct print?

a

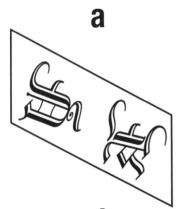

b

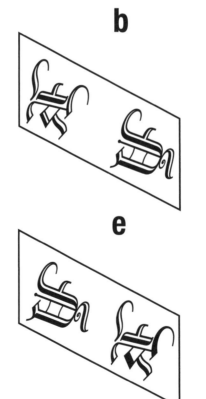

c

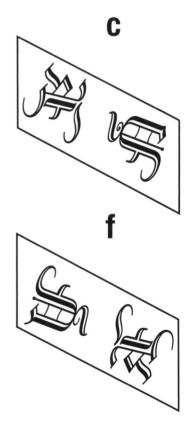

d

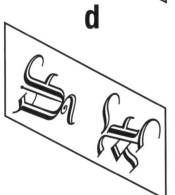

e

f

5 DIFFICULTY ✪✪✪✪✪☆☆☆☆☆  ③ Minutes

Which of the four boxed figures (a, b, c, or d) completes the set?

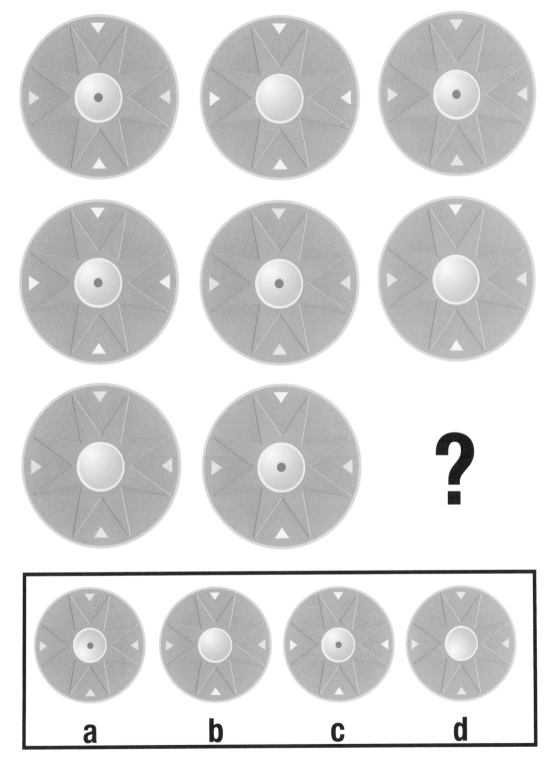

a   b   c   d

6 DIFFICULTY ✪✪✪✪✪☆☆☆☆☆   **6** Minutes

A famous mathematical theorem says that any political map (where no two bordering countries are colored the same) can be completed using just four colors. Grab four different pens and see if you can color the mainland of Europe correctly. Don't worry about the small islands.

7 DIFFICULTY ✪✪✪✪☆☆☆☆☆☆   **3** Minutes

Can you cut this cake into four slices, each containing the same number and type of decorations, with just two straight cuts of the knife? Although the knife may pass between the candles, no decoration may be cut!

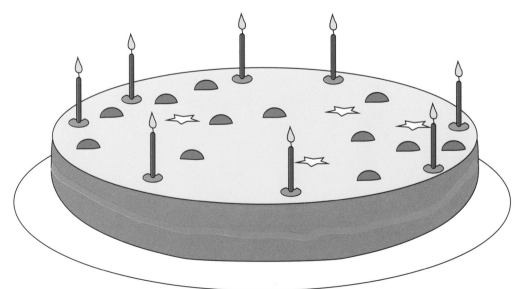

Kirsty played a game of Snakes and Ladders with her brother Tom. He threw the first 6, so started first, placing his playing piece on the 6. After that, every time it was Kirsty's turn, her die followed the sequence 6, 4, 2, 5, 3, 1; so her first move was to square 6, her second was to square 10, her third was to 12, etc. After his first turn when he threw the 6, Tom's die followed the sequence 2, 4, 6, 1, 3, 5 each time, so his second move was to square 8, his third was to 12, etc. The normal rules of the game were followed, so whenever someone landed on a square that had the foot of a ladder, the piece was moved to the top of the ladder. Whenever someone landed on a square that had the head of a snake, the piece was moved to the tail of the snake. The number thrown to end the game didn't necessarily matter, since the first person to move a piece completely off the board won. Who won the game—Kirsty or Tom?

9 DIFFICULTY ⭐⭐⭐⭐⭐✩✩✩✩✩ ② Minutes

Keith's magic mirror reflects very strangely!
Can you match each leaf to its correct
(although misplaced and somewhat distorted)
image in the mirror?

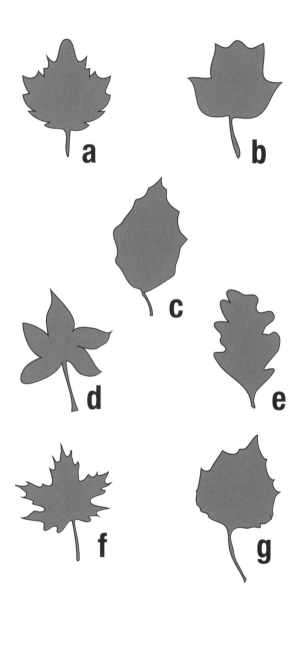

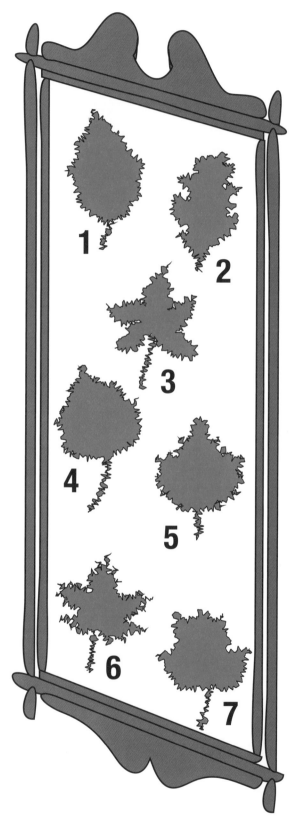

10 DIFFICULTY ✪✪✪✪✪✪☆☆☆☆

In this two-player game, the aim is to make a continuous path in your color across the board. Choose a red or blue pen, then decide who goes first. To begin, the first player draws a line from any dot of his or her color to the nearest dot horizontally or vertically next to it. The second player does the same between two dots of their own color.

Players continue to make moves in turns. Because each player is using his or her own set of dots and paths, there cannot be a tie. Lines must not cross at any point. The winner is the first player to achieve a continuous path in his or her color, from his or her starting side to the opposite edge.

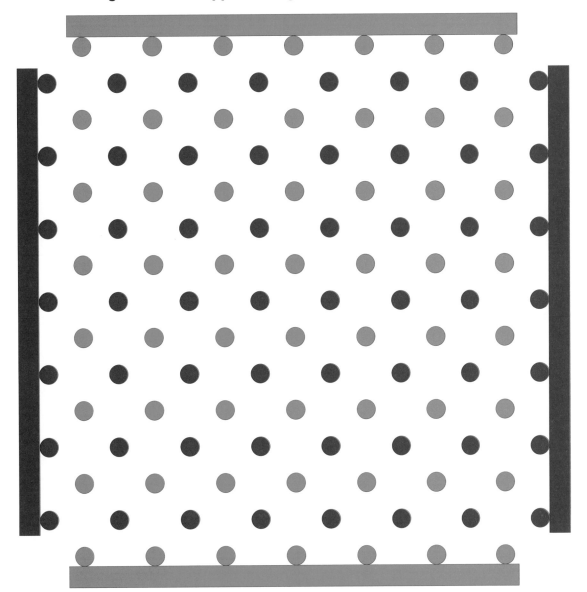

11 DIFFICULTY ✪✪✪✪✪✪✩✩✩✩ ⏱ **8** Minutes

In each of the four buildings below, one type of brick is used more or less frequently than it is in the other three buildings. Can you discover the different brick in each construction? The ten brick types are as follows:

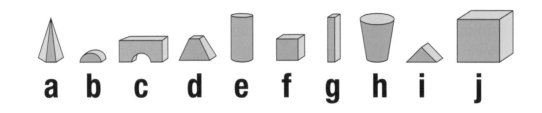

a b c d e f g h i j

Building 1

Building 2

Building 3

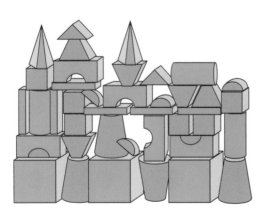

Building 4

12 DIFFICULTY ●●●●●○○○○○ ③ Minutes

At the local casino, they play a dice gambling game that involves throwing two dice and betting a stake of $12. What are the rules and how much did Gary Gambler win or lose when he threw a 2 followed by a 3? Study the clues below to discover the answer.

1. Gina threw a 4 followed by a 5 and got $6 back, losing $6.

2. Gordon threw a 1 followed by a 5 and broke even, so got $12 back.

3. Graham threw a 1 followed by a 3 and got $24 back, so won $12.

13 DIFFICULTY ●●●●●●●○○○ ④ Minutes

By drawing three straight lines, can you divide this room into five sections, each containing a bed, a storage unit, a table, and two chairs?

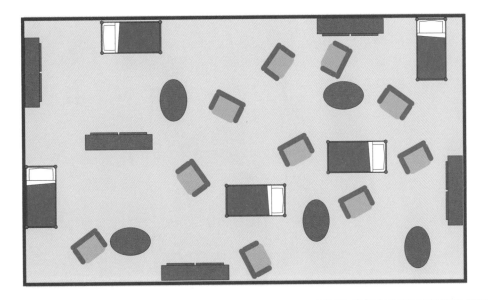

14 DIFFICULTY ✪✪✪✪✪✪☆☆☆☆ ② Minutes

A circular loop of string lies flat on a table. Part of the string has been hidden from view by the black border. If X is inside the loop, what can you say about Y? Here's a hint: coloring in some of the areas may help you.

15 DIFFICULTY ✪✪✪✪✪☆☆☆☆☆ ③ Minutes

Which three pieces can be fitted together to form an identical copy of this shape? Pieces may be rotated, but not flipped over.

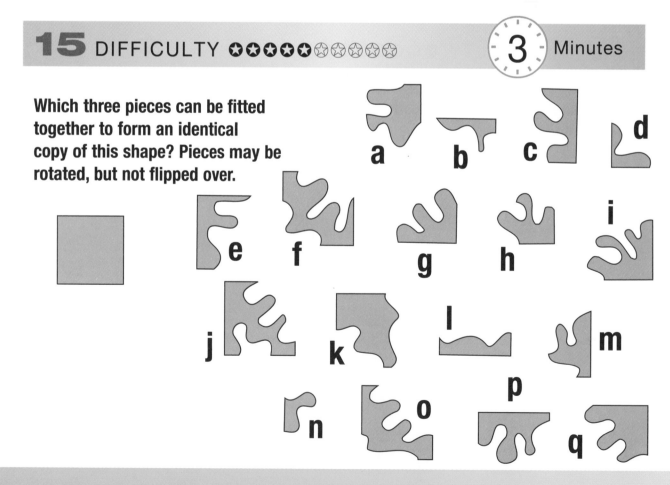

16 DIFFICULTY ✪✪✪✪✪✪☆☆☆☆

4 Minutes

Try to make your way to the center of this circular maze.

17 DIFFICULTY ★★★☆☆☆☆☆☆☆　　⏱ **5** Minutes

Can you spot the eight differences between these two pictures? Circle them in the lower drawing.

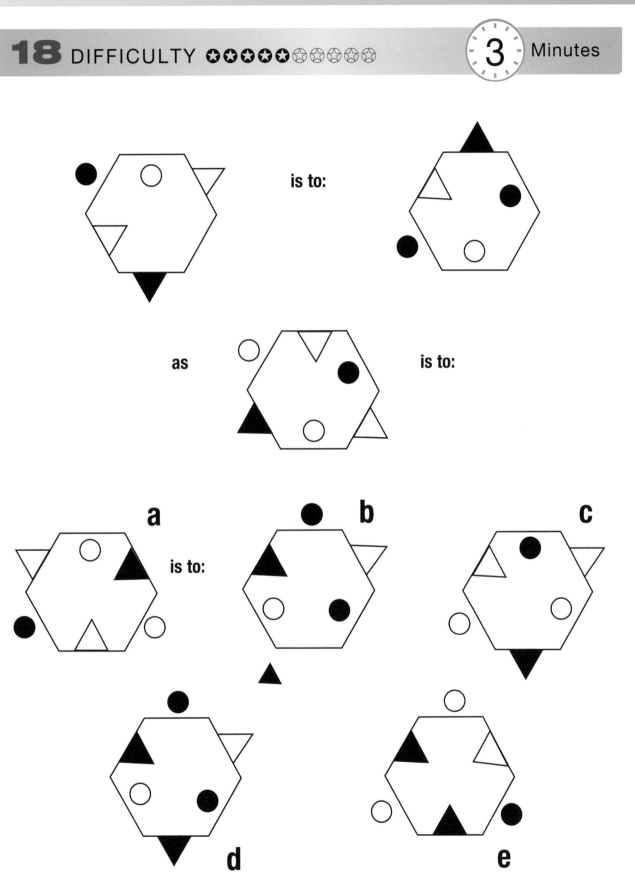

is to:

as

is to:

a

is to:

b

c

d

e

When the shape below is folded into a cube, which one of the following (a, b, c, d, or e) is produced?

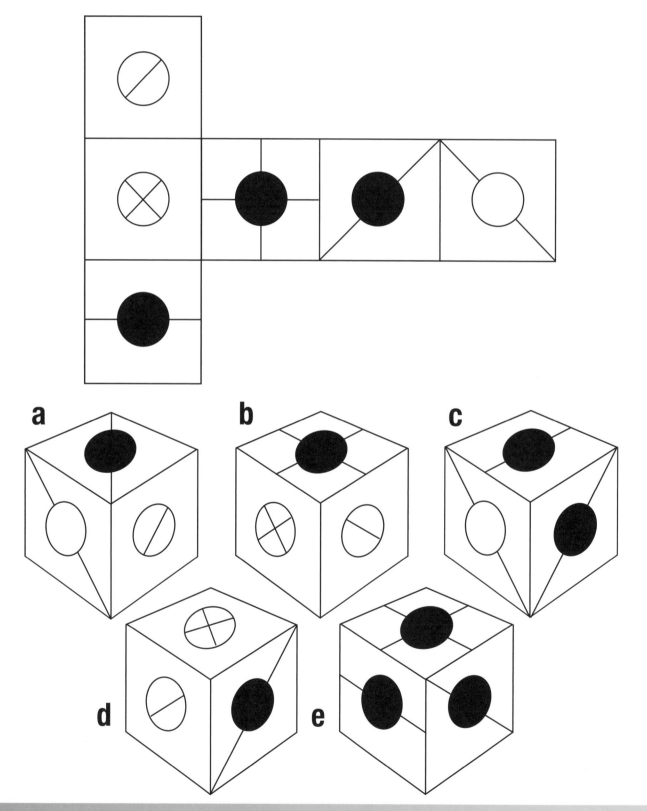

This cross is hidden only once in the large grid of squares below. The pattern may be rotated but not reflected. Can you find it?

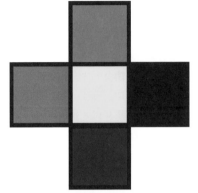

21 DIFFICULTY ✪✪✪✪✪✪✪☆☆☆ ⏱ 30 Minutes

Think deeply and you might find a way to complete this numeropic.

How to do a numeropic:

Along each row or column, there are numbers that indicate how many blocks of black squares are in a line. For example, "3, 4, 5" indicates that from left to right or top to bottom, there is a group of three black squares, then a group of four black squares, then another group of five black squares.

Each block of black squares on the same line must have at least one white square between it and the next block of black squares. Blocks of black squares may or may not have a number of white squares before and after them.

It is sometimes possible to determine which squares will be black without reference to other lines or columns. It is helpful to put a small dot in a square you know will be empty.

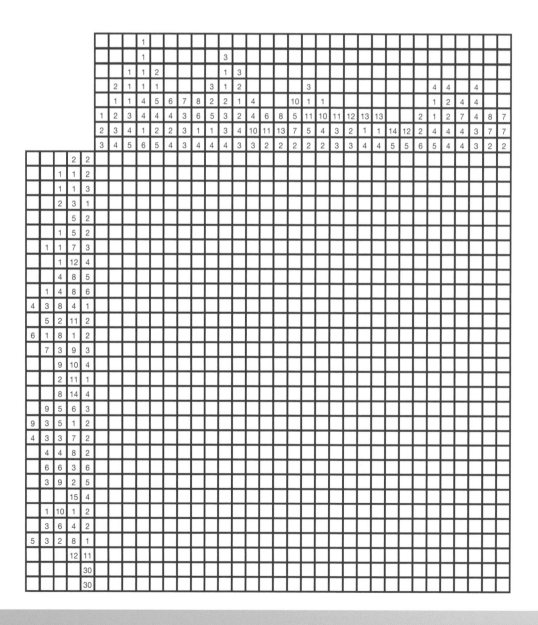

22 DIFFICULTY ✪✪✪✪✪✪✪✩✩✩✩ ⏱ 5 Minutes

What shape should be in the middle?

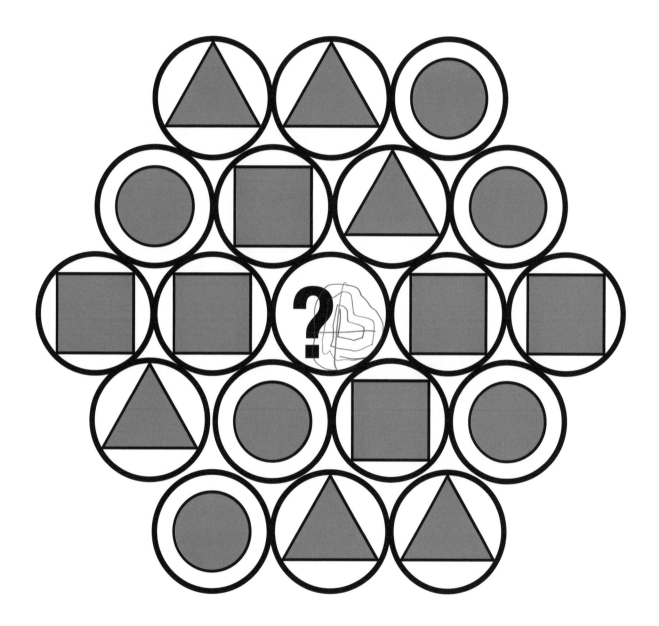

23 DIFFICULTY ✪✪✪✪✪✪✪✪✫✫ — 6 Minutes

How many differences can you spot between these two pictures, given that one is supposed to be an exact mirror image of the other? Circle them in the drawing on the right.

24 DIFFICULTY ✪✪✪✪✪✪✫✫✫✫ — 5 Minutes

Using three of the four different mathematical operators (+, −, x, ÷), can you find the correct totals for each of these dice problems?

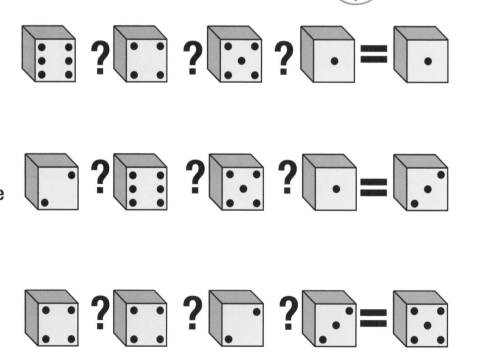

25 DIFFICULTY ✪✪✪✪✪☆☆☆☆☆ 5 Minutes

When the shape below is folded into a cube, which one of the following
(a, b, c, d, or e) is produced?

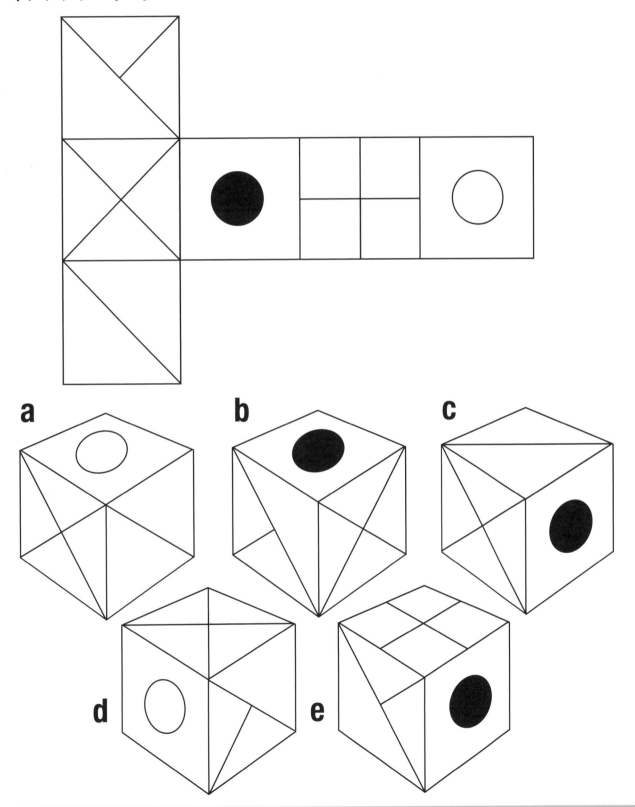

26 DIFFICULTY ✪✪✪✪✪✩✩✩✩✩

1 Minute

Study this picture for one minute, then see if you can answer the questions on the next page.

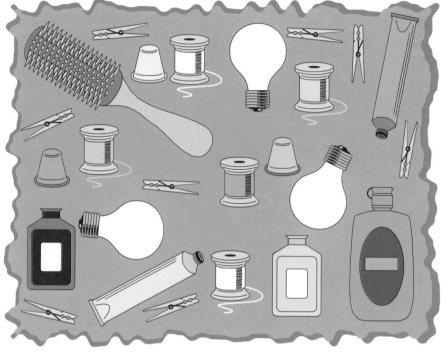

27 DIFFICULTY ✪✪✪✪✩✩✩✩✩✩

2 Minutes

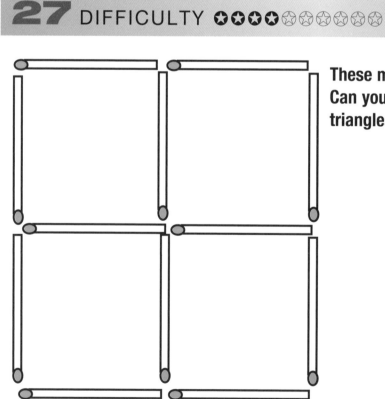

These matches make five squares. Can you move two to make five triangles?

[26] DIFFICULTY ●●●●●○○○○○○ | **3** Minutes

Can you answer these questions about the puzzle on the previous page without looking back?

1. What color is the hairbrush?

2. How many thimbles appear in the picture?

3. What color is the tube at the top right corner of the picture?

4. How many lightbulbs appear in the picture?

5. How many spools of thread have white thread?

6. How many clothespins appear in the picture?

7. How many bottles have a white label?

8. How many objects are in the picture?

28 DIFFICULTY ●●●●○○○○○○○ | **3** Minutes

By drawing three straight lines, can you divide this cloud into four sections, each containing five different symbols?

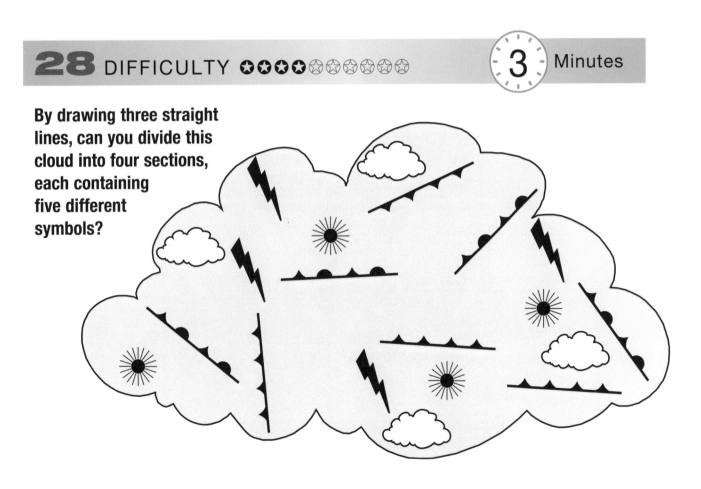

29 DIFFICULTY ⭐⭐⭐⭐☆☆☆☆☆⭐ | 🕐 **4** Minutes

Starting at a, see if you can make your way to b in this difficult triangular maze.

What is the missing shape?

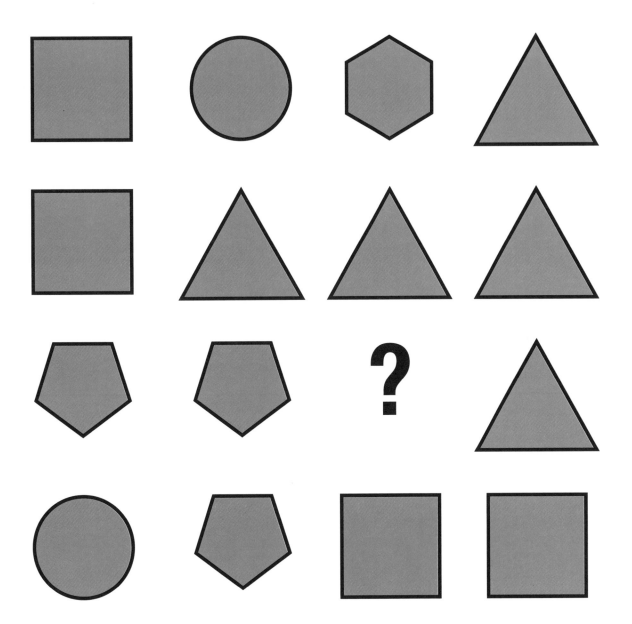

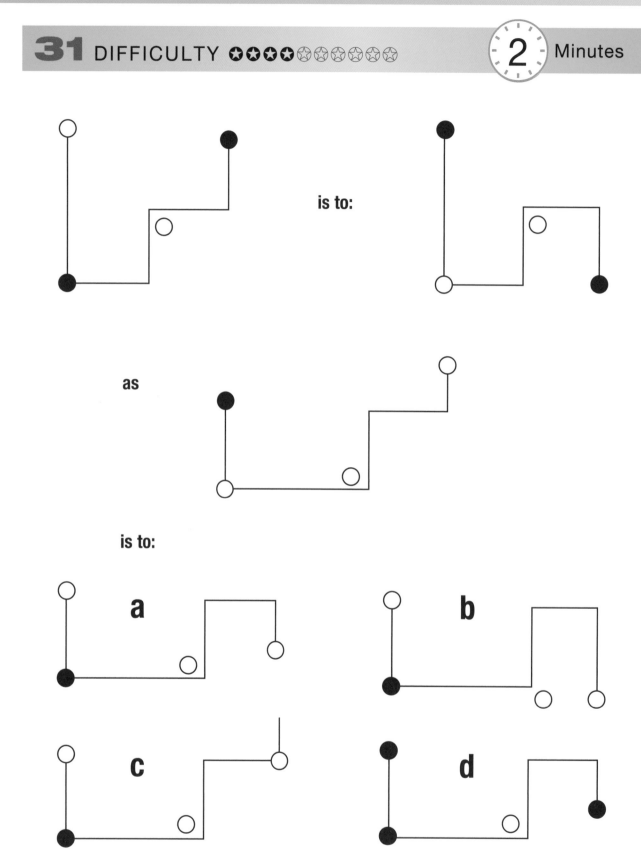

is to:

as

is to:

a

b

c

d

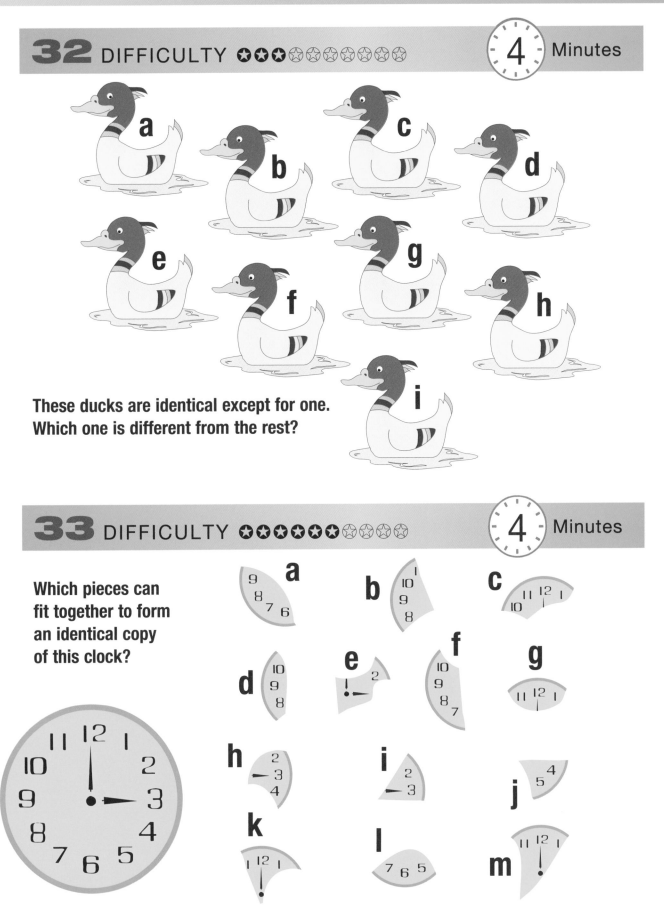

32 DIFFICULTY ✪✪✪☆☆☆☆☆☆☆ | 4 Minutes

These ducks are identical except for one.
Which one is different from the rest?

33 DIFFICULTY ✪✪✪✪✪✪☆☆☆☆ | 4 Minutes

Which pieces can
fit together to form
an identical copy
of this clock?

34 DIFFICULTY ●●●●●○○○○○

2 Minutes

Study this picture for two minutes, then see if you can answer the questions on the next page.

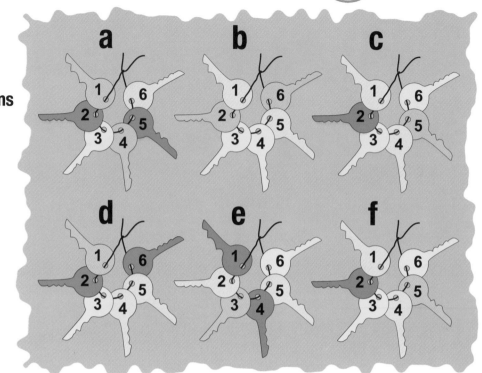

35 DIFFICULTY ●●●●●●○○○○

4 Minutes

By drawing three straight lines, can you divide this rectangle into four sections, each containing eight different birds?

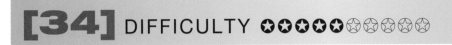

[34] DIFFICULTY ✪✪✪✪✪✪☆☆☆☆☆ ③ Minutes

Can you answer these questions about the puzzle on the previous page without looking back?

1. How many keys are there in total?

2. Which two bunches of keys are identical?

3. How many blue keys appear in total?

4. Which letter identifies the key ring with no red keys?

5. How many keys with the number 6 are yellow?

6. Which letter identifies the key ring with two blue keys touching one another?

7. How many odd-numbered keys are purple?

8. Which letter identifies the only key ring with a purple key numbered 6?

36 DIFFICULTY ✪✪✪✪✪✪✪☆☆☆☆ ④ Minutes

Here are ten matches. What is the smallest number you have to take away to leave two?

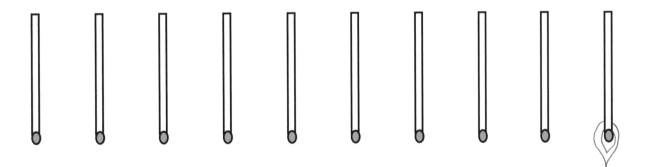

37 DIFFICULTY ⬤⬤⬤⬤⬤☆☆☆☆☆   2 Minutes

Which number should follow in this dice sequence?

23   **14**   **8**   **?**

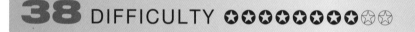

38 DIFFICULTY ⬤⬤⬤⬤⬤⬤⬤⬤☆☆   5 Minutes

Juliette has lined up these three dice on her coffee table. She can see the same seven faces that you can see. Angelica (her friend, sitting opposite) can see the top three faces of the dice, as well as another four faces you and Juliette cannot see. None of you can see the bottom three faces of these dice. What is the total number of spots on all the faces of the dice that Angelica can see, given that this is a different number from the total number of dots you can see?

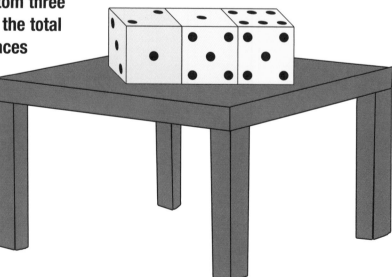

39 DIFFICULTY ★★★★★★☆☆☆☆

30 Minutes

Face facts in order to complete this numeropic. Refer to the instructions on puzzle 21 for help on how to do this kind of puzzle.

Row clues (top to bottom):

- 15
- 13 6
- 13 7
- 4
- 13 7
- 4 6 6
- 13
- 4 6 6
- 6 6 7
- 6 11 4
- 7 1 9 7
- 19 6
- 20
- 9 7 6
- 20 7
- 5 7 4
- 16 7
- 13 6
- 1 8 2
- 12 2 6
- 1 8 2 7
- 1 8 2 4
- 13 2 7
- 13 2 6
- 14 2
- 14 2
- 14 2
- 7
- 8

40 DIFFICULTY ●●● ✪✪✪✪✪✪✪   ④ Minutes

David's magic mirror reflects very strangely! Can you match each lamp to its correct (although misplaced and somewhat distorted) image in the mirror?

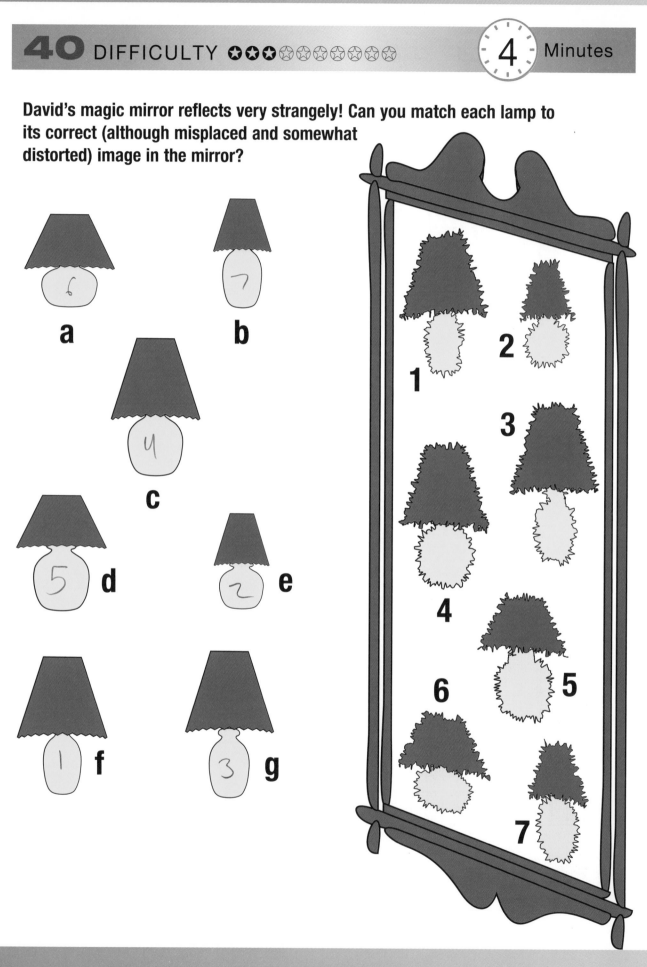

41 DIFFICULTY ✪✪✪✪✪✪☆☆☆☆   ④ Minutes

Carefully study the rocking horses below. Which is different from the rest?

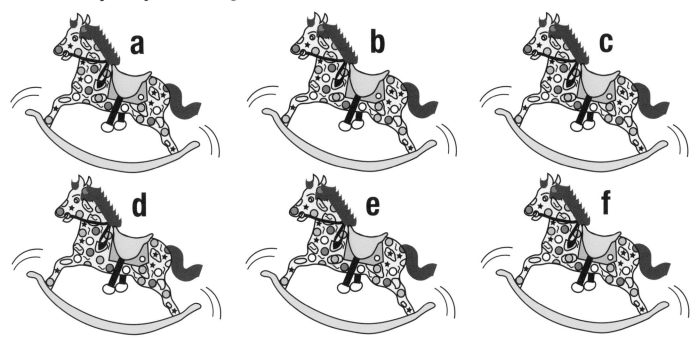

42 DIFFICULTY ✪✪✪✪✪☆☆☆☆☆   ③ Minutes

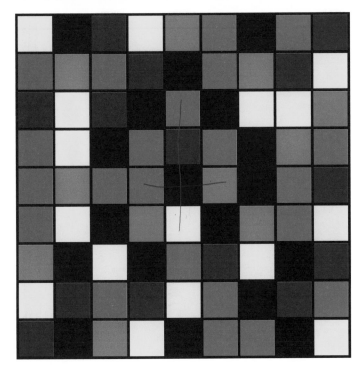

Where can the cross be found in the larger grid? The pattern may be rotated but not reflected.

43 DIFFICULTY ●●●●●○○○○○ | 4 Minutes

Using three colored pens (e.g., red, yellow, and blue), color in this diagram so that no two bordering areas have the same color.

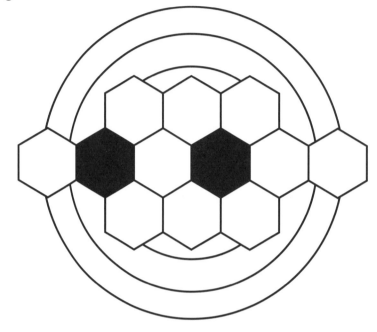

44 DIFFICULTY ●●●●●●○○○○ | 5 Minutes

Using straight lines only, can you divide this T-shirt into sections, each containing the same number of differently colored T-shirts?

45 DIFFICULTY ✪✪✪✪✪✪✪✩✩✩ ⏱ 8 Minutes

Starting at the top hexagon in the maze, make your way to the bottom hexagon by moving from shape to adjacent shape. You may ONLY move from a blue shape to a green one, from a green shape to a red one, or from a red shape to a blue one.

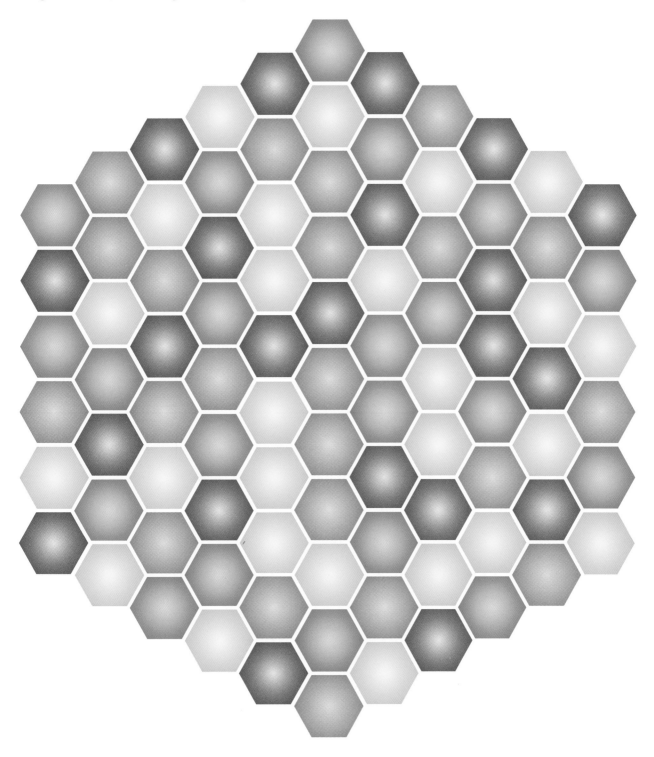

46 DIFFICULTY ✪✪✪✪✪☆☆☆☆☆ ⏱ 5 Minutes

Can you spot the ten differences between these two pictures?
Circle them in the lower drawing.

47 DIFFICULTY ✪✪✪✪✪✪✪☆☆☆

6 Minutes

Mary would like to buy two identical T-shirts for her twin brothers. Which two should she buy?

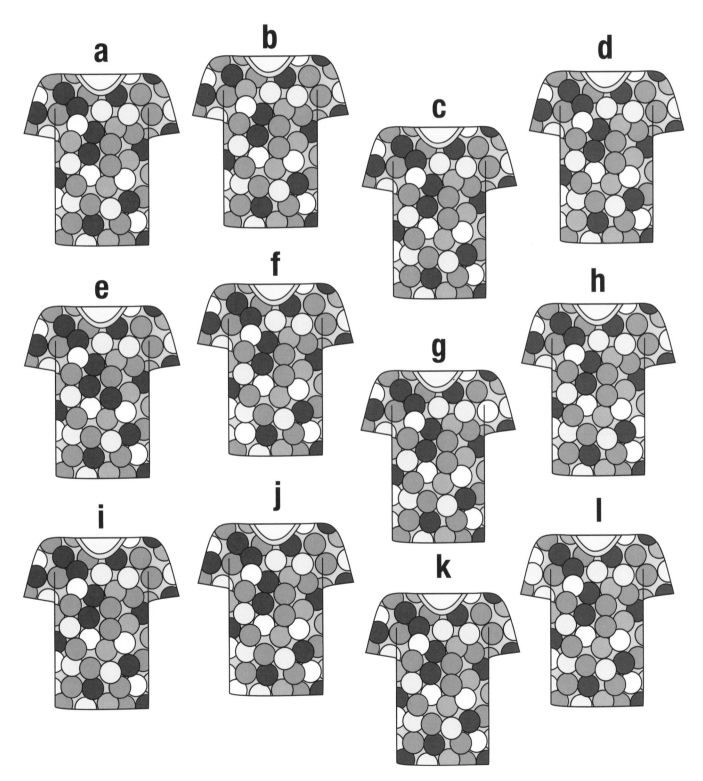

48 DIFFICULTY ✪✪✪✪✪☆☆☆☆☆ ⏱ 8 Minutes

In each of the four buildings below, one type of brick is used more or less frequently than it is in the other three buildings. Can you discover the different brick in each construction? The ten brick types are as follows:

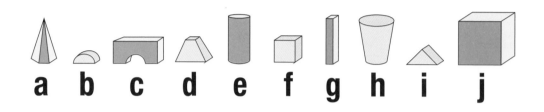

Building 1

Building 2

Building 3

Building 4

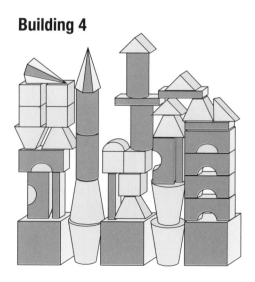

49 DIFFICULTY ✪✪✪✪✪✪☆☆☆☆  **4** Minutes

What shape is missing?

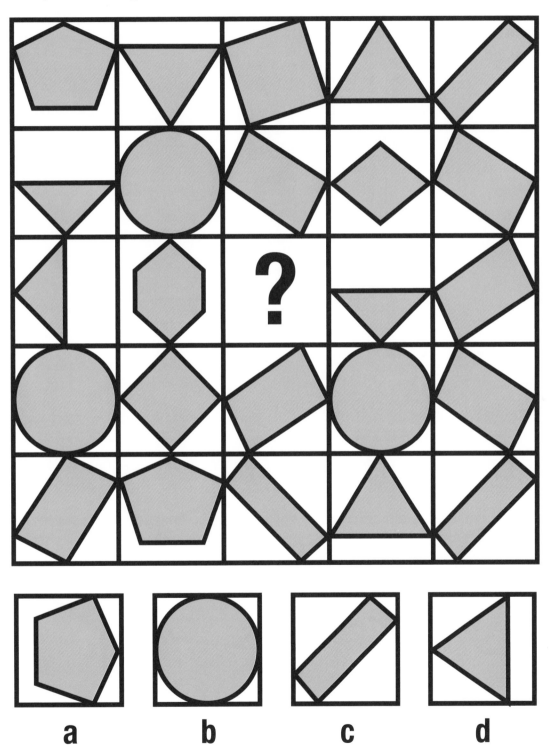

a   b   c   d

50 DIFFICULTY ★★★★★☆☆☆☆☆ ② Minutes

Study this picture for two minutes, then see if you can answer the questions on the next page.

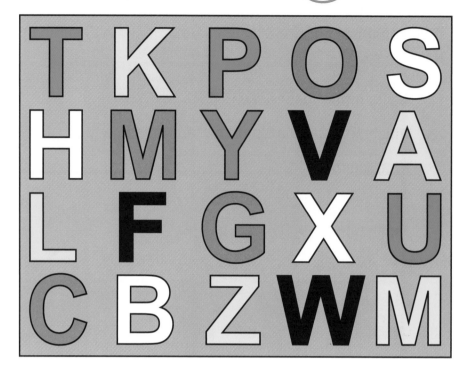

51 DIFFICULTY ★★★★★★☆☆☆☆ ② Minutes

Think laterally to make a perfect square out of these four heptagonal coins.

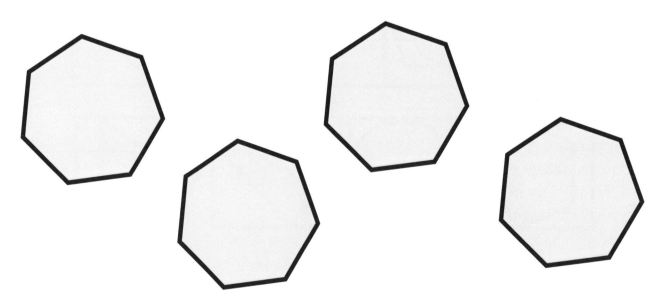

[50] DIFFICULTY ✪✪✪✪✪☆☆☆☆☆ ③ Minutes

Can you answer these questions about the puzzle on the previous page without looking back?

1. Which letter appears twice?

2. Which color is used for more letters than any other color?

3. What color is the Y?

4. What color is the letter above the Y?

5. Which letter is directly below the F?

6. Which letter is between the C and the H?

7. What color is the V?

8. Which letter is left of the S?

52 DIFFICULTY ✪✪✪✪✪✪✪✪☆☆ ④ Minutes

It is not possible to color in this diagram with just three different pens so that no two bordering areas have the same coloring. Can you manage it by resorting to a fourth color for only one area?

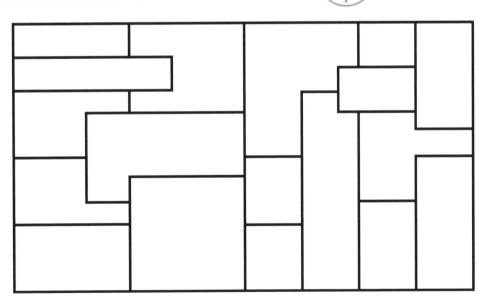

53 DIFFICULTY ✪✪✪✪✪✪✪☆☆☆☆

In this two-player network game, all you need to start are three + signs drawn on a piece of paper. The first player connects up any two of the "crossroads" and adds a third + sign somewhere along that route, in effect adding two new spur roads. The second player does the same, making sure that the lines do not cross. The play continues back and forth between both players until no valid move can be made.

The illustration shows the first three moves in a sample game.

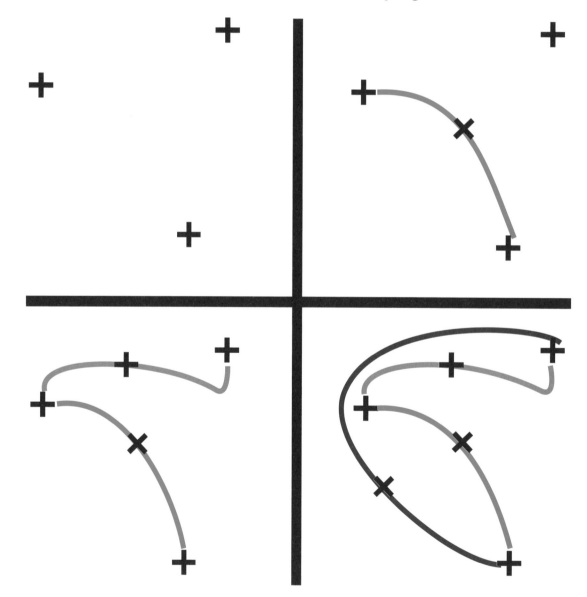

54 DIFFICULTY ✪✪✪✪✩✩✩✩✩✩ ⑤ Minutes

is to:

as

is to:

a

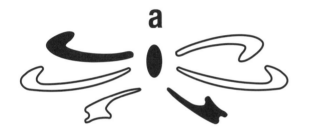

b

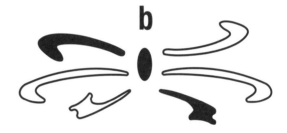

c

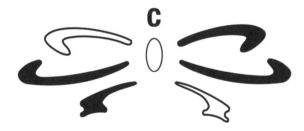

d

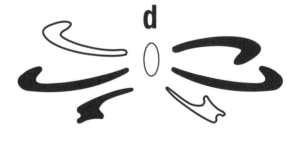

e

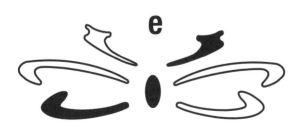

f

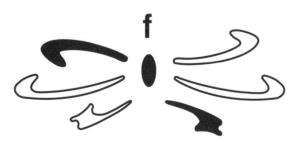

55 DIFFICULTY ✪✪✪✪✪✪☆☆☆☆ ⏱30 Minutes

Make the connections between the numbers to complete this numeropic.
See puzzle 21 for instructions on how to complete this kind of puzzle.

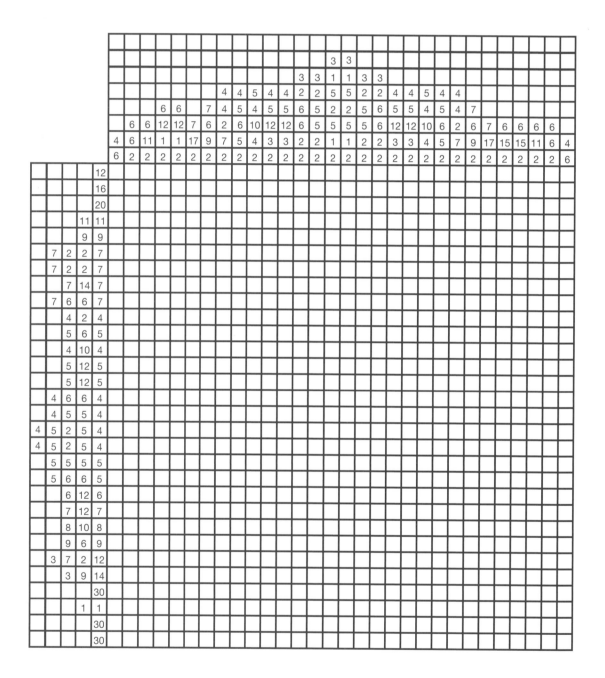

56 DIFFICULTY ✪✪✪✪✪✪✪✪☆☆ ③ Minutes

Can you match this potted plant with its shadow?

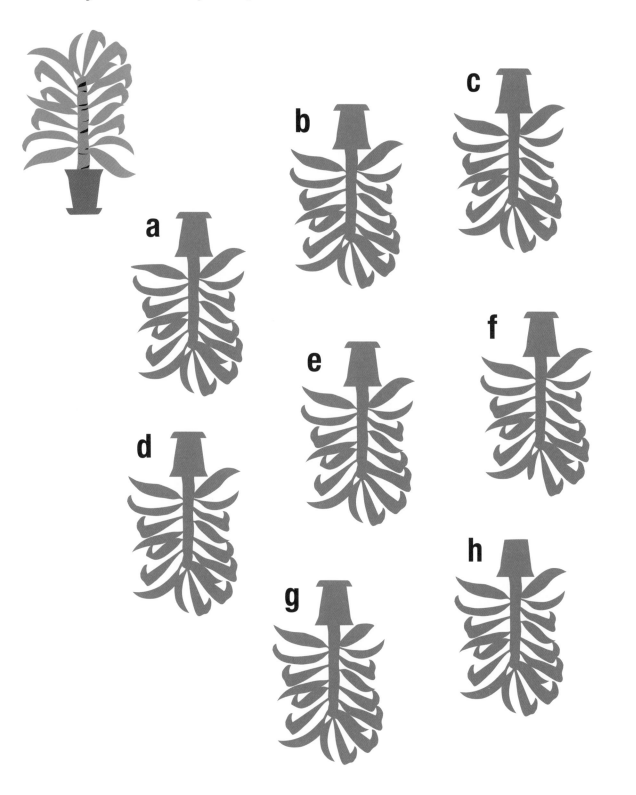

57 DIFFICULTY ★★★★★★★☆☆ ⑤ Minutes

Travel from any star on the top row of the grid to any star on the bottom row by moving from one square in the grid to an adjacent one. You may ONLY move from a star to a square, from a square to a circle, or from a circle to a star. You may not move diagonally. Colors are only there to confuse.

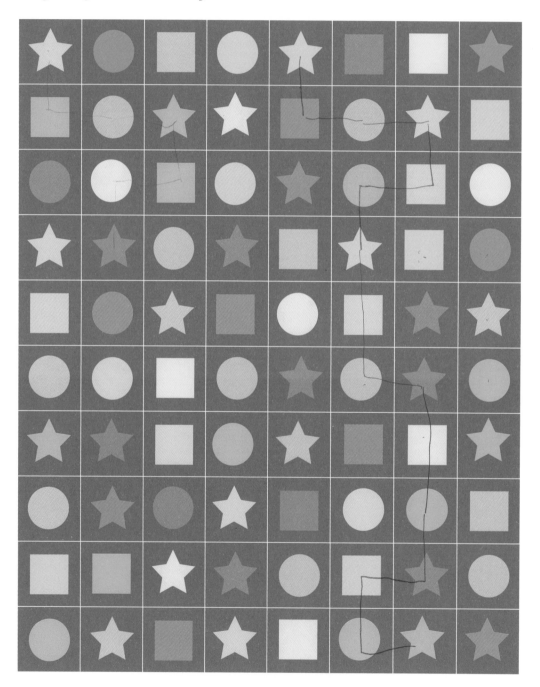

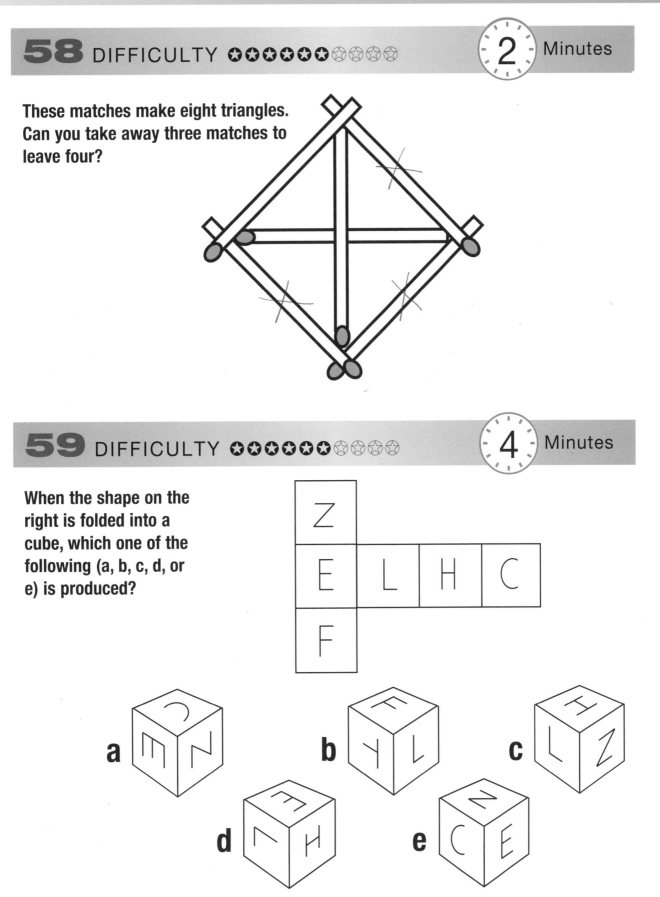

58 DIFFICULTY ✪✪✪✪✪✪☆☆☆☆ ⏱ 2 Minutes

These matches make eight triangles. Can you take away three matches to leave four?

59 DIFFICULTY ✪✪✪✪✪✪☆☆☆☆ ⏱ 4 Minutes

When the shape on the right is folded into a cube, which one of the following (a, b, c, d, or e) is produced?

Z
E L H C
F

a

b

c

d

e

60 DIFFICULTY ✪✪✪✪✪☆☆☆☆☆ ③ Minutes

These balls have been kicked around, but all are identical except for one. Which one is different from the rest?

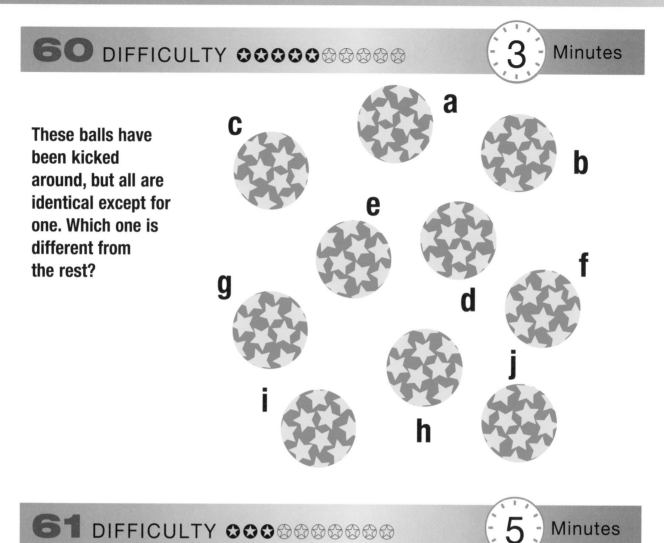

61 DIFFICULTY ✪✪✪☆☆☆☆☆☆☆ ⑤ Minutes

Can you spot the ten differences between these two pictures? Circle them in the drawing on the right.

62 DIFFICULTY ✪✪✪✪☆☆☆☆☆☆ | 3 Minutes

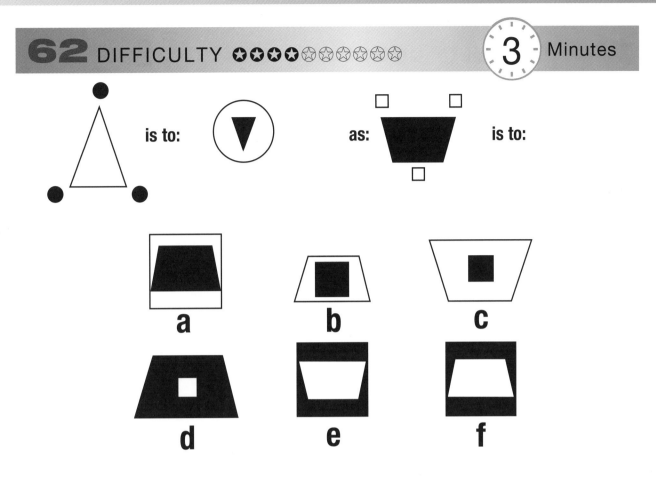

63 DIFFICULTY ✪✪✪✪✪✪✪☆☆☆ | 5 Minutes

At the local casino, they play a dice gambling game, which involves throwing two dice and betting a stake of $6. What are the rules and how much did Gary Gambler win or lose when he threw a 6 followed by a 1? Study the clues below to discover the answer.

1. Gina threw a 3 followed by a 2 and got $2 back, so lost $4.

2. George threw a 2 followed by a 6 and got $8 back, thus won $2.

3. Graham threw a 4 followed by a 1 and got $6 back, so broke even.

64 DIFFICULTY ✦✦✦✦✦☆☆☆☆☆ ⏱ 2 Minutes

Study this picture for two minutes, then see if you can answer the questions on the next page.

65 DIFFICULTY ✦✦✦✦✦☆☆☆☆☆ ⏱ 4 Minutes

Can you pair up these door keys with the imprints of their ends?

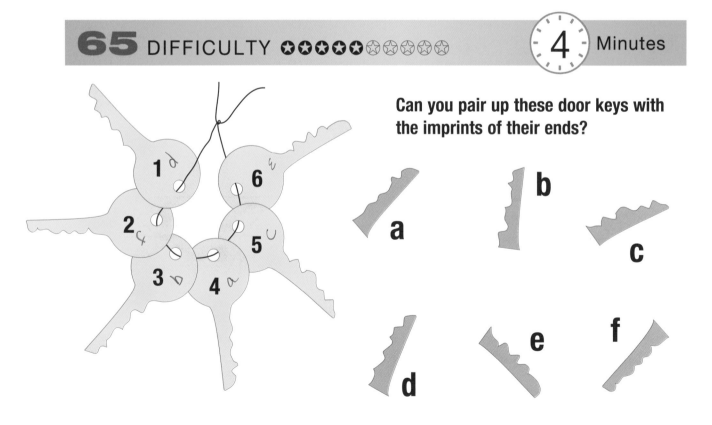

[64] DIFFICULTY ✪✪✪✪✪✪☆☆☆☆☆   ③ Minutes

Can you answer these questions about the puzzle on the previous page without looking back?

1. Which number appears on a square with a blue background?

2. What is the color of the letter K?

3. What color is the question mark?

4. What color is the triangle?

5. Which letter appears above the K?

6. How many letters appear on squares with a green background?

7. How many yellow stars appear in the picture?

8. Which letter appears diagonally between the letter S and the letter B?

66 DIFFICULTY ✪✪✪✪☆☆☆☆☆☆   ③ Minutes

What is the sum total of the spots on the fifteen hidden sides of these four dice?

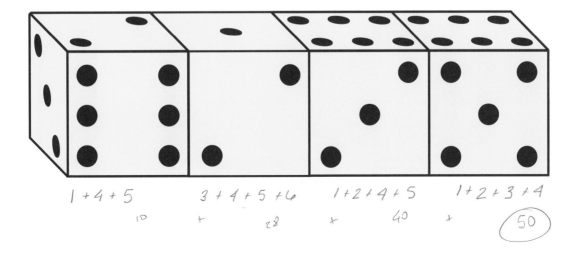

1 + 4 + 5   3 + 4 + 5 + 6   1 + 2 + 4 + 5   1 + 2 + 3 + 4

10   +   28   +   40   +   50

67 DIFFICULTY ✪✪✪✪✪✪✩✩✩✩   ⏲ **7** Minutes

In how many different places can the shape shown be found in the larger grid?
The pattern may be rotated but not reflected.

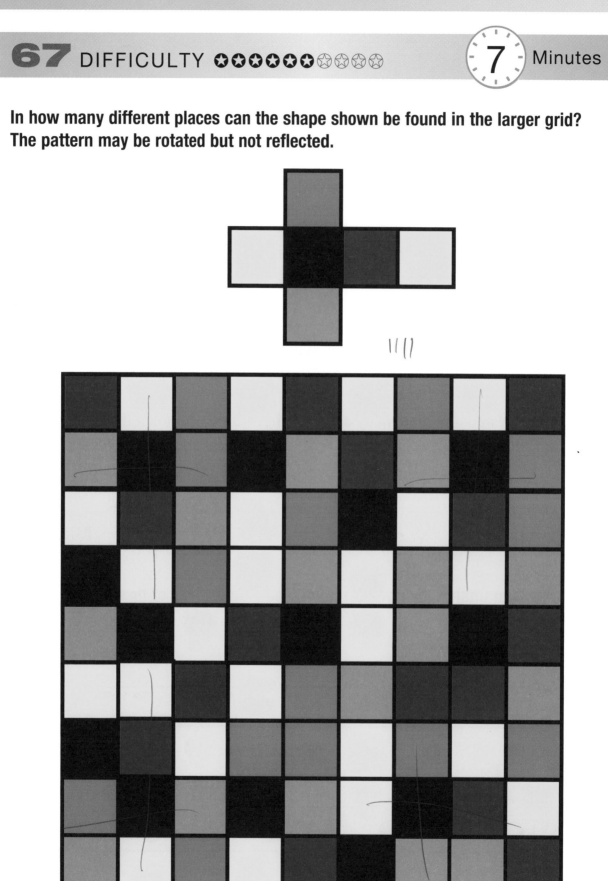

68 DIFFICULTY ✪✪✪✪✪✪✩✩✩✩ (10) Minutes

Kirsty played a game of Snakes and Ladders with her brother Tom. He threw the first 6, so started first, placing his playing piece on the 6. After that, every time it was Kirsty's turn, her die followed the sequence 6, 5, 4, 3, 2, 1; so her first move was to square 6, then square 11, etc. After his first turn when he threw the 6, Tom's die followed the sequence 1, 2, 3, 4, 5, 6 each time, so his second move was to square 7, his third was to 9, etc. The normal rules of the game were followed, so whenever someone landed on a square that had the foot of a ladder, the piece was moved to the top of the ladder. Whenever someone lands on a square that had the head of a snake, the piece was moved to the tail of the snake. The number thrown to end the game didn't necessarily matter, since the first person to move a piece completely off the board won. Who won the game—Kirsty or Tom?

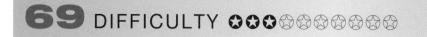

Can you spot the ten differences between these two pictures? Circle them in the drawing on the right.

70 DIFFICULTY ✪✪✪✪✪✩✩✩✩✩   ③ Minutes

These witches are identical except for one. Which witch is different from the rest?

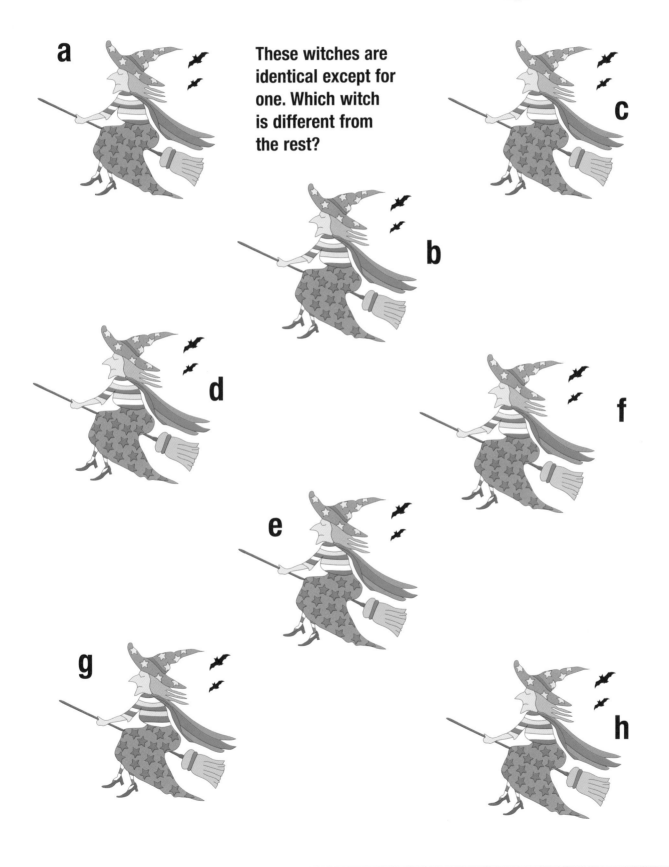

71 DIFFICULTY ✪✪✪✪✪☆☆☆☆☆   6 Minutes

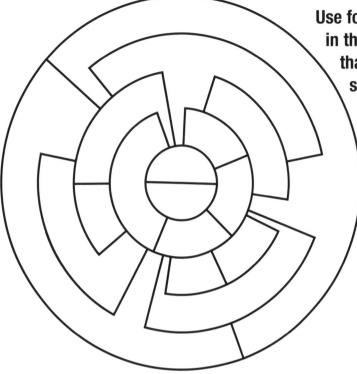

Use four different colored pens to shade in this diagram like a political map so that no two bordering areas have the same color. It's trickier than it looks!

72 DIFFICULTY ✪✪✪✪✪✪☆☆☆☆   3 Minutes

Look carefully—which of the ten clock hands is in the wrong position? Where should it be instead?

73 DIFFICULTY ★★★☆☆☆☆☆☆☆   (4) Minutes

Mrs. R. Teest would like to buy two identical abstract paintings, but is rather confused by the choice at the art gallery. Can you help by finding two that are exactly the same?

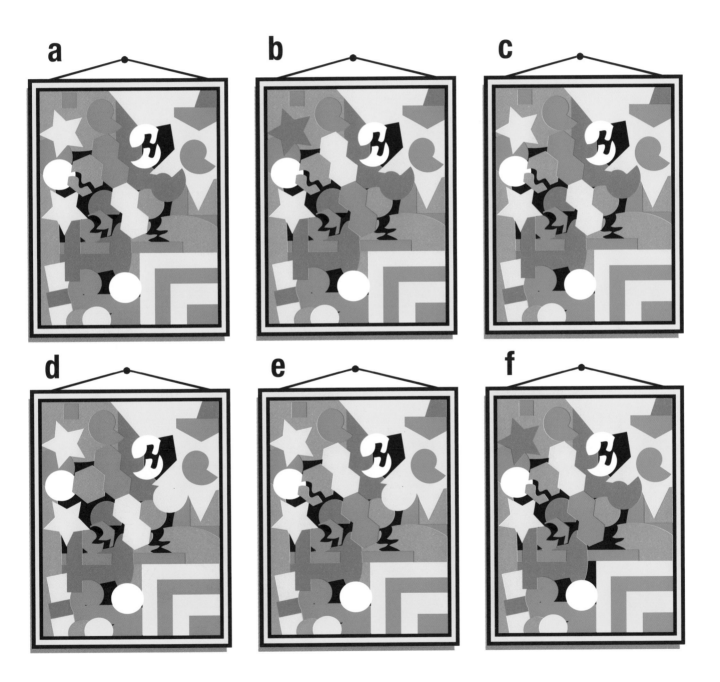

a
b
c
d
e
f

74 DIFFICULTY ✪✪✪✪✪✪☆☆☆  3 Minutes

Make your way from A to B collecting just one of each of the four shapes. You can pick them up in any order but you may NOT travel over the same path more than once.

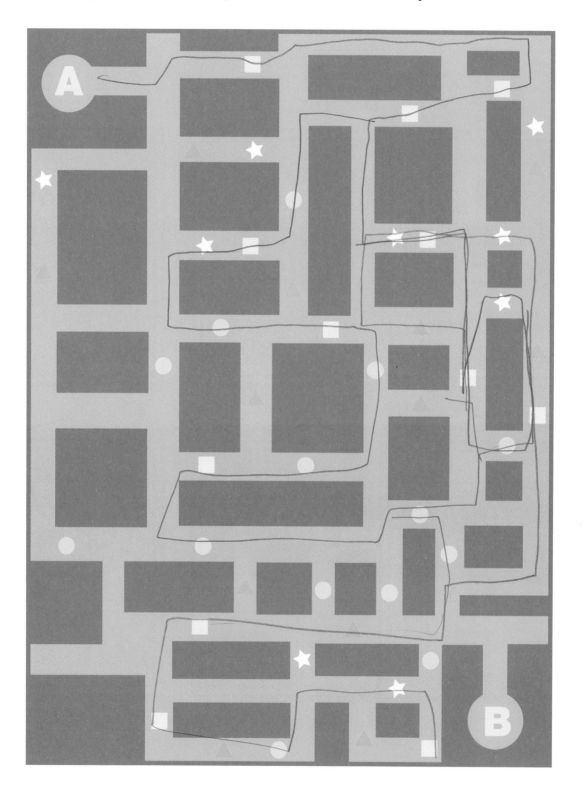

75 DIFFICULTY ✪✪✪✪✪☆☆☆☆☆ ⏱ 5 Minutes

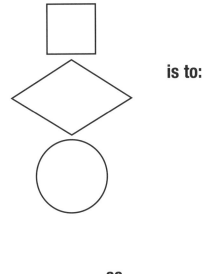

is to:

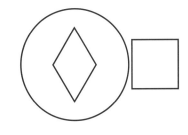

as

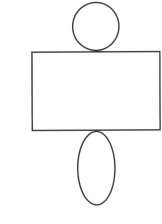

is to:

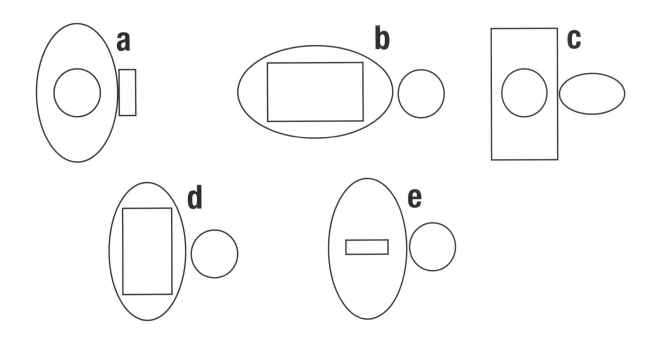

MINDWORKS BRAIN TRAINING

76 DIFFICULTY ★★★★★☆☆☆☆ ③ Minutes

In how many different places can the pattern shown be found in the grid below? The pattern may be rotated but not reflected.

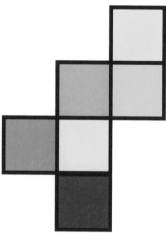

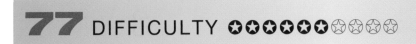

77 DIFFICULTY ★★★★★★☆☆☆☆

30 Minutes

Once you've completed this numeropic, you'll never forget how it's done. See puzzle 21 for instructions on how to complete this type of puzzle.

Column clues (top):

					2																										
					3																										
		1		2	3	3					3														1	2	3				
3	2	2	1	8	3				3	2	2	3	4	5										1	2	3					
1	1	2	11	3	1	4		5	3	8	5	8	10	12	20	16	20	20	16	20	19	1		19	16	12	10				
3	2	4	17	7	1	1	7	14	19	13	7	5	2	2	2	2	2	3	3	2	2	3	3	19	2	2	1	1	2		
1	1	1	1	1	1	1	1	1	2	3	3	3	3	4	4	1	1	2	2	1	1	2	2	1	1	5	2	2	3	3	2

Row clues (left):

- 1 2 1
- 2 2 2
- 3 2 1 1
- 3 2 1
- 4 14 2
- 18
- 5 13
- 6 13
- 7 2 13
- 7 4 12
- 3 7 12
- 4 7 12
- 8 2 13
- 8 1 14
- 4 4 1 14
- 1 2 5 1 14
- 8 15
- 10 15
- 5 5 15
- 3 19
- 3 4 4 2 4
- 2 4 4 2 4
- 2 4 4 2 4
- 2 1 2 1 2 2 1 2
- 2
- 2 1 14
- 2 15 1
- 1 7 2 3 2
- 6 2 2 6
- 30

78 DIFFICULTY ✪✪✪✪✪☆☆☆☆☆

6 Minutes

At first glance, these photos may look identical. However, only two are exactly the same. Can you spot them?

a

b

c

d

e

f

79 DIFFICULTY ●●●☆☆☆☆☆☆☆

4 Minutes

Can you spot the eight differences between these two seasonal pictures? Circle them in the lower drawing.

80 DIFFICULTY ●●●●●●☆☆☆☆

3 Minutes

Can you rearrange these matches so that the area enclosed is twice as large?

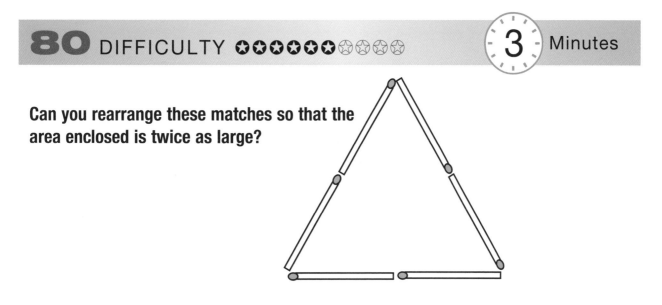

81 DIFFICULTY ★★★★★☆☆☆☆☆ ④ Minutes

Which of the figures below (a, b, or c) completes the grid above?

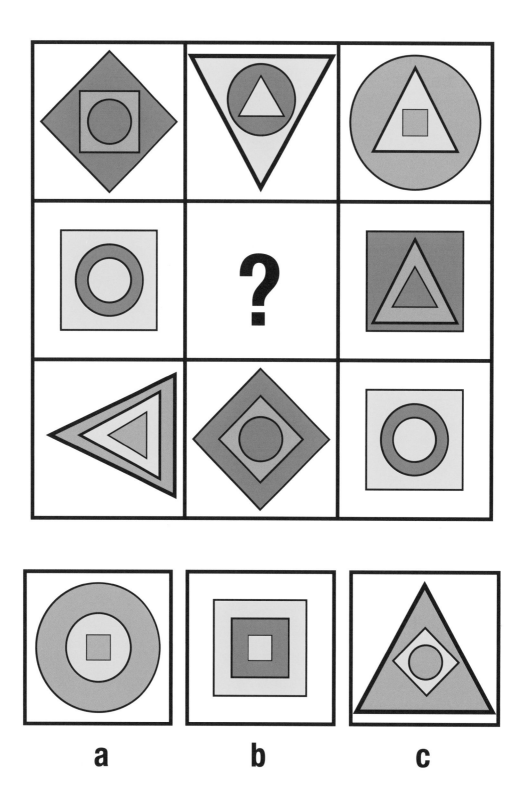

a   b   c

82 DIFFICULTY ✪✪✪✪✪☆☆☆☆☆ ⑤ Minutes

Which three pieces can fit together to match the chair on the right? Any piece may be rotated, but not flipped over.

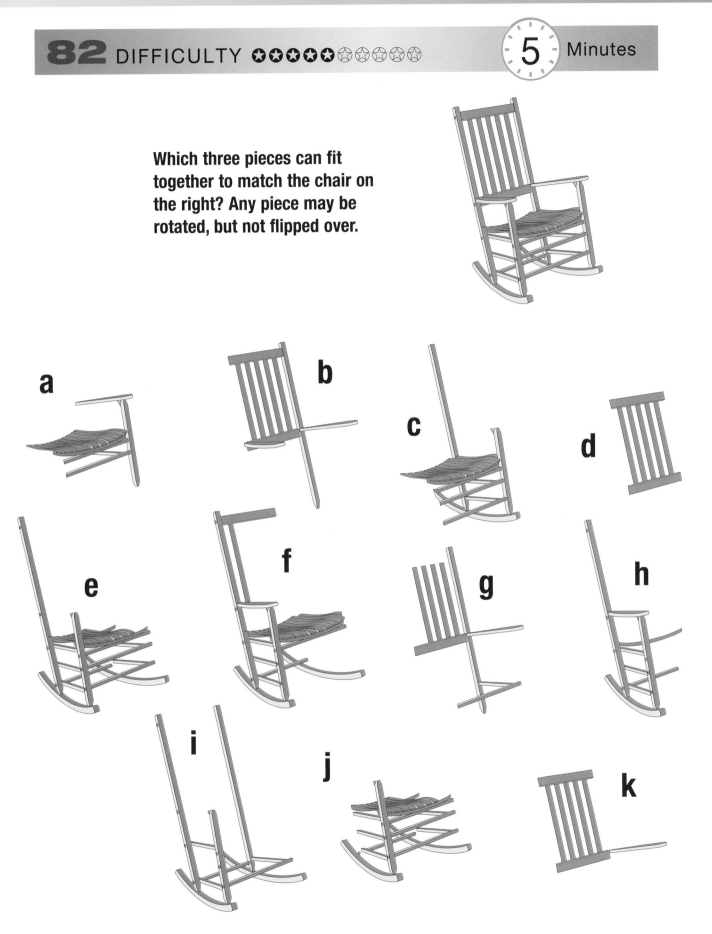

83 DIFFICULTY ✪✪✪✪✪✰✰✰✰✰   ⏱ 8 Minutes

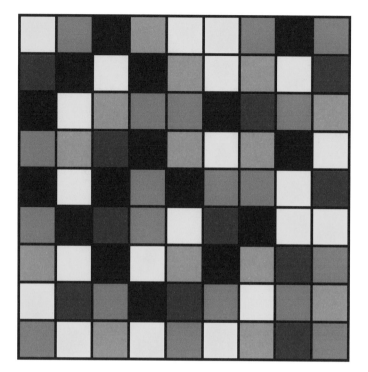

Where can this specific pattern of squares be found in the larger grid? The pattern may be rotated but not reflected.

84 DIFFICULTY ✪✪✪✪✪✰✰✰✰✰   ⏱ 4 Minutes

Arrange these fourteen coins into seven lines of four coins each.

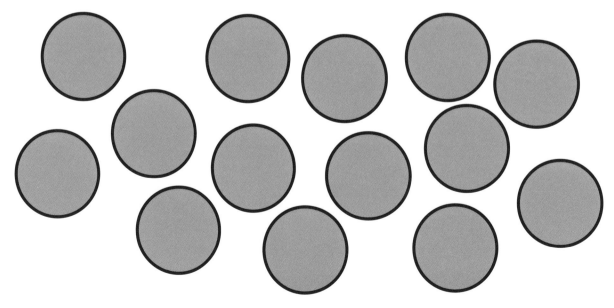

85 DIFFICULTY ✪✪✪✪✪✫✫✫✫✫   ⏱ 3 Minutes

By drawing four straight lines, can you divide this shape into five sections, each containing seven letters?

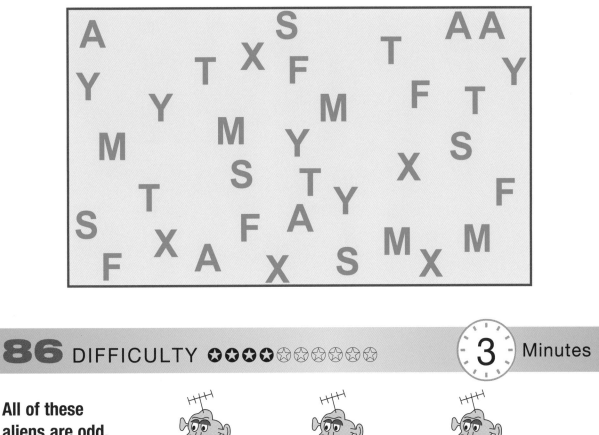

86 DIFFICULTY ✪✪✪✪✫✫✫✫✫✫   ⏱ 3 Minutes

All of these aliens are odd, but which is the odd one out?

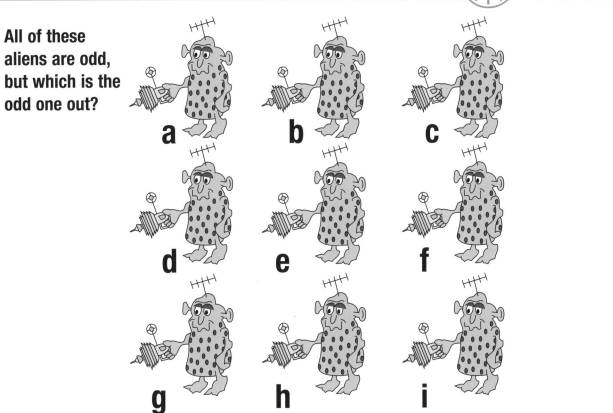

a   b   c

d   e   f

g   h   i

87 DIFFICULTY ✪✪✪✪✪✩✩✩✩✩ ⏱ 2 Minutes

Study this picture for two minutes, then see if you can answer the questions on the next page.

88 DIFFICULTY ✪✪✪✪✪✩✩✩✩✩ ⏱ 3 Minutes

Which number should follow next in this dice sequence?

36   **12**   **4**   **?**

[87] DIFFICULTY ✪✪✪✪✪✪☆☆☆☆☆  3 Minutes

Can you answer these questions about the puzzle on the previous page without looking back?

1. How many white-petaled flowers have white centers?

2. How many blue-petaled flowers appear in total?

3. How many blue-petaled flowers have blue centers?

4. What color petals does the flower at the very tip of the leaf have?

5. How many red-petaled flowers have yellow centers?

6. How many white-petaled flowers appear in total?

7. What is the total number of flowers in the picture?

8. How many petals does each flower have?

89 DIFFICULTY ✪✪✪✪✪✪✪☆☆☆  6 Minutes

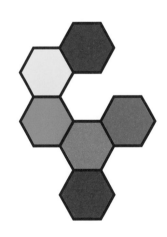

In how many different places can the pattern shown be found in the larger grid? The pattern may be rotated but not reflected.

90 DIFFICULTY ●●●☆☆☆☆☆☆☆   4 Minutes

Can you draw appropriate-colored lines from dot to dot (e.g., a yellow line from yellow dot to yellow dot) so that all the pairs of dots are connected up? None of the colored lines may cross or touch, even at a corner.

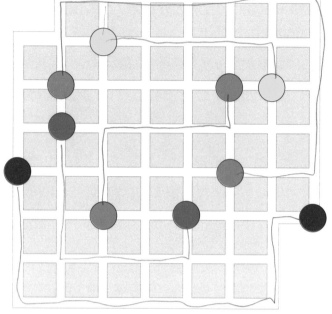

91 DIFFICULTY ●●●●●☆☆☆☆☆   4 Minutes

When this shape is folded to form a cube, which is the only one of the following that can be produced?

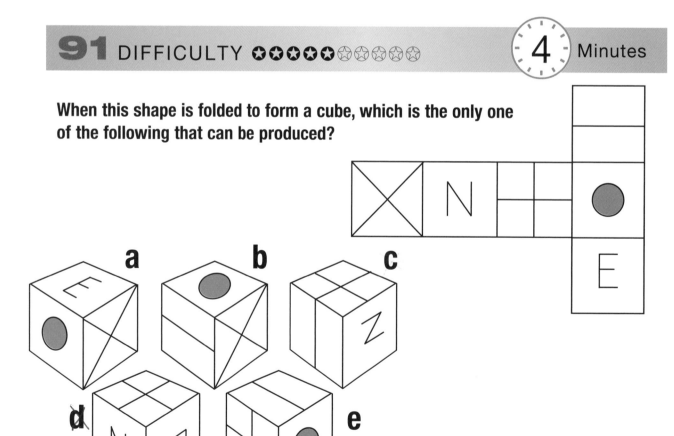

1

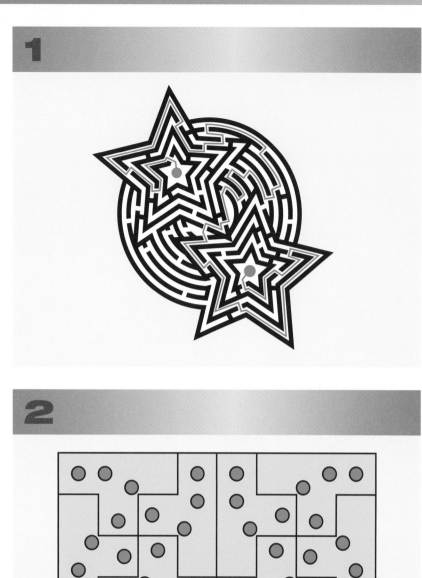

2

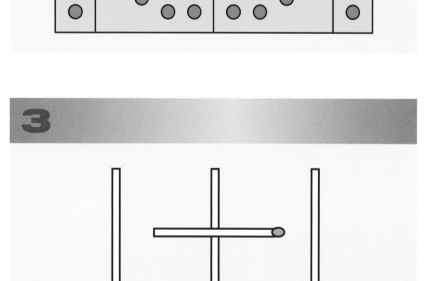

3

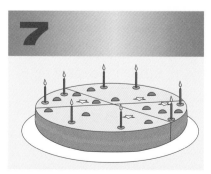

4

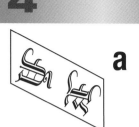

a

5

c; each vertical and horizontal line contains one shape with all green triangles, one with all pink triangles, and one with half pink and half green triangles. Each line also contains two shapes with a red dot in the center and one with no red dot. The missing shape must have all green triangles and a red dot.

6

7

8

Kirsty wins in the fewest moves.

9

a=5, b=7, c=1, d=3, e=2, f=6, and g=4

10

Place stepping stones on the grid rather than making consecutive steps.

11

Building 1
e

Building 2
g

Building 3
h

Building 4
b

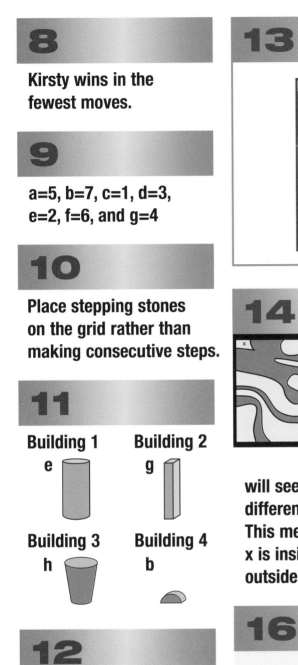

12

Gary won $8. The total payback is the number of spots on the opposite side of the first die multiplied by the number of spots on the opposite side of the second. Thus Gary got back $20 (5 x 4 = 20), winning $8.

13

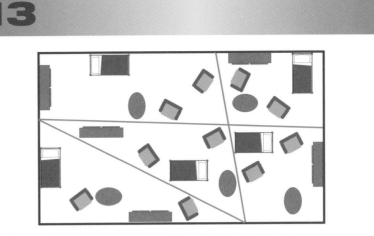

14

If you color in the areas like a political map, you will see that x and y are different colored areas. This means that since x is inside the loop, y is outside the loop.

15

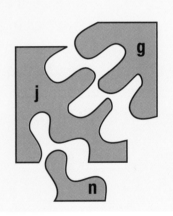

16

17

18

d; all figures originally outside the hexagon transfer to the inside of the hexagon, and vice versa. Also, black circles turn to white triangles, white circles turn to black triangles, and vice versa.

19

C

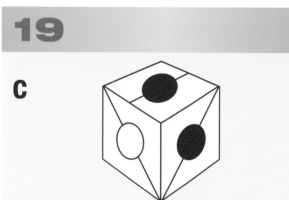

20

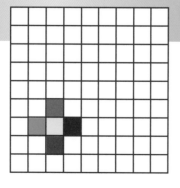

21

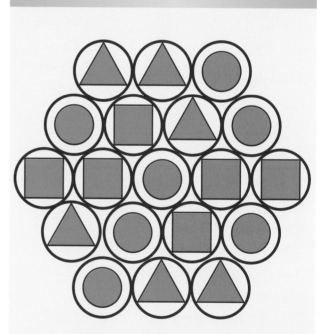

22

A circle. Every triangle of six circles, or , must contain different numbers of circles, squares, and triangles.

23

There are ten differences between the two pictures.

24

$([6 + 4] \div 5) - 1 = 1$

$([2 + 6] - 5) \times 1 = 3$

$([4 \times 4] \div 2) - 3 = 5$

25

e

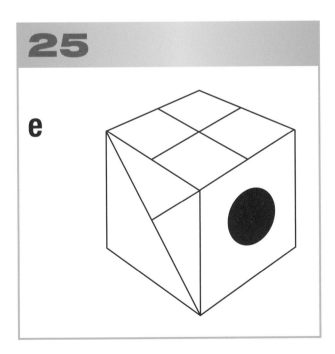

26

1. Blue
2. 3
3. Green
4. 3
5. 2
6. 8
7. 2
8. 25

27

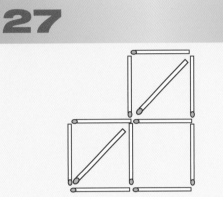

28

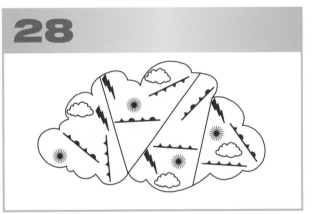

29

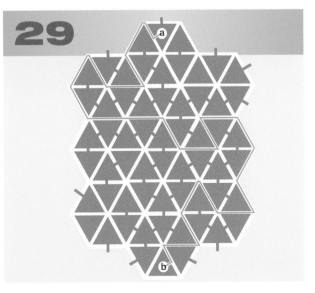

30

A circle. Each row and column, across and down, has thirteen corners.

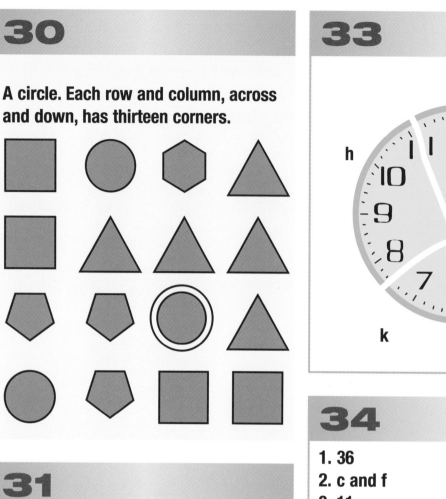

31

a; the circles on the line at the extreme left change places. The line on the extreme right points down instead of up.

32

a; it is looking in a different direction.

33

34

1. 36	5. 3
2. c and f	6. d
3. 11	7. 5
4. b	8. b

35

36

None. Rearrange them as follows:

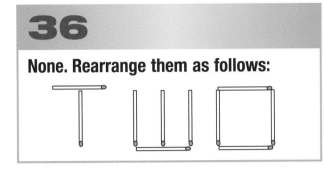

37

48; multiply the number of dots on the top face of each die by the total of the number of dots on the (visible) front and side, then deduct the sum of the dots on the three hidden faces of each die.

38

22; Angelica can see the top faces of all three dice, thus a total of nine spots. The opposite sides of a die have spots that add up to seven. On the left die, the side face Angelica can see has six spots. On the central die, the side face Angelica can see has two spots. On the right die, the side face Angelica can see also has two spots. On the bottom face of the right die there is one spot, so the end face of this die (hidden from you) has either three or four spots. If this end face has four spots, then the total number of spots Angelica can see is twenty-three. But Angelica can see a different number of spots than you—and you can see twenty-three. So the end face Angelica can see has three spots. Thus,

Angelica can see a total of nine spots on the top faces, ten spots on the side faces, and three on the end face for a combined total of twenty-two spots.

39

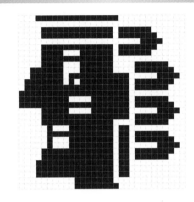

40

a=6, b=7, c=4, d=5, e=2, f=1, and g=3

41

d

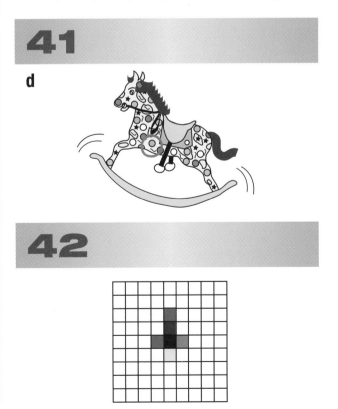

42

43

46

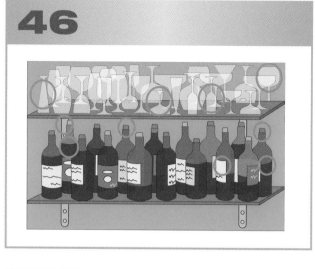

47

c and i

44

48

Building 1
a

Building 2
c

Building 3
i

Building 4
b

45

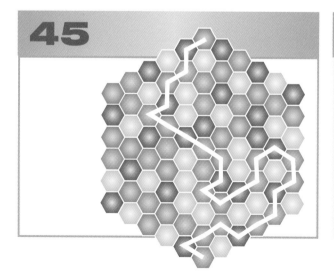

49

a; where shapes touch the side of the square, the shape in the adjacent square must also touch.

50

1. M
2. Yellow
3. Red
4. Red
5. B
6. L
7. Black
8. O

54

b; the image is the same except that each white arm that points down in the original now points up, and vice versa.

51

Put them on their edges.

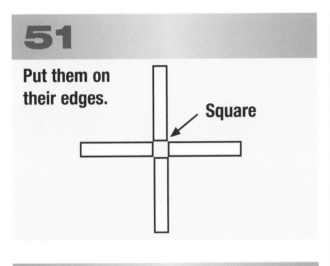

Square

55

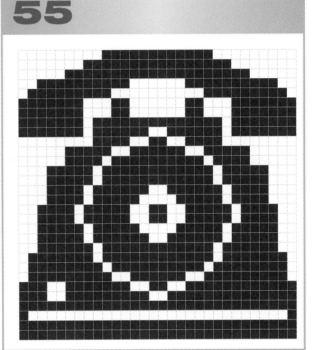

52

56

d

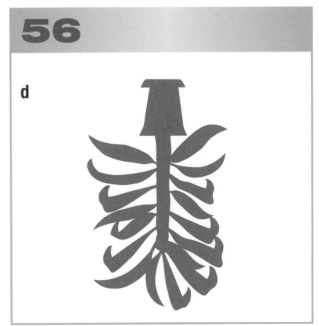

53

Drawing lines inside existing loops will reduce the length of the game but won't guarantee you a win. It's best to plan carefully.

57

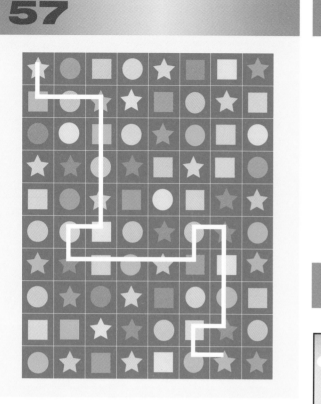

58

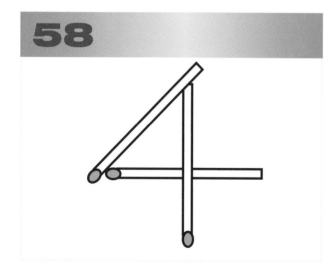

59

a

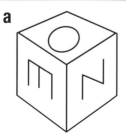

60

f; the points of the central three stars are not aligned.

61

62

f; the figure in the middle rotates 180º and turns from black to white. The three small white squares become one large black square and enclose the figure in the middle.

63

Gary won $4. The total payback is double the difference of the number of spots on the two dice. Thus Gary got back $10: (6 – 1) x 2 = 10, winning $4.

64

1. 5
2. Blue
3. Green
4. White
5. S
6. 3: the T, the S, and the W
7. 2
8. T

65

1=d, 2=f, 3=b, 4=a, 5=c, 6=e

66

There are 21 dots on each die, thus a total of 84 dots on the four dice. Since 34 dots are visible, the total number of dots on the sides that are not visible amounts to 50.

67

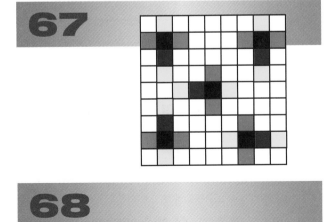

68

Tom wins in the fewest moves.

69

70

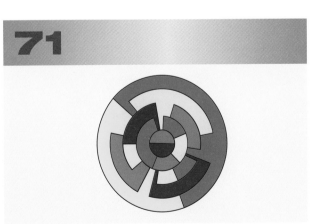

g; the bottom two stripes on her shirt are different.

71

72

The minute hand of the clock in the bottom-right corner is incorrect. It should be pointing at the five minutes to the hour position. Now each hour hand points to the minute hand on one of the other clocks so that they lie on the same extended line.

73

a and c

74

75

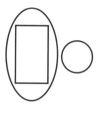

d; the figure in the middle (the rectangle) reduces in size, rotates 90º, and goes inside the figure originally at the bottom (the oval), which increases in size. The figure at the top (the circle) attaches itself to the right-hand side of the oval.

76

77

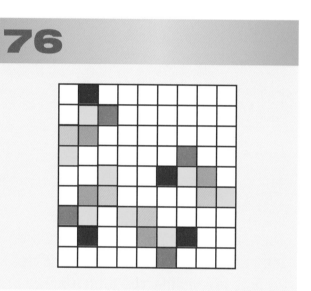

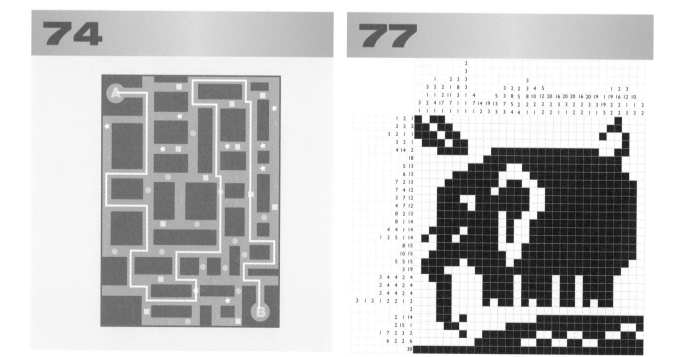

78

c and f

79

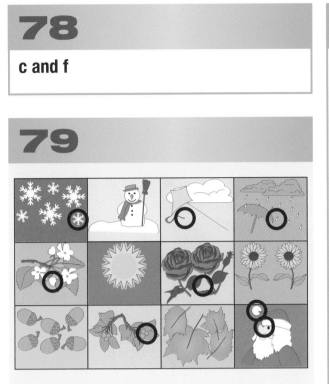

80

The triangle can be seen to consist of four isosceles triangles, each side being one match in length. The hexagon consists of six of the same-sized triangles, which is twice as big in area.

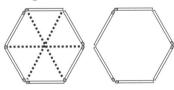

81

c; on each row and column, each shape and each color appears three times.

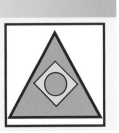

82

c, h, and k

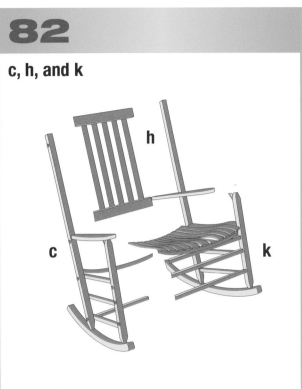

83

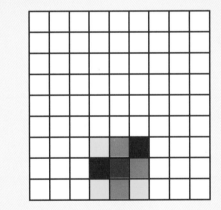

84

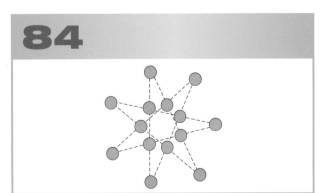

85

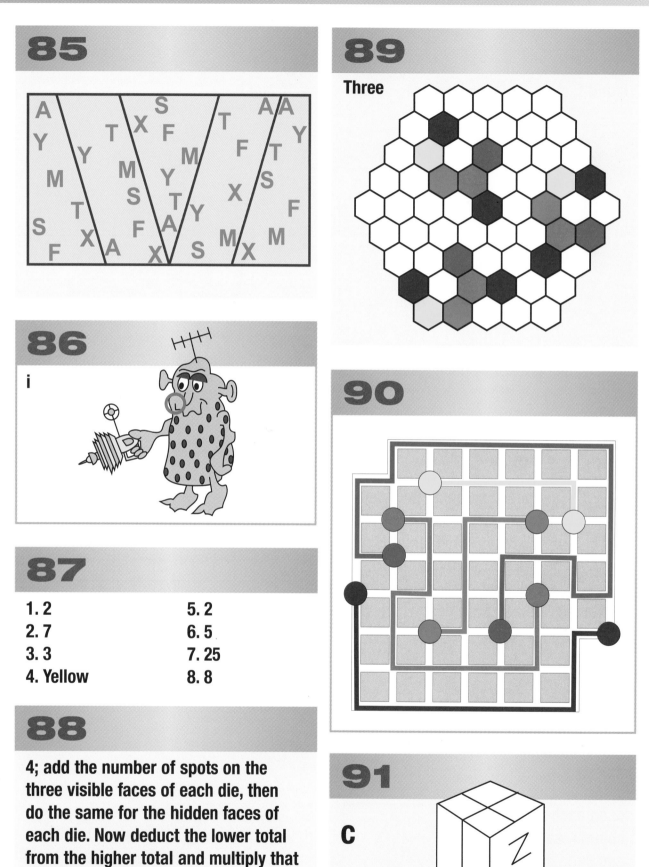

86

i

87

1. 2	5. 2
2. 7	6. 5
3. 3	7. 25
4. Yellow	8. 8

88

4; add the number of spots on the three visible faces of each die, then do the same for the hidden faces of each die. Now deduct the lower total from the higher total and multiply that answer by four.

89

Three

90

91

C